Metaboli

574.13 BOY

03 DEC	11 MAY	– 8 NOV 2016
18 DEC	10 JUL 1996	– 5 NOV 2019
06 OCT	18 DEC 2002	
03 MAY	8-7-05	
29 FEB	– 9 JAN 2012	
29 FEB	15 MAR 2012	
19 APR	14 NOV 2012	
07 JUL	28 NOV 2012	
	– 2 NOV 2015	

CANCELLED
RETURNED

FOUNDATIONS OF BIOLOGY
General editor L. M. J. Kramer
A major advanced biology course for schools and colleges

Metabolism, movement and control

A. Boyce, B. Sc., Cert. Ed.

Biology department, Maynard School, Exeter

C. M. Jenking, B. Sc., Cert. Ed.

Head of Biology department, Maynard School, Exeter

Macmillan Education

London and Basingstoke

First published 1980
Reprinted 1982, 1983

Published by
Macmillan Education Limited
Houndmills Basingstoke Hampshire RG21 2XS and London
Associated companies in Delhi Dublin Hong Kong
Johannesburg Lagos Melbourne New York Singapore
and Tokyo

Printed in Hong Kong

British Library Cataloguing in Publication Data
Boyce, A
Metabolism, movement and control.
(Foundations of biology series)
1. Metabolism
I. Title   II. Jenking, C M   III. Series
574.1'33   QH521
ISBN 0-333-26776-9

Contents

Acknowledgements

The authors would like to acknowledge the tolerance of their husbands during the writing of this book and to thank Dr G. F. C. Hawkins and Dr J. K. Scott for advice.

The authors and publishers wish to acknowledge the following photograph sources:

Booth's, London Figure 117(a), p. 269;
Dr L. M. J. Kramer as originator and source of Figure 115, p. 258;
Tom Molland Limited Figure 117(c), p. 269;
Harry Smith Figure 112(b), p. 253;
Studio Cole Limited Figure 117(b), p. 269;
United States Department of Agriculture, Office of Information Figure 112(a), p. 253.

The publishers have made every effort to trace the copyright holders but if they have inadvertently overlooked any they will be pleased to make the necessary arrangements at the first opportunity.

Preface

Foundation of biology aims to provide a complete pre-university course in biological science. Accordingly, the work is covered in a few handy volumes, not in a single bulky one or numerous monographs. The questions at the ends of the chapters are to test the comprehension of the material covered in the chapters and their contents are not necessarily similar to those set in biological examinations which often require knowledge in several branches of biology if they are to be answered properly. Suggestions are provided for further reading.

The course consists of five books written by experienced teachers with special knowledge of biological science, who believe through their experience that fresh approaches to teaching biology are desirable at pre-university level. The books in the series are:–

The diversity of life
The cell concept
Heredity, development and evolution
Movement, metabolism and control
Man and the ecosystem

Biologists will realise the difficulty of subdividing the course into a number of books and opinions will undoubtedly differ on how it should best be done. One difficulty is that a number of topics are based upon knowledge of others. So that if each book is to be helpful some overlap must occur with others in the series. In fact the necessity for overlap has proved to be relatively small and where it occurs the treatment of topics is consistent from one book to another.

It is wise to remember that no branch of science is more 'fundamental' than any other, so no suggestion has been made that the books need to be studied in a given order. Teachers will be free to use them in any sequence or combination which suits their own courses.

All the authors concerned with the series have felt keenly the inadequacy of purely descriptive biology in giving insight into the basis of science today. It has been necessary therefore for them to introduce some mathematics, physics and organic chemistry to which biology is so closely related. The names of chemical compounds are accompanied by their new names under the *IUPAC rules* and in *The cell concept* there is an introduction to the new uses which seems difficult at first but which are in fact logical and easy to follow once the principles have been grasped.

Metabolism, movement and control has close links with other books in the series. It deals with most of the physiology of animals and plants, which is important in examination answers. On one hand it is related to the cellular biology in *The cell concept*, where some work, chiefly cell energetics and the movements of substances, is more fully developed, and on the other hand it is related to the accounts of reproduction, growth and development in *Heredity, development and evolution*, which are associated naturally with genetics.

L. M. J. KRAMER
General Editor

1 Introduction to metabolism

A good modern dictionary defines metabolism as 'the process in organisms, or in single cells, by which nutritive material is built up into living matter, or protoplasm is broken down into simpler substances'. This is a fairly adequate definition but it does concentrate on the processes of growth and breakdown, and largely ignores other activities of cells such as the production of enzymes, hormones and mucus – substances which, although they do not contribute directly to the structure of the organism, do nonetheless perform vital functions. Metabolism can be more inclusively defined as 'the sum total of all the chemical activities that go on inside each living cell'. The number of chemical reactions involved is very large, ranging from several hundred to several thousand in a single cell.

All the activities of organisms such as feeding, excretion, locomotion, and the transmission of nerve impulses, ultimately depend on chemical changes in cells. A knowledge of the most important metabolic processes is thus essential to any understanding of the functioning, or *physiology*, of organisms.

Metabolism as a homeostatic process

The main function of metabolism is to enable the organism to maintain itself in a given condition. The ability to maintain internal conditions in a more or less steady state is called *homeostasis* (see chapter 9). Metabolic processes can thus be thought of as homeostatic mechanisms, as they are concerned with preserving the organism's structural and functional status. Obviously some changes do occur. All organisms increase in size sometime during their lives, just as they all age and eventually die.

Anabolism and Catabolism

The chemical reactions that go on inside cells are of two kinds, *anabolic* and *catabolic*. 'Anabolic' describes reactions in which organic molecules are built up or synthesised. Such reactions are involved in photosynthesis, growth, the replacement of worn out or damaged organelles or cells, reproduction, and the synthesis of substances like hormones and mucus that are subsequently used outside the cell in which they were made (a process known as *secretion*). Anabolic reactions are generally *endergonic*, that is, they require a supply of energy to drive them. The energy is mainly used to form bonds between the reactant molecules.

'Catabolic' describes the types of reaction which bring about the breakdown of organic molecules and living structures. Such reactions play a vital part in the replacement of worn out or damaged parts of the organism, as well as supplying the energy requirements of the cell. Catabolic reactions are generally *exergonic* or energy-yielding.

In young organisms, anabolism outpaces catabolism resulting in net growth. As organisms get older the capacity for repair and regeneration decreases, so that catabolism predominates. This leads eventually to the death of the organism.

Energy flow through organisms

As just described, anabolic reactions require energy, and even catabolic reactions generally require an input of energy to start off the reaction (*activation energy*). Most of the energy used by living organisms is ultimately supplied by the sun. The flow of energy through living organisms starts with the photosynthetic cells of green plants and chlorophyll-containing bacteria. These cells trap solar energy and convert it into chemical energy stored in food molecules. The chemical energy literally holds the food molecule together and can be released if the food molecule is broken down. The breakdown of energy-containing food molecules, usually carbohydrates, is known as *respiration*, and it is the way in which animal cells and non-photosynthetic plant cells obtain all the energy they need for their metabolic processes.

Photosynthesis and respiration both involve a complicated sequence of reactions (these are described in later chapters), but they can be summarised in the following equations:

photosynthesis $\quad 6CO_2 + 6H_2O \rightarrow C_6H_{12}O_6 + 6O_2$
$\qquad\qquad\qquad\qquad\qquad$ glucose

respiration $\qquad C_6H_{12}O_6 + 6O_2 \rightarrow 6CO_2 + 6H_2O$

The two processes thus comprise a natural cycle which can be represented diagrammatically as follows:

The capacity to use energy to maintain a constant structure is perhaps the most fundamental characteristic of living organisms.

The main types of reaction involved in metabolism

In multicellular organisms different cells are specialised for particular functions. Accordingly, the reactions that go on in cells will differ from one cell type to another, but certain reactions and types of reaction are common to all cells.

When considering the functioning of a cell, it is tempting to draw comparisons between the cell and a factory. Both require an input of raw materials and an energy source (fuel). A variety of products are manufactured, some for internal use such as maintenance (repair) and expansion (growth), while others are produced for export (secretions). As a result of these processes unwanted waste materials are produced and must be removed (excretion). The scheme in Figure 1 sets out the most important metabolic processes. It is obviously greatly simplified and, for example, does not show that some of the energy made available from respiration is used in the transport of certain substances across the membrane, nor does it show the synthesis of enzymes and the vital part they play in all the other reactions. It does illustrate however, that the chemical reactions that go on inside cells are inter-related, not isolated, processes.

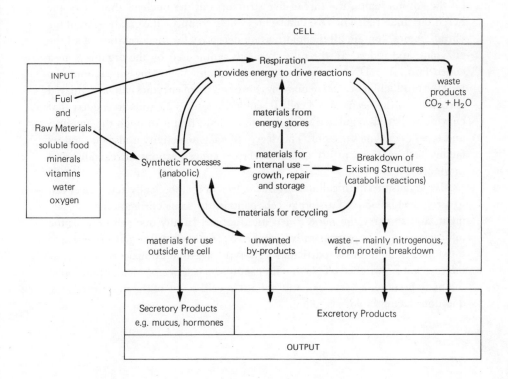

Figure 1   A scheme showing the main metabolic processes in a generalised (non-photosynthetic) cell

The role of enzymes in metabolism

Most metabolic processes are fairly complicated and involve a whole sequence of reactions; for example, respiration involves about thirty different reactions. The majority of these reactions are controlled by *enzymes*, biological catalysts, which enable reactions to proceed more rapidly than they would otherwise. All cells produce many hundreds or even thousands of enzymes, each of which is fairly specific in its action, that is, it will only catalyse one particular reaction or type of reaction. The properties of enzymes are discussed in greater detail in chapter 4.

The control of enzyme activity

Enzymes play a vital role in the cell, directing and controlling reactions within the cell, and maintaining a balance between the different processes, so that, for example, each product is produced in just the required amount. Continuing the factory analogy, the enzymes can be thought of as a combination of workers and machines. This raises the question of what controls the enzymes. In other words, which part of the cell plays the supervisory or managerial role? The answer is quite simple. The enzymes are produced under the direction of the *genes* – regions on the chromosomes, the thread-like structures in the nucleus, that carry the hereditary material. The DNA molecules which comprise the greater part of the chromosomes, contain all the information necessary for the formation of all the enzymes, and indeed all the other proteins synthesised by the organism, in a coded form. The DNA molecule also incorporates 'switching mechanisms' so that the production of a particular enzyme or group of enzymes can be regulated according to the needs of the cell. It would be a simplification to suggest that enzyme activity is regulated solely by the nucleus, that is through the amounts and types of enzymes present. The degree of enzyme activity is also affected by factors such as temperature and the relative concentrations of reactants and products.

All the cells in a multicellular organism, from a metabolically active liver cell to a relatively inactive fat-storage cell, contain the same chromosome complement, and so carry the same coded information. In any one cell most of the information must be permanently 'switched off' so that only the genes relevant to the functioning of that particular cell type are operational. Exactly how information is 'switched off' so that for example, a cell in a particular position in the body becomes a nerve cell and not a skin cell, is one of the most intriguing questions facing biologists today.

2 Respiration

As explained in the previous chapter, organisms maintain themselves by the continual expenditure of energy. Most cells derive this energy from the breakdown of food molecules, a process known as *cellular* or *internal respiration*. Substances that are broken down to yield energy are called *respiratory substrates*. Although most organisms can respire a mixture of substrates, that is, fats, proteins and carbohydrates, the latter are by far the most important and widely used energy source.

The respiratory process generally starts with the breakdown of some of the organism's carbohydrate reserves (usually glycogen in animals and starch in plants) to the monosaccharide glucose. In most organisms the glucose is broken down to carbon dioxide and water in a process which requires molecules of oxygen, and is known as *aerobic respiration*. This process can be summarised as follows:

$$C_6H_{12}O_6 + 6O_2 \rightarrow 6CO_2 + 6H_2O + \text{energy}$$

$$\text{glucose} \qquad \text{oxygen} \qquad \text{carbon} \quad \text{water}$$
$$\text{dioxide}$$

Respiration can also proceed in the absence of oxygen molecules, a process known as *anaerobic respiration*, in which glucose is partially broken down, to lactic acid in animals, and to carbon dioxide and alcohol in plants. The latter process is also called *alcoholic fermentation*. The anaerobic processes can be summarised as follows:

anaerobic respiration in plants $\quad C_6H_{12}O_6 \rightarrow 2C_2H_5OH + 2CO_2 + \text{energy}$
$$\text{ethyl}$$
$$\text{alcohol}$$

anaerobic respiration in animals $\quad C_6H_{12}O_6 \rightarrow 2CH_3CHOH.COOH + \text{energy}$
$$\text{lactic acid}$$

The partial breakdown of glucose yields only a fraction of the potential energy stored in the molecule. The energy yield from anaerobic respiration is accordingly much lower than that of aerobic respiration (see p. 15).

The equation given for aerobic respiration also applies to the burning of glucose in air. Although the final energy yield is the same however, the two processes are very different. The combustion of glucose in air proceeds extremely rapidly and most of the molecule's energy is dissipated as heat. This method of glucose breakdown is not only wasteful of energy, it is also incompatible with conditions inside living cells. The sudden release of such a large amount of heat would raise the temperature in cells to a level that would destroy the enzymes on which the continued existence of cells depends. Thus, in the cell, glucose is broken down in a series of carefully controlled reactions, during which energy is made available in relatively small amounts which can be harnessed and made to perform work. A much smaller proportion of the energy in the glucose molecule is dissipated as heat during this process (at most about forty per cent).

The energy made available during the respiratory process is stored in molecules of *adenosine triphosphate*, usually called ATP.

THE ROLE OF ATP AS A STORE AND SUPPLIER OF ENERGY

ATP occurs in all living cells. It is the universal energy 'currency'. All the energy-requiring activities of the organism, such as synthetic processes, muscle contraction, production of electrical impulses, and many others, depend on ATP as their immediate source of energy. The structure of ATP can be represented as follows:

Energy is supplied by the splitting of the bond that attaches the terminal phosphate group to the rest of the molecule. The bond is broken by *hydrolysis*, the splitting of a substance by the addition of a water molecule. This reaction yields a large amount of energy (about 33 kJ mol^{-1}). Because of this high energy yield ATP is often called an 'energy-rich' or 'high-energy' molecule, and the bond holding the terminal phosphate is called a '*high-energy*' *bond*. The latter is generally represented by the symbol $\sim$, as in the formula above. Actually the term 'high-energy bond' is rather misleading as some of the energy possessed by the molecule as a whole is released, in addition to the bond energy of the terminal phosphate group. The terminal phosphate group of ADP can also be removed by hydrolysis with the same high energy yield but this reaction does not proceed as readily.

ATP thus provides a source of energy that is easily and rapidly accessible to any energy-requiring process. The relationship between ATP and glucose as energy sources can be compared to the difference between currency and cheques. If ATP is the 'energy currency' which can be rapidly 'spent' by hydrolysis, glucose molecules are the 'energy cheques', which can be 'cashed' by respiration. It is tempting to take this analogy further and compare the carbohydrate reserves, starch and glycogen, to energy 'current accounts' which are used up and replaced steadily, and the longer term fat reserves to energy 'deposit accounts' which are paid in intermittently in times of plenty and cashed only in special circumstances.

THE FORMATION OF ATP

Molecules of ATP are constantly being 'spent' and must be replaced. They are formed from ADP and inorganic phosphate by *condensation* (the joining of two substances by the removal of a molecule of water). This reaction is also a *phosphorylation*. This is a term used to describe any reaction in which phosphate is added to a molecule.

The regeneration of ATP requires a supply of energy equal to that which it yields on hydrolysis. This energy is supplied by respiration. There are two mechanisms which direct the energy yield from respiration into the formation of ATP; namely substrate-linked phosphorylation and oxidative phosphorylation.

Substrate-linked phosphorylation

At two stages in the respiratory sequence (see Figure 3) phosphate is detached from one of the intermediate compounds of glucose breakdown (*respiratory intermediates*), together with sufficient energy to form a bond with ADP. This process occurs in the cytoplasm and, unlike the other process (oxidative phosphorylation) does not require a supply of oxygen molecules.

Oxidative phosphorylation

As its name suggests, this process involves *oxidation* reactions. Such reactions tend to have a high energy yield, and it is this energy that is used to combine inorganic phosphate and ADP. Before going any further, it will be as well to clarify exactly what constitutes an oxidation reaction. The following types of reaction are all described as oxidations.

1 The addition of oxygen to a molecule,

$$\text{e.g.} \quad C + O_2 \rightarrow CO_2 \text{ (the burning of carbon in air)}$$

2 The removal of hydrogen from a molecule (*dehydrogenation*). The general equation for this reaction can be written thus:

$$AH_2 + B \rightarrow A + BH_2$$

3 The removal of an electron from a charged ion, e.g.

$$Fe^{++} - e^- \text{(an electron)} \quad \rightarrow \quad Fe^{+++}$$

ferrous	ferric
iron	iron
(iron II)	(iron III)

The term *reduction* is used to describe reactions which are the reverse of oxidation, namely the removal of oxygen or the addition of hydrogen or electrons. It will be seen that oxidation and reduction are interdependent in that one substance cannot be oxidised without another being reduced.

All three types of oxidation are involved in oxidative phosphorylation. First, pairs of hydrogen atoms are removed from a number of respiratory intermediates by dehydrogenase enzymes; the respiratory intermediates are thus oxidised. The hydrogen removed from the respiratory intermediates is transferred to special *hydrogen-carrier* or *hydrogen-acceptor* molecules, usually *nicotinamide adenine dinucleotide* (NAD) or *flavoprotein* (FAD). These molecules are also described as coenzymes because they are essential for the functioning of the dehydrogenase enzymes (these enzymes require the presence of a molecule which will accept the hydrogen they remove).

The hydrogen removed by the hydrogen-acceptors is eventually combined with oxygen to form water (the hydrogen is thus oxidised). The hydrogen is not passed directly to the oxygen however. It is first passed along a chain of intermediate carriers. The whole sequence of carriers, including the initial hydrogen-acceptors, comprise the *respiratory chain* (see Figure 2). Each of the carriers in the respiratory chain is successively reduced and then oxidised as it first accepts and then hands on the hydrogen. In fact, after the flavoprotein, it is only the electrons of the hydrogen atoms that are passed along the chain. Flavoprotein is an enzyme that splits hydrogen atoms into hydrogen ions and electrons thus:

$$H \rightarrow H^+ + e^- \quad \text{(an electron)}$$

The hydrogen ion remains in solution and is reunited with the electron at the end of the respiratory chain.

The part of the respiratory chain after flavoprotein is known as the *electron transport chain*. Each carrier in this chain has a greater affinity for electrons than its predecessor so there is a one-way flow of electrons along the chain. The electron transport chain consists of ubiquinone and several *cytochromes*. The latter are a group of closely related proteins, each of which is combined with an iron-containing ring compound called *haem*. (In this they resemble another important respiratory protein, haemoglobin.) The state of the iron is altered from the oxidised ferric (Fe^{+++}) form to the reduced ferrous (Fe^{++}) form, and then back to the oxidised form as the cytochrome accepts and then passes on electrons.

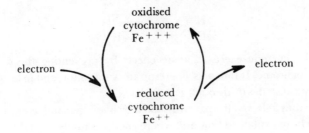

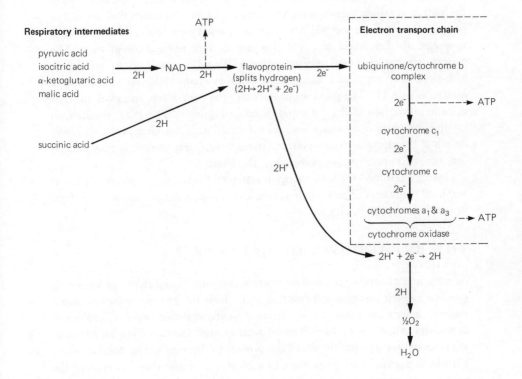

Figure 2   The respiratory chain

Hydrogen with 'excited' electrons is removed from the respiratory intermediates to NAD or flavoprotein. Flavoproteins split the hydrogen into hydrogen ions and electrons. The electrons then pass from carrier to carrier in the electron-transport chain, losing energy in the process. This energy is directed into the formation of ATP from ADP and inorganic phosphate at the points indicated. The electrons are eventually reunited with the hydrogen ions and then combined with oxygen to form water.

At the final cytochromes in the chain, a_1 and a_3, which together comprise cytochrome oxidase, the electrons are reunited with the hydrogen ions, and then combine with molecules of oxygen to form water.

$$2H^+ + 2e^- \longrightarrow 2H$$
$$2H + \tfrac{1}{2}O_2 \longrightarrow H_2O$$

Incidentally, cyanide exerts its toxic effects by preventing the oxidation of reduced cytochrome. It thus acts as a respiratory inhibitor, and in large amounts can rapidly cause death through energy lack.

We have thus followed the pathway taken by hydrogen and its electrons, but it has not yet been explained how and where energy is made available during this process. Energy is derived from the original splitting away of hydrogen atoms from the respiratory intermediates. This energy is transferred to the electrons of the hydrogen raising them to a higher energy level, in which state they are said to be 'excited'. As these 'excited' electrons are passed from one carrier to another they give up their extra energy and return to their normal energy state. The energy they give up is used to join together ADP and inorganic phosphate. A pair of hydrogen atoms passed along the respiratory chain yields on average three molecules of ATP. The positions in the carrier system where energy is directed into the formation of ATP are indicated in Figure 2. The exact mechanism linking the respiratory chain and ATP formation is not clear. Indeed, many details of the electron carrier system are not completely settled. It may well be that other components are involved in the chain.

Having examined the way energy is removed during the respiratory process and used to make ATP, we will now consider the sequence of reactions involved in the degradation of glucose.

THE BREAKDOWN OF GLUCOSE

Aerobic and anaerobic respiration share a common initial pathway known as *glycolysis* (which means sugar-splitting), in which the glucose is broken down through a series of reactions to pyruvic (2-oxopropanoic) acid. Glycolysis is sometimes called the *Embden-Meyerhof pathway* after the two German scientists who worked out the full details of the process in the 1930s. The breakdown of glucose to pyruvic acid takes place in the cytoplasm and does not require the presence of oxygen molecules. The reactions of glycolysis are summarised in Figure 3.

The energy yield of glycolysis

As each molecule of glucose is degraded to two molecules of pyruvic acid, four molecules of ATP are formed by substrate-linked phosphorylation. Two molecules of ATP are 'spent' in the phosphorylation of glucose and fructose phosphate. Thus, the net yield is two molecules of ATP per glucose molecule. However, if oxygen is present the two pairs of hydrogen atoms removed by NAD (one pair from each triose phosphate) can be passed to the respiratory chain and will there yield a further six molecules of ATP (by oxidative phosphorylation). Thus in conditions where oxygen is available the net gain from glycolysis is eight molecules of ATP per glucose molecule.

The fate of pyruvic acid differs according to whether oxygen is present or not and, in the latter circumstance, according to whether plant or animal cells are being considered.

The final anaerobic pathway in plants

In the absence of oxygen pyruvic acid is converted to acetaldehyde (ethanal) and carbon dioxide.

$$CH_3 - C(=O) - COOH \rightleftharpoons CH_3 - C(\!\!\!/\!\!\!\diagdown\ O\ H) + CO_2$$

pyruvic acid   acetaldehyde

The $NADH_2$ formed during glycolysis is then used to reduce the acetaldehyde to ethanol. The oxidised NAD is then free to pick up more hydrogen atoms.

$$CH_3 - C(\!\!\!/\!\!\!\diagdown\ O\ H) + NADH_2 \rightleftharpoons CH_3 - CH_2OH + NAD$$

acetaldehyde   ethanol

The final anaerobic pathway in animals

In animal cells the pyruvic acid is reduced by the $NADH_2$, formed during glycolysis, to lactic (2-hydroxypropanoic) acid.

$$CH_3 - C(=O) - COOH + NADH_2 \rightleftharpoons CH_3 - CHOH - COOH + NAD$$

pyruvic acid   lactic acid

The energy yield of anaerobic respiration

There is no further energy yield in the anaerobic pathways after glycolysis. The net yield from anaerobic respiration is thus two molecules of ATP per glucose

Figure 3 An outline of glycolysis

This is the initial pathway shared by both aerobic and anaerobic respiration. The process takes place in the cytoplasm and is not dependent on the presence of oxygen. It comprises two stages: in the first, glucose is phosphorylated to fructose disphosphate, and this is provided with activation energy enabling the subsequent breakdown of the molecule to proceed. After phosphorylation, the substrate breaks down to pyruvic acid and, in so doing, makes energy available which is used to form ATP. Each of the reactions shown above is catalysed by an enzyme.

Glucose is a rather unreactive molecule. Before it can participate in the reactions that follow, it must be supplied with activation energy. This is achieved by phosphorylation. The terminal phosphate of ATP together with some energy is added to the glucose forming glucose phosphate.

The glucose phosphate molecule is reorganised to form fructose phosphate.

Another ATP molecule is 'spent' to provide more activation energy as fructose phosphate is phosphorylated to fructose diphosphate.

Fructose diphosphate splits into two, interconvertible, 3-carbon compounds known as triose phosphates. Only one of these, glyceraldehyde phosphate, can participate in the reactions that follow, but the other, dihydroxyacetone phosphate, is reorganised to form glyceraldehyde phosphate thus ensuring that both halves of the original 6-carbon molecule are used.

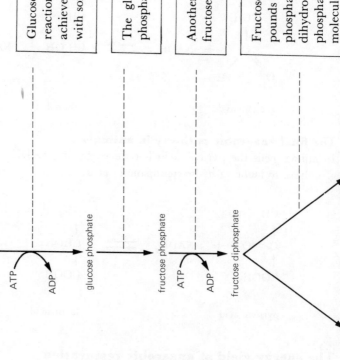

glucose → glucose phosphate → fructose phosphate → fructose diphosphate

ATP → ADP

ATP → ADP

glyceraldehyde phosphate

dihydroxyacetone phosphate ⇌ glyceraldehyde phosphate

Hydrogen is removed by NAD and inorganic phosphate is added to form diphosphoglyceric acid. The 'new' phosphate group differs from the other one in that it is joined to the rest of the molecule by an energy-rich bond (this bond derives it's energy from the reorganisation of energy within the molecule).

Diphosphoglyceric acid reacts with ADP to form ATP (substrate linked phosphorylation) and phosphoglyceric acid (PGA).

The PGA is rearranged to alter the position of the phosphate group. The elements of water are then removed forming phosphoenol pyruvic acid. The removal of water transforms the phosphate bond into a high-energy bond.

The phosphate group of phosphoenol pyruvic acid is transferred to ADP forming ATP. The enolpyruvic acid that remains is spontaneously rearranged to form pyruvic acid.

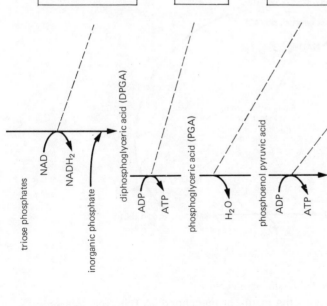

molecule respired or two moles of ATP per mole of glucose (a mole is a molecular weight in grams). Two moles of ATP represent an energy store of about 66 kJ. This is a small return from glucose, which stores about 2800 kJ mol^{-1}.

The aerobic pathway

If oxygen is present the pyruvic acid enters a mitochondrion (see p. 15) and there embarks on a sequence of reactions that involves the removal of hydrogen atoms to the respiratory chain, and the removal of carbon dioxide molecules. These reactions are outlined in Figure 4. The removal of carbon dioxide is always linked to a dehydrogenation and so is called *oxidative decarboxylation*.

The first step in this sequence is the conversion of pyruvic acid to acetyl coenzyme A (acetyl-coA) by oxidative decarboxylation. The 2-carbon acetyl part of the acetyl-coA is then combined with a 4-carbon compound, oxaloacetic acid, to form a 6-carbon compound, citric acid (2 hydroxypropane-1,2,3-tricarboxylic acid), and in so doing enters the *tricarboxylic acid cycle* – so called because several of the key substances in the cycle are acids with three carboxyl (COOH) groups. The tricarboxylic acid cycle or TCA is also known as the *Krebs cycle*, after the British biochemist who contributed most to its discovery.

In the Krebs cycle the 6-carbon citric acid is gradually broken down by four

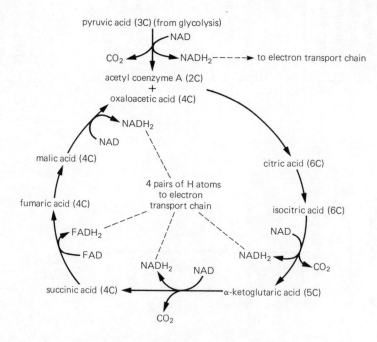

Figure 4   The Krebs or tricarboxylic acid cycle
These reactions take place in the matrix of mitochondria. The cycle will only operate if molecules of oxygen are available to combine with the hydrogen removed from the respiratory intermediates. As in glycolysis each of the reactions shown above is catalysed by a specific enzyme.

dehydrogenations and two decarboxylations to reform the 4-carbon oxaloacetic acid. This compound then combines with another molecule of acetyl-coA, and the cycle continues. The Krebs cycle can be simply represented as follows:

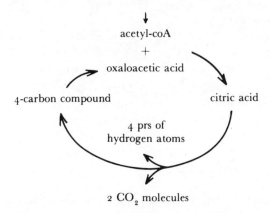

The energy yield of aerobic respiration

Five pairs of hydrogen atoms are removed as pyruvic acid is broken down in the aerobic pathway, four pairs from each turn of the Krebs cycle and one pair from the initial conversion of pyruvic acid into acetyl-coA. The total yield from this part of the respiratory process is thus ten pairs of hydrogen atoms per glucose molecule (each glucose molecule is broken down to two molecules of pyruvic acid). As each pair of hydrogen atoms provides sufficient energy to form three molecules of ATP, thirty ATP molecules will be formed by oxidative phosphorylation. To this must be added the two molecules of ATP formed during glycolysis, and we must not forget the two pairs of hydrogen atoms removed during this process, which, in the presence of oxygen, can yield a further six molecules of ATP.

The total yield from aerobic respiration is thus thirty-eight molecules of ATP. This represents an energy store of about 1188 kJ per mole of glucose, approximately twenty times greater than can be obtained by anaerobic respiration.

The site of the aerobic process

Mitochondria are found in nearly all cells. They tend to be most abundant in cells with a high energy requirement. Their structure is illustrated in Figure 5. They are sausage-shaped organelles comprising two unit membranes which enclose an aqueous solution, the matrix. The inner membrane is folded into cristae which project into the matrix. Attached to the cristae are tiny spheres or granules.

Mitochondria contain more than seventy enzymes and coenzymes. The matrix contains the enzymes involved in the Krebs cycle and the breakdown of fatty acids (see the section that follows on the use of fats as respiratory substrates), while the inner mitochondrial membrane contains the enzymes and electron

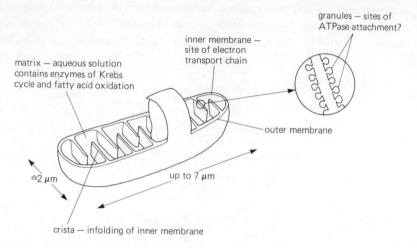

Figure 5 Diagram of mitochondrial structure (most of the top half has been removed to show the internal arrangement)

carriers of the electron transport system. It is generally supposed that the carriers and enzymes are embedded in the membrane, spaced in such a way that electrons can flow easily from one to the other. There is some evidence to suggest that the spheres on the inner membrane may be the sites of ATPase, the enzyme that brings about the formation of ATP from ADP and inorganic phosphate (when sufficient energy is available). The cristae presumably serve to increase the surface area for enzyme and carrier attachment. Supporting this, it has been observed that the cristae are more numerous in cells with a high energy requirement.

The mitochondria are thus the 'power plants' of the cell, responsible for most of the ATP production in aerobic organisms.

RESPIRATION USING OTHER SUBSTRATES

As already mentioned, carbohydrates are not the only source of energy. In certain circumstances, fats and proteins can supply part of the organism's energy needs. The breakdown of fats and proteins is largely dependent on the presence of oxygen as they are converted into substances, most of which enter the Krebs cycle where they are oxidised to yield their energy. The interrelationships between proteins, fats and carbohydrates are summarised in Figure 6.

You will find it helpful to refer to chapter 4, where the structure of fats and proteins is described, before reading the following sections.

The use of fats as a respiratory substrate

Fats form the long-term energy stores in many organisms. They are generally

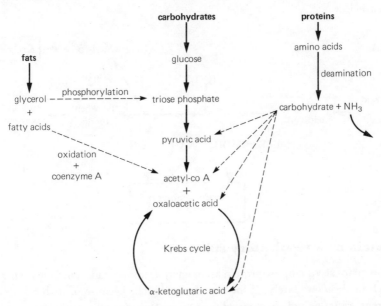

Figure 6   Diagram summarising the interrelationships of fats, carbohydrates and proteins

used only when the carbohydrate reserves are exhausted. Fats usually have a much higher energy yield than glucose. Therefore, weight for weight, far more energy can be stored in the form of fat.

The way in which fats are broken down to yield energy is best known in mammals, and so will be described here. The fats are first removed from the fat depots (under the skin and around various internal organs), a process known as mobilisation. They are then transported to the liver where they split into fatty (alkanoic) acids and glycerol (propane 1,2,3-triol). These two substances then follow separate pathways. The glycerol is phosphorylated to form triose phosphate which enters the respiratory sequence. The fatty acids are split in a series of oxidations. They are first combined with coenzyme A forming a fatty acid/coA complex. The energy required for this first step is derived from the splitting of ATP to AMP. The fatty acid/coA complex is carried from the cytoplasm into the mitochondrial matrix. In the reactions that follow, two hydrogen atoms are removed and passed to flavoprotein, and then to the electron transport chain. Water is then added and two more hydrogen atoms are removed to the electron transport chain, this time by NAD. Finally, the two terminal carbon atoms of the fatty acid are removed together with coenzyme A, as acetyl coA, which enters the respiratory sequence. The rest of the fatty acid then combines with more coenzyme A, and the process is repeated again and again with a 2-carbon portion of the fatty acid removed at each stage until the entire fatty acid molecule has been broken up and oxidised. The longer the fatty acid chain, the greater will be the energy yield. An outline of fatty acid breakdown is given below.

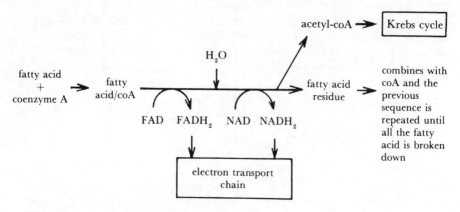

Protein as a respiratory substrate

Many plant seeds employ protein as an energy storage material. One such seed, much in the news lately, is the soya bean which, because of its high protein content, is increasingly being used as a meat substitute. Animals do not generally employ protein as an energy reserve. Thus, if they use protein as an energy source, they do so at the expense of their own tissue proteins. Accordingly, proteins are only respired by animals as a last resort in cases of prolonged starvation.

When proteins are respired they are first broken down into their constituent amino acids. These are then deaminated, that is, their nitrogen-containing amino group is removed. The products of deamination are ammonia and a carbon-containing residue (different amino acids yield different residues). An example of a deamination is shown below.

$$CH_3CH.NH_2COOH + \tfrac{1}{2}O_2 \rightarrow \underset{\text{Krebs cycle}}{\nearrow}\; CH_3CO.COOH + NH_3$$

| alanine | pyruvic acid | ammonia |

(2-amino propanoic acid)

The ammonia is toxic and must be removed from the body. The residue enters the respiratory sequence, either directly as in the example above, or indirectly, via further reactions. The points at which most of the carbohydrates derived from amino acids enter the respiratory sequence are set out in Figure 6.

As with fats, the energy yield from protein breakdown is generally much higher than that of carbohydrates.

SURVIVAL IN CONDITIONS OF OXYGEN SHORTAGE

It is generally believed that the first forms of life on this planet were anaerobic, and that part of the anaerobic process (glycolysis) was retained as organisms evolved the biochemical machinery to complete the breakdown of the respiratory substrate and so extract a much greater proportion of the energy contained in the molecule. The majority of organisms today are so dependent on the aerobic process, *aerobiosis*, that they will die if deprived of oxygen for more than a few minutes. Such organisms are described as *aerobes*. At the other extreme, some organisms depend entirely on anaerobic respiration. These organisms are called *anaerobes*, and include many parasitic flatworms, as well as many of the bacteria that bring about the decay of organic material. Both of these live in conditions where oxygen is not readily available. Some anaerobes are actually poisoned by oxygen.

Certain organisms, notably yeast and some other fungi, are described as *partial anaerobes* because, although they normally respire aerobically, they can respire anaerobically for extended periods if oxygen is not available. It is sometimes mistakenly supposed that yeast can go on respiring anaerobically indefinitely. This is not the case, yeast is unable to grow and reproduce when respiring anaerobically, and the toxic alcoholic end-product of the process will kill the yeast if it exceeds a certain concentration, usually about eighteen per cent.

Returning to aerobic organisms, while it is true that they are rapidly killed by total oxygen deprivation, most have evolved mechanisms which enable them to survive periods of oxygen shortage. One such adaptation is the possession of tissues which can respire anaerobically for limited periods. The muscles of vertebrates provide an example of such a tissue. They can survive anaerobic conditions for many minutes, much longer than, for example, brain cells which suffer irreparable damage if deprived of oxygen for more than one or two minutes. One value of this is that in conditions of oxygen shortage, blood can be diverted away from the muscles to the tissues that need it most. This mechanism is particularly well developed in diving animals such as the seal. During a dive, constriction of the blood vessels supplying the muscles cuts off their blood supply and diverts blood (carrying oxygen) to the heart and brain. The muscles respire anaerobically and the heart rate slows to accommodate the reduced circulation. In this way these animals can remain submerged for up to twenty minutes without harm. Similar modifications are found in the circulatory systems of alligators and diving birds such as cormorants and puffins.

Human muscles 'switch over' to anaerobic respiration during strenuous activity, such as running, when the circulatory system cannot supply oxygen to the muscles sufficiently quickly to supply their energy needs. When the muscles respire anaerobically, lactic acid accumulates. The length of time that the muscles can respire anaerobically is largely determined by their tolerance to lactic acid. Regular exertion can build up tolerance to lactic acid.

The accumulation of lactic acid creates what is known as the *oxygen debt*. After the exercise, the lactic acid is converted back to pyruvic acid and enters the aerobic pathway. The debt must then be repaid, that is, extra oxygen must be taken in to complete the breakdown of the pyruvic acid derived from lactic acid. This is usually achieved by panting rapidly in the period immediately after the activity.

Some organisms vary their respiratory habits during their life history. For example, many plant seeds respire anaerobically, and the pupal stages of certain insects enter an inactive stage (diapause) during which they respire anaerobically.

MEASURING RESPIRATORY RATES

The rate of respiration is usually measured in terms of the amount of oxygen consumed or the amount of carbon dioxide produced. The apparatus used to measure respiratory rates is called a *respirometer* (see Figure 7). There are many different designs, but most types share the following features. The respiring organisms are placed in an airtight vessel and changes in gas volume are measured at selected time intervals, usually by recording changes in the level of liquid in a manometer tube connected to the vessel. If oxygen uptake is to be investigated, sodium hydroxide is placed in the apparatus to absorb carbon dioxide and then any decrease in gas volume can be attributed to oxygen consumption by the respiring tissue. The weight of the respiring tissues should be recorded so that respiratory rate can be expressed per gramme of respiring tissue; this is essential if the respiratory rates of different tissues or organisms are to be compared.

The respiratory rate is generally taken as a measure of the *metabolic rate*. The two rates are approximately equivalent, as all metabolic processes require energy at some stage, and this is provided by respiration. Thus, the higher the metabolic rate, the higher the respiratory rate, and vice versa.

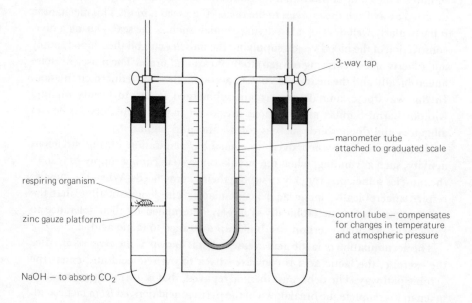

Figure 7 A simple respirometer

RESPIRATORY QUOTIENTS

The ratio of carbon dioxide produced to oxygen absorbed $\left(\dfrac{CO_2 \text{ produced}}{O_2 \text{ absorbed}}\right)$ is known as the *respiratory quotient* or *RQ*. The respiratory quotient of a respiring tissue gives an indication of the type of respiration involved (whether aerobic or anaerobic) and the nature of the respiratory substrate.

If the production of carbon dioxide exceeds the oxygen uptake ($RQ > 1$), this generally means that some anaerobic respiration is taking place, and if the RQ is very high (>6) it is almost certain that respiration is entirely anaerobic.

The theoretical respiratory quotients of the different respiratory substrates can be calculated by studying their complete oxidation equations. The complete oxidation of glucose is represented as follows:

$$C_6H_{12}O_6 + 6O_2 \rightarrow 6CO_2 + 6H_2O$$

Thus when one molecule of glucose is completely oxidised, six molecules of oxygen are absorbed and six molecules of carbon dioxide are produced;

$$RQ = \frac{6}{6} = 1.0$$

An RQ of 1.0 thus indicates that carbohydrates are being respired. Comparing this with the complete oxidation of a fat, triolein:

$$C_{57}H_{104}O_6 + 80\ O_2 \rightarrow 57\ CO_2 + 52\ H_2O$$

$$RQ = \frac{57}{80} = 0.71$$

Other fats, having different fatty acids, give slightly different values, but they mostly have RQs around 0.7. The RQs of proteins are even more variable but usually lie between 0.5 and 0.8.

The interpretation of respiratory quotients requires some caution. The following are just a few of the factors that can produce a misleading RQ value:

 (i) if a mixture of substrates is respired
 (ii) if some anaerobic respiration is taking place (the RQ will be raised)
(iii) if carbohydrate is being converted to fat, carbon dioxide will be produced which will raise the RQ (this happens in animals about to hibernate).

In spite of these limitations, RQs have proved a useful tool, especially in studies of the respiratory changes that occur during an organism's development, or when an organism is subjected to certain external changes. In such studies, variations in RQ not only pinpoint when a respiratory change occurs, but also provide some indication as to the nature of the change. These indications can then be checked by detailed analyses of the energy reserves.

QUESTIONS

1 Explain what is meant by the following terms:
  (a) cellular respiration
  (b) respiratory substrate
  (c) alcoholic fermentation.

2 Discuss the circumstances in which (a) carbohydrate (b) fat and (c) protein are the substrates for cell respiration, and the circumstances in which (i) carbon dioxide and (ii) lactic acid are the end-products.

3 Explain the part played by the following processes in glycolysis:
  (a) phosphorylation of glucose and fructose phosphate,
  (b) substrate-linked phosphorylation.

4 Describe the part played by the electron transport chain in the respiratory process. Why is oxygen necessary for its functioning?

5 Explain why the mitochondrion is described as the 'power plant' of the cell.

6 Aerobic respiration involves two major steps, glycolysis and the Krebs cycle. Explain, in outline only, what each of these steps involves and how energy is obtained from them. Explain why anaerobic respiration yields a smaller amount of energy than aerobic respiration.

7 What is meant by the term 'oxygen debt'? How is such a debt
  (a) built up, and (b) repaid?

3 Gas exchange

Aerobic respiration demands a continuous flow of oxygen into cells accompanied by the rapid removal of the carbon dioxide they produce. These two processes comprise *external respiration* or *gas exchange*.

Two evolutionary changes have played a major part in shaping gas exchange mechanisms, namely *increasing size*, which has tended to accompany increasing complexity of structure, and the *colonisation of land*, which occurred separately in many different groups of organisms.

Consider first the difficulties presented by increased size. The respiratory gases pass into and out of cells by diffusion along a concentration gradient. They do so in aqueous solution. Diffusion in water is a fairly slow process whose efficiency as a means of transport is determined by the following factors:

(i) the concentration gradient, which in the case of oxygen depends on the external oxygen concentration (oxygen tension) and the rate at which oxygen is used up;
(ii) the area over which diffusion takes place;
(iii) the distance over which the concentration gradient must operate (the length of the diffusion pathway).

From the above it is apparent that two structural features of the organism will determine whether diffusion through the body surface can supply its gas exchange needs, namely surface area and the distance from the surface to the innermost respiring cell. If the surface area through which gases enter and leave is large enough, and the distance they must travel inside the body is small enough, diffusion will suffice as the means of transport.

In animals these conditions are only met in unicells, flatworms, and certain other small animals whose surface is very large relative to their volume. Diffusion also supplies the respiratory needs of coelenterates, whose actively-metabolising cells are restricted to a single layer in contact with the water (both inside and outside the body) thus limiting the distance the gases have to travel even in the largest forms.

As animals increase in size their surface area to volume ratio decreases so that, above a certain size, diffusion alone cannot supply the respiratory needs. In animals like the earthworm, the body surface is still large enough to supply the gas exchange requirements but the movement of the respiratory gases within the organism is speeded up by a special transporting system – the blood circulatory system. In larger or more active animals, or in animals living in conditions of oxygen shortage, the body surface is not usually large enough to supply the respiratory needs – even with a circulatory system to speed the delivery of the respiratory gases. In such circumstances large, specialised gas exchange or *respiratory surfaces* such as *lungs* and *gills* have developed, that either replace, or supplement, respiration through the skin. Another development frequently associated with gas exchange in large or active animals is some kind of *ventilating mechanism*. Such mechanisms ensure the constant renewal of the respiratory medium (either air or water) at the respiratory surface and, in so doing, help to maintain the concentration gradient.

The situation in plants is rather different; even the largest forms rely on diffusion alone to supply their respiratory needs. Gas exchange in plants is discussed in detail at the end of this chapter.

Consider next the colonisation of land. Organisms leaving the water to live on land faced the difficulty of keeping the respiratory surface moist in drying terrestrial conditions. The respiratory gases can only diffuse through cells in aqueous solution. For this reason water must be present on the respiratory surface, to allow carbon dioxide to pass out of the cells at this surface, and to dissolve oxygen so that it can enter the cells. Another difficulty presented by life on land is that the soft gills animals use for gas exchange in water are unsuitable for terrestrial respiration, because they depend (at least in part) on the surrounding water for support, and so collapse in air. Both these difficulties were overcome by the development of internally situated respiratory organs such as lungs and tracheae.

A comparison of air and water as respiratory media

Apart from the lack of support for respiratory structures and the drying effects of air, other differences between the two media have had significant effects on respiration in organisms. Perhaps the most obvious difference is that a given volume of air contains much more oxygen than the same volume of water; air contains about 210 cm^3 of oxygen per litre, or about twenty one per cent, as compared with 5 to 10 cm^3 per litre, or 0.5 to 1.0 per cent in water, according to the temperature. The greatly increased amount of oxygen available to terrestrial organisms has enabled them to develop much higher metabolic rates than would be possible in water. This in turn has allowed them to achieve a generally higher degree of physiological complexity.

The greater weight of transporting medium needed to bring a given amount of oxygen to the respiratory surface (some 100 000 times greater in water than in air), and the greater viscosity of water (some fifty times greater than that of air), necessitate a one-way flow of water through the gas exchange organs of aquatic animals. Too much energy would otherwise have to be expended stopping, and then reversing, the flow of liquid. This contrasts with the situation in terrestrial animals where the flow of air through the respiratory organs is often two-way.

In the sections that follow, three important respiratory mechanisms, namely teleost (bony fish) gills, mammalian lungs and insect tracheae are described.

GAS EXCHANGE IN A TELEOST

Fish gills consist of several paired gill arches lying on either side of the buccal cavity, protected by a muscular flap, the *operculum* (Figure 8(a)). From each gill arch extend two rows of *gill filaments* or *primary lamellae*. These are spread like curtains to separate the buccal cavity and the opercular cavity (Figure 8(b)). Each filament bears rows of closely packed, shelf-like *secondary lamellae* on both surfaces. The secondary lamellae contain a capillary network. Gas exchange occurs between the blood in these capillaries and the water current flowing past them. The water passing through the gills and the blood travelling in the lamellar capillaries flow in opposite directions (Figures 8(c) and (d)). This type of arrangement is called *counter current flow*, and it greatly increases the efficiency of gas exchange, as we shall see later.

Other devices, apart from the opercular flaps, serve to protect the delicate gills. In many fish the gill arches bear comb-like *gill rakers* which project across the openings into the opercular cavity and strain out any particles that might otherwise injure the gill filaments. In fish lacking gill rakers, the flow of water can be reversed suddenly to dislodge any particles caught in the gills, a mechanism analogous to coughing in mammals.

From the description of fish gills above, it is apparent that they provide a very extensive surface area for gas exchange. The gill surface may be as much as ten times larger than the body surface area. As might be expected, the more active the fish, the larger the gill surface area relative to body weight. Thus the highly active mackerel has a gill surface area, expressed per gramme body weight, some ten times greater than that of the relatively inactive flounder, and fifty times greater than the sluggish goosefish.

Ventilation

If water were to remain in contact with the gills for any length of time, the oxygen would soon be used up. Some sort of ventilating mechanism must therefore be employed. A few fast-moving fish, such as mackerel and tuna, maintain a continuous current of water through the gills by swimming along with the mouth open. This method suffers from the disadvantage that, if the fish stops swimming for extended periods of time, it will die of asphyxiation (oxygen deprivation).

Most fish employ muscular movements of the operculum and buccal cavity to ventilate the gills. The sequence of events involved in ventilation is illustrated in Figure 9. Starting with inspiration, the floor of the buccal cavity is lowered, reducing the pressure in the buccal cavity and causing water to pass in through the open mouth. The mouth is then closed and the floor of the buccal cavity is raised. This increases the pressure in the buccal cavity and causes water to pass through the gills into the opercular cavity. The flow of water from the buccal cavity into the opercular chamber is assisted by movements of the opercular flaps. These bulge outwards, while the opercular valves remain closed, thus lowering the pressure in the opercular cavity relative to the pressure in the buccal cavity.

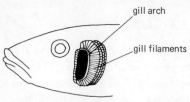

(a) head with operculum removed to show gills

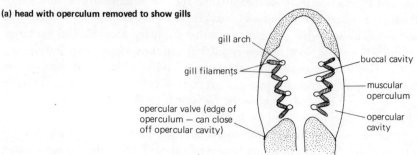

(b) gill arrangement

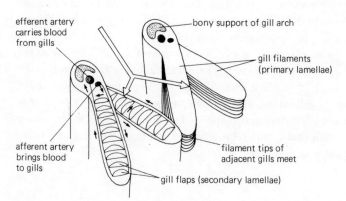

(c) gill filaments and their blood supply

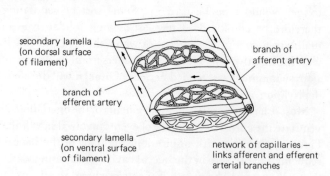

(d) portion of primary lamella

Figure 8 (a) – (d) The gas exchange apparatus of a bony fish, showing the counter current flow of the water and the blood in the lamellar capillaries. White arrows show direction of water flow; dark arrows show direction of blood flow.

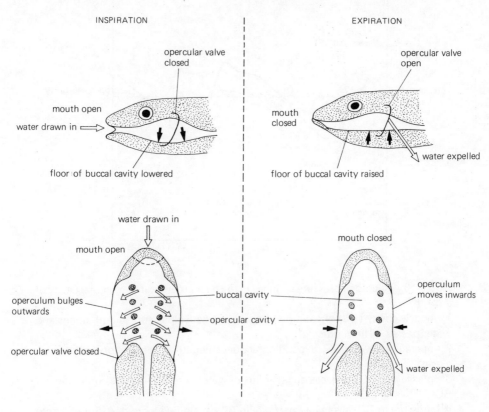

opercular valve closed

mouth open

water drawn in ⇨

floor of buccal cavity lowered

opercular valve open

mouth closed

water expelled

floor of buccal cavity raised

water drawn in

mouth open

mouth closed

operculum bulges outwards

buccal cavity

opercular cavity

operculum moves inwards

opercular valve closed

water expelled

Figure 9   Ventilation movements in a bony fish (see text)

During expiration the opercular flap moves inwards, increasing the pressure in the opercular cavity and eventually forcing water out through the opercular valves. Water does not pass back into the buccal cavity during expiration because the pressure in the latter is higher than the pressure in the opercular cavity. This can be demonstrated by inserting polythene tubes attached to manometers into the opercular and buccal cavities, and then recording pressure changes in the two chambers during the ventilation cycle. Figure 10 shows the results of such an experiment, and reveals that the pressure in the buccal cavity is higher than that in the opercular cavity throughout most of the ventilation cycle. This difference in pressure thus provides an almost continuous, one-way flow of water across the gills.

Gas exchange at the gill surface

Oxygen diffuses from the water into the blood in the lamellar capillaries along a concentration gradient. Carbon dioxide diffuses in the opposite direction. The layer of cells that separates the blood and the water is very thin and offers little resistance to the passage of gases. Once in the blood, most of the oxygen combines with haemoglobin; the oxygenated blood is then carried to all parts of the body.

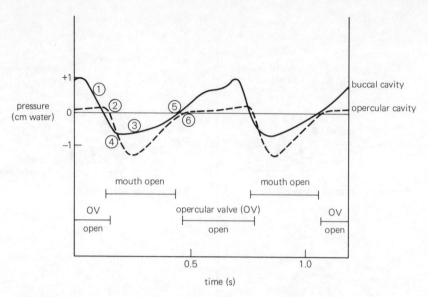

Figure 10 Record of pressure changes in the buccal cavity and opercular cavity of a roach

1 buccal cavity (BC) expanding acquires a negative pressure; mouth opens and water passes in from outside:

2 opercular cavity (OC) expanding acquires negative pressure; opercular valve closes:

3 pressure in BC increases due to influx of water from outside and contraction of BC:

4 pressure in OC falls below pressure in BC causing water to pass from BC into OC:

5 buccal cavity continues to contract and acquires positive pressure; mouth closes and water is forced from BC into OC:

6 OC contracts and acquires positive pressure; opercular valve opens and water is expelled.

The concentration gradient of oxygen at the gill surface is maintained by:
(i) the continuous removal of oxygen from solution by haemoglobin,
(ii) blood flow which removes oxygenated blood from the gills,
(iii) continuous ventilation of the gill surface.

Similar factors operate to maintain the concentration gradient of carbon dioxide namely, ventilation, the continuous transport of carbon dioxide to the gills, and the action of the enzyme carbonic anhydrase. In the conditions of high oxygen tension that prevail at the gill surface, this enzyme brings about the release of large amounts of carbon dioxide into the plasma (this process is described in detail on p. 114–115).

As mentioned earlier, the counter current flow of water and blood has a significant effect on the efficiency of gas exchange. Considering first how exchange would proceed if blood and water flowed in the same direction

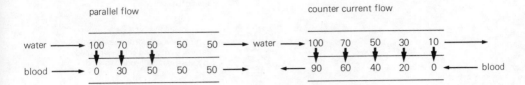

Figure 11   A comparison of exchange in parallel flow and counter current flow
systems; Figures represent oxygen concentrations in arbitrary units
Bold arrows indicate the direction of oxygen movement.
Fine arrows indicate the direction of water and blood flow.

(parallel flow), it is easier to appreciate the advantages of counter current exchange.

With parallel flow, oxygen would diffuse into the blood until the concentration of oxygen in the blood and in the water was in equilibrium, after which there would be no further exchange (see Figure 11). With the counter current exchange system, the oxygen concentration in the water exceeds that of the blood along the entire length of the lamella. This enables blood to remove as much as ninety six per cent of the oxygen from the water passing through the gills.

Counter current exchange systems also occur, in the placenta, where the maternal blood flows in the opposite direction to the foetal blood, in the kidney (see chapter 10), and in the peripheral blood vessels of many animals where they serve for heat conservation (see chapter 9).

In many fish, the efficiency of gas exchange can be modified by allowing blood to flow through non-respiratory vessels embedded deep in the filaments, rather than through the superficial capillaries of the lamellae. Presumably, such pathways are used when the oxygen requirement is low.

GAS EXCHANGE IN MAMMALS

Mammalian lungs lie in the thoracic cavity, bounded by the ribs and a dome-shaped muscle, the *diaphragm* (see Figure 12(a)). They are enclosed in a double layer of membranes; the *pleural membranes*. These are separated by a thin layer of *pleural fluid* which acts as a lubricant, allowing the membranes to slide over one another without friction during ventilation movements.

The lungs consist of two elastic sacs, each of which is sub-divided into numerous tiny sacs or *alveoli* (see Figure 12(b)). The latter are lined with a film of moisture and provide the very extensive respiratory surface. The area of the human lungs is between thirty and ninety square metres, that is, some thirty to fifty times the body surface area. It has recently been discovered that the surface tension of the water film in the alveoli would cause them to collapse were it not

(a)

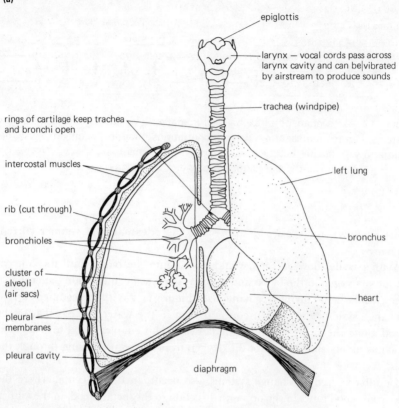

epiglottis

larynx — vocal cords pass across larynx cavity and can be vibrated by airstream to produce sounds

trachea (windpipe)

rings of cartilage keep trachea and bronchi open

intercostal muscles

rib (cut through)

bronchioles

cluster of alveoli (air sacs)

pleural membranes

pleural cavity

left lung

bronchus

heart

diaphragm

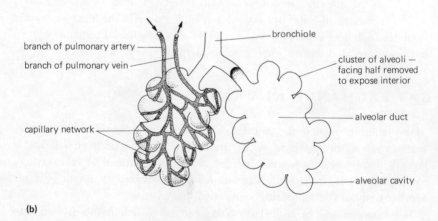

bronchiole

branch of pulmonary artery

branch of pulmonary vein

cluster of alveoli — facing half removed to expose interior

alveolar duct

capillary network

alveolar cavity

(b)

Figure 12 (a) and (b)   Diagrams of human gas exchange apparatus.
(a) Respiratory structures in neck and thorax with interior of right lung shown exposed.
(b) Alveoli and their blood supply.

for the presence of detergent-like substances called *surfactants*, secreted by certain alveolar cells, which reduce the surface tension.

The lungs communicate with the outside through a system of air-tubes. The main air-tube, the *trachea*, leads from the pharynx where its entrance, the glottis, is guarded by a flap, the *epiglottis*. The latter closes during swallowing to prevent food entering the air passages. The trachea divides into two, and one branch or *bronchus* passes to each lung. The bronchi branch on entering the lungs to form a mass of smaller tubes, the *bronchioles*, the smallest branches of which lead via alveolar ducts into the alveoli. The trachea, bronchi and bronchioles have a similar structure, being composed of smooth muscle lined with mucous membrane. Embedded in the wall of the trachea and bronchi are c-shaped rings of cartilage which serve to keep the air passageways open.

The nasal passages, the trachea, the bronchi and their larger branches, have a ciliated lining membrane. The cilia waft particles, that become entangled in mucus, to the back of the throat where they can be swallowed.

Ventilation

The air passageways just described connect the lungs with the outside air at atmospheric pressure. Ventilation is achieved by lowering or raising the pressure in the lungs relative to atmospheric pressure, so that air either passes into or out of the lungs. These pressure changes are brought about by contraction and relaxation of the diaphragm and the *intercostal* muscles.

During inspiration the diaphragm contracts and flattens, enlarging the thoracic cavity. The latter is further enlarged by the contraction of the intercostal muscles, which move the ribcage upwards and outwards. As the thoracic cavity enlarges, the elastic lungs, being attached to the ribcage and diaphragm by the pleura, also expand. The expansion of the lungs lowers the pressure inside the lungs relative to atmospheric pressure and air passes in from outside (see Figure 13).

Expiration results mainly from the relaxation of the diaphragm and the intercostal muscles. Released from the restraints imposed by the intercostal muscles, the ribcage returns to its former position. The resulting reduction in lung volume increases the pressure within the lungs and causes air to pass out (see Figure 13).

In mammals that move on all four legs, diaphragm movements play a more important part in ventilation because the ribcage is required to support the thorax, and so its movements must be limited.

The volume of air that passes in and out at each breath during normal unforced breathing is called the *tidal volume*. During quiet breathing a man exchanges about half a litre at each breath. This represents only about one tenth of the *total capacity* of the two lungs. The *vital capacity* of the lungs is the maximum volume of air which can be exchanged during forced breathing; in man this is usually about three litres. From these figures you can see that some air always remains in the lungs. This *residual air* does not stagnate as it is constantly renewed by exchange with the tidal air.

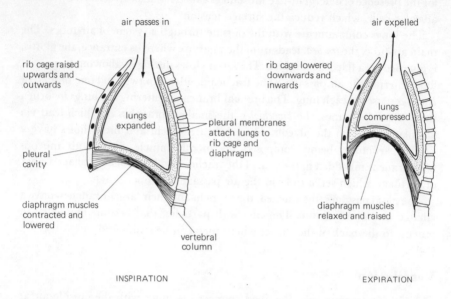

air passes in

rib cage raised
upwards and
outwards

lungs
expanded

pleural
cavity

diaphragm muscles
contracted and
lowered

vertebral
column

pleural membranes
attach lungs to
rib cage and
diaphragm

INSPIRATION

air expelled

rib cage lowered
downwards and
inwards

lungs
compressed

diaphragm muscles
relaxed and raised

EXPIRATION

Figure 13 Diagrams of sections through mammalian thorax summarising
ventilation mechanisms

Gas exchange in the alveolus (Figure 14)

The alveolar wall consists of a single layer of cells, the epithelium, 1 μm thick.
Each alveolus is surrounded by a network of capillaries; these receive blood from
a branch of the pulmonary artery and convey it to a branch of the pulmonary
vein.

Oxygen dissolves in the film of moisture that lines the alveolus, and then
diffuses along a concentration gradient into the blood; carbon dioxide diffuses in
the opposite direction. The two-cell-thick layer that separates the blood and the
alveolar air offers little resistance to the passage of the respiratory gases. The
concentration gradient of carbon dioxide and oxygen between the alveolar
cavity and the blood is maintained by blood flow, ventilation, haemoglobin and
carbonic anhydrase, as already described in fish.

Control of respiratory gases in mammals

The adjustment of the depth and rate of breathing plays an important part in the
homeostatic control of the respiratory gases. The supply of oxygen and removal
of carbon dioxide must keep pace with the varying needs of the animal. As the
metabolic rate increases, so the oxygen requirement and carbon dioxide
production will also increase. If the blood contains insufficient oxygen to meet
the body's requirements, asphyxiation results; if it contains too much oxygen,
cells will be destroyed by unwanted oxidations. An inadequate supply of oxygen
is generally accompanied by an accumulation of carbon dioxide, and this also

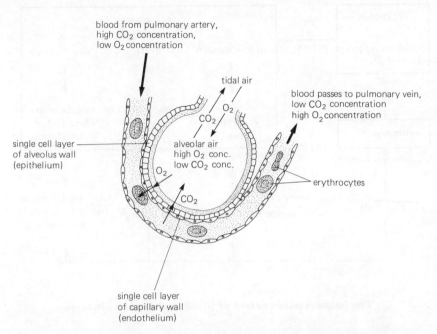

blood from pulmonary artery,
high CO_2 concentration,
low O_2 concentration

tidal air

O_2

CO_2

blood passes to pulmonary vein,
low CO_2 concentration
high O_2 concentration

single cell layer
of alveolus wall
(epithelium)

alveolar air
high O_2 conc.
low CO_2 conc.

O_2

CO_2

erythrocytes

single cell layer
of capillary wall
(endothelium)

Figure 14   Diagram summarising gas exchange in the mammalian alveolus.
Fine arrows indicate the direction of diffusion of the respiratory gases. Bold arrows
indicate the direction of blood flow.

has undesirable effects. It will tend to lower the pH (increase the acidity) of the body fluids, which can cause enzyme inhibition.

The most important factor determining the rate and depth of ventilation is not, as might be expected, the concentration of oxygen in the blood, but the concentration of carbon dioxide. The latter is usually expressed as partial pressure of carbon dioxide or pCO_2. Changes in pCO_2 are detected by chemoreceptors in the respiratory centres of the medulla (part of the hind brain). These receptors actually respond to a decrease in the pH (increased acidity) of the cerebrospinal fluid, but this accurately reflects increased arterial pCO_2.

During increased activity the level of carbon dioxide rises and stimulates the medullary chemoreceptors, causing nerve impulses to be sent along efferent nerves to the muscles of the thorax. The arrival of these impulses increases the ventilation rate or *ventilation minute volume* (respiratory rate × tidal volume), and so speeds up the removal of carbon dioxide. Impulses are also sent out from the medulla to the heart and certain blood vessels: the way in which these impulses facilitate the removal of carbon dioxide is explained in the diagram on p. 34.

In common with most other homeostatic processes, blood carbon dioxide concentration is regulated by a negative feedback mechanism (see chapter 9), and is under autonomic or involuntary control.

As already mentioned, the levels of carbon dioxide and oxygen are inversely related (as carbon dioxide rises oxygen falls, and vice versa). Thus the

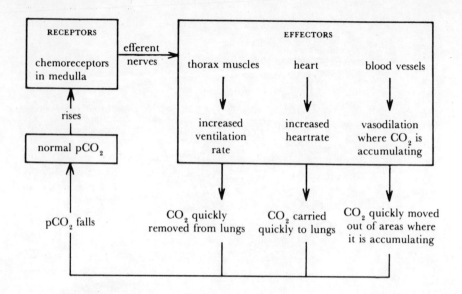

The homeostatic control of blood carbon dioxide level

mechanisms that tend to reduce the blood pCO_2, and so restore it to normal, will also restore the blood oxygen level to normal by increasing the rate of oxygen intake.

Chemoreceptors sensitive to pCO_2 are also found in the carotid and aortic bodies, nodules of tissue on the carotid arteries and aorta respectively. These receptors monitor the arterial pCO_2 directly, but seem to play a subsidiary role to the medullary chemoreceptors. If the nerves that connect the carotid and aortic bodies to the brain are severed, little if any effect on the response to lowered pCO_2 is observed. Some of the chemoreceptors in the carotid and aortic bodies respond to decreased oxygen concentration (pO_2). In normal circumstances they appear to enhance the effects of increased pCO_2 rather than initiate corrective mechanisms themselves.

Ventilation is not solely determined by chemical factors $(pCO_2$ and $pO_2)$. It is possible to exert a degree of voluntary (conscious) control over breathing, as when speaking or singing.

GAS EXCHANGE IN INSECTS

The gas exchange system in insects consists of a network of interconnecting, air-filled tubes, the *tracheae*. In contrast to the gas exchange mechanisms already described, the insect system is independent of the circulatory system, as the tracheae deliver air directly to the tissues.

Tracheae arise as inpushings of the body surface, and are lined with cuticle. Rings or spirals of chitin, called *taenidia*, in the walls of the tracheae serve to keep them open. In many insects portions of the air-tubes are expanded to form *air sacs* (see Figure 15(a)). These lack taenidia and consequently play an important role in ventilation; this is discussed later.

Air enters the tracheae through pores or *spiracles*. Typically there are two pairs of spiracles on the thorax and seven to eight pairs on the abdomen. In primitive insects the spiracles are simple holes that open directly into the tracheal system. In most insects however, a pore at the surface opens into a pit or *atrium*, and the tracheae open into the base of this pit (see Figure 15(b)). The openings into the tracheae are generally guarded by a closing, or valve, mechanism, as well as some sort of filtering apparatus such as hairs, hairy pads or perforated plates. The *spiracular valves* and filtering devices prevent dust particles and parasites from entering the tracheal system, but, more importantly, they help to restrict water loss.

The internal arrangement of the tracheal system varies from species to species but there is usually a pair of longitudinal tubes linked by cross-connections (see Figure 15(a)). Branching tracheae arise from these main trunks and pass to all regions of the body. The finest branches, the air capillaries or *tracheoles*, are about one micrometre or less in diameter, and arise from cells called *tracheole cells*. The tracheoles comprise the main region for the exchange of respiratory gases. Each tracheole branches to form a fine network that pushes into the membrane of respiring cells, and has even been found to penetrate the very active, flight muscle cells in some insects.

Gas exchange at the tracheoles (Figure 15c)

The ends of the tracheoles are filled with fluid. Oxygen dissolves in this fluid and diffuses into the respiring tissues. In 1942 Wigglesworth, an insect physiologist, observed that the amount of fluid in the tracheoles decreases when the tissues they supply are actively metabolising. This has an obvious adaptive value in that it will accelerate the delivery of oxygen to the cells, since oxygen diffuses about 30 000 times more quickly in air than it does in aqueous solution. Wigglesworth suggested that the accumulation of metabolites during activity might be responsible for the osmotic withdrawal of the fluid from the tracheoles into the surrounding tissues.

Ventilation

Diffusion along a concentration gradient from the spiracles to the respiring tissues can supply enough oxygen for many small insects, but forms that weigh more than one gramme, or are highly active, require some form of ventilation to speed up the delivery of oxygen to the tissues. This is usually achieved by the contraction and relaxation of the abdominal muscles which pump air in and out of the tracheal system. The air sacs, lacking taenidia, can be easily compressed to create air flow. Ventilation is often visible externally as a dorso-ventral flattening of the abdomen in insects such as beetles and grasshoppers, and a telescoping of the abdomen in insects such as bees and flies. You may well have observed bumble bees indulging in this pumping operation.

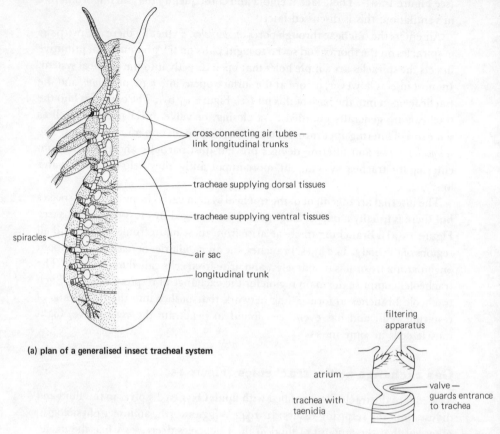

cross-connecting air tubes — link longitudinal trunks

tracheae supplying dorsal tissues

tracheae supplying ventral tissues

spiracles

air sac

longitudinal trunk

(a) plan of a generalised insect tracheal system

filtering apparatus

atrium

valve — guards entrance to trachea

trachea with taenidia

(b) spiracle with atrium, valve and filtering apparatus

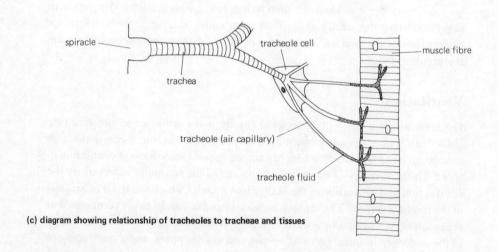

spiracle

tracheole cell

muscle fibre

trachea

tracheole (air capillary)

tracheole fluid

(c) diagram showing relationship of tracheoles to tracheae and tissues

Figure 15 (a) – (c) The gas exchange apparatus of an insect

In many insects, the efficiency of gas exchange is increased by the imposition of a one-way air flow through the main air trunks. This is achieved by the opening and closing of the spiracles in time with the ventilation movements, but out of phase with one another. In most insects studied, the thoracic spiracles are used mainly for inspiration, while the abdominal spiracles serve for expiration.

It is probable that, despite these ventilation mechanisms, the slowness of gas transport imposed by the tracheal system has limited the size of insects.

Water conservation and gas exchange

The interior of the tracheal system provides a very extensive, moist surface. Necessary though this moisture is for the transport of the respiratory gases, keeping the tracheoles moist poses considerable problems, because the water tends to diffuse out of the animal. As already indicated, spiracular valves and filtering devices help to reduce this water loss. Filtering devices trap humid air in the atria; this effectively reduces the concentration gradient and so inhibits water loss. This adaptation is reminiscent of the sunken stomata encountered in plants living in dry conditions. (See p. 161.)

Spiracular valves can be closed by muscles, enabling the organism to exert a measure of control over water loss. The pattern of spiracle opening – which spiracles open, how often, and for how long – varies from species to species, and within species according to the degree of activity and the temperature. In most insects, the opening and closing of the spiracles is determined by the carbon dioxide concentration. When the valves are closed the pCO_2 inside the animal builds up. When it reaches a certain level, it triggers the opening of the spiracular valves, and gas exchange can recommence. This mechanism allows the insect to balance the needs of respiration and water conservation.

GAS EXCHANGE IN PLANTS

Plants are considerably less active than animals and so generally have a much lower oxygen requirement. In addition, plants produce oxygen during photosynthesis. These facts help to explain many of the differences between gas exchange mechanisms in the two kingdoms. In contrast to the situation in animals, even the largest plants rely on diffusion alone to supply their gas exchange needs. This is partly attributable to their relatively low oxygen requirements, and partly to the very extensive gas exchange surfaces provided by plant organs such as leaves and roots.

In common with animals, plants colonising the land had to overcome the difficulty of keeping the respiratory surface moist in terrestrial conditions. Early colonisers like mosses and liverworts are imperfectly adapted to life on land. Like their aquatic ancestors, these plants respire through the body surface and as a consequence are restricted to moist habitats. The truly terrestrial higher plants developed a special, waterproof covering, the *cuticle*, on their aerial parts (leaves and stems) perforated by pores or *stomata* to allow gas exchange. The process of respiratory exchange through stomata is summarised in Figure 16(a). Within the

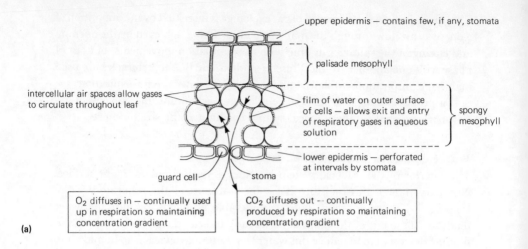

(a)

upper epidermis — contains few, if any, stomata

palisade mesophyll

intercellular air spaces allow gases to circulate throughout leaf

film of water on outer surface of cells — allows exit and entry of respiratory gases in aqueous solution

spongy mesophyll

lower epidermis — perforated at intervals by stomata

guard cell

stoma

O_2 diffuses in — continually used up in respiration so maintaining concentration gradient

CO_2 diffuses out — continually produced by respiration so maintaining concentration gradient

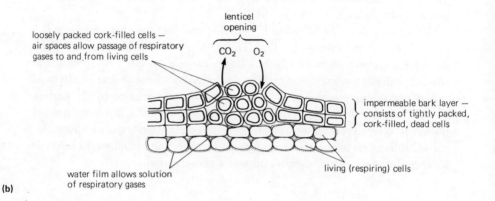

(b)

lenticel opening

loosely packed cork-filled cells — air spaces allow passage of respiratory gases to and from living cells

CO_2 O_2

impermeable bark layer — consists of tightly packed, cork-filled, dead cells

water film allows solution of respiratory gases

living (respiring) cells

Figure 16   Diagrams of gas exchange in the aerial parts of a flowering plant
(a) in a leaf
(b) at a lenticel

leaves, and, to a lesser extent in the stem and roots, air spaces ensure that air can circulate freely and that no cell is very far from a supply of oxygen. Each living cell inside the plant is covered with a thin film of water which allows the respiratory gases to enter and leave.

In stems that become secondarily thickened and acquire an outer layer of bark for protection, the stomata are replaced by *lenticels* – areas where the cork-filled cells of the bark are loosely packed, allowing air to circulate between the outside and the living cells that lie under the bark (see Figure 16(b)). Lenticels appear as elongate or spherical, slightly raised areas on the bark.

The younger parts of roots lack a waterproofing cuticle and so gas exchange can take place through their surface; an impermeable, protective outer layer generally develops on the older parts of the root.

QUESTIONS

1 Explain what is meant by the following terms:
   (a) gas exchange
   (b) ventilation
   (c) tidal volume.

2 Explain how diffusion alone can supply the oxygen needs of even the largest tree, while the smallest insect requires supplementary gas exchange mechanisms.

3 What part do the following play in maintaining the concentration gradient of respiratory gases at the gas exchange surface of a mammal;
   (a) ventilation movements,
   (b) haemoglobin,
   (c) carbonic anhydrase?

4 Explain how a) fish gills, and b) the mammalian lungs, are suited to their function of gas exchange.

5 How are the amounts of respiratory gases in the blood regulated in a mammal? Why is such regulation necessary?

6 What essential features are shared by the gas exchange mechanisms of (a) a flowering plant, (b) an insect, and (c) a mammal?

4   Introduction to nutrition

Nutrition is a collective term for the processes by which an organism obtains chemical compounds for the release of energy, for growth and repair, the production of secretions and the maintenance of a steady internal environment. The chemical compounds are nutrients and their sources vary according to the type of nutrition concerned. *Autotrophic* (self-feeding) organisms include the pigmented plants and chemosynthetic bacteria. They are able to build up complex organic nutrients from simple inorganic substances by methods described in chapter 5. *Heterotrophic* organisms need a supply of readymade organic nutrients from their environment and include all the animals and fungi, most bacteria and a few flowering plants which lack photosynthetic pigment. Heterotrophic nutrition is discussed in chapter 6.

We shall now look briefly at the various food types and their uses in living organisms.

FOOD TYPES AND THEIR USES

Carbohydrates

Carbohydrates contain carbon, oxygen and hydrogen only and include sugars, starches and some structurally important substances like cellulose. The general formula for a single sugar molecule is $(CH_2O)_n$ where n may vary from three to six e.g. triose $C_3H_6O_3$ or hexose $C_6H_{12}O_6$. Pentoses (five carbon sugars) and hexoses (six carbon sugars) are ring-shaped molecules as shown below, the ring consisting of five carbon atoms and one oxygen atom. The thick lines project towards you and the thin ones go back away from you. (The numbers 1 to 6 refer to the position of the carbon atoms.)

α glucose – a hexose

A single hexose or pentose molecule is a *monosaccharide*. Two monosaccharides may be combined to form a *disaccharide* by condensation, the removal of water, forming a *glycoside bond*. Sucrose is a disaccharide formed by the union of two hexoses, glucose and fructose:

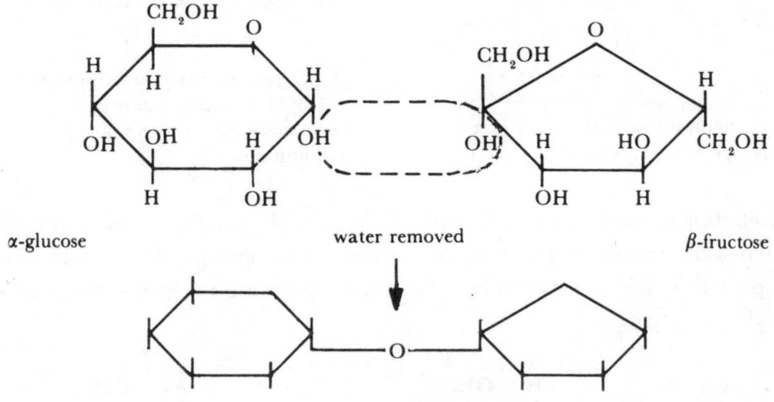

α-glucose   water removed   β-fructose

sucrose $C_{12}H_{22}O_{11}$

Similarly, maltose, a sugar found in germinating seeds, is a disaccharide formed by condensation of two glucose molecules, and lactose (milk sugar) is formed by the condensation of glucose and galactose. In each case the reaction can be reversed by hydrolysis, replacing the water molecule removed to establish a glycoside bond and thereby separating the two monosaccharides again.

Condensation of many monosaccharides results in a polysaccharide with the general formula $(C_6H_{10}O_5)_n$, where n may be in excess of 200. These large molecules are insoluble and chemically inert and this, together with their compact shape, makes them ideal as food reserves, which can then be hydrolysed to monosaccharides as needed. Plants use starch as a polysaccharide food store and animals use animal starch or glycogen. The unbranched amylose form is shown below.

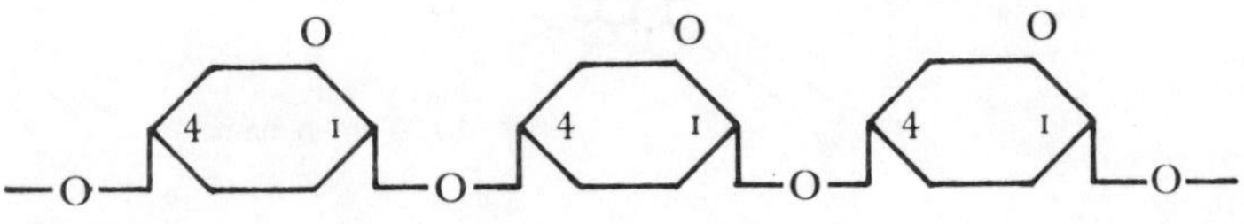

A short length of an amylose chain. There are usually 200–1000 glucose molecules joined by 1-4 linkages. The molecule is arranged as a helix with every sixth glucose molecule beginning the next turn of the spiral.

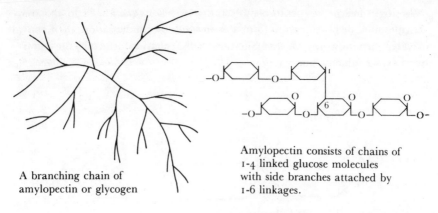

A branching chain of
amylopectin or glycogen

Amylopectin consists of chains of
1-4 linked glucose molecules
with side branches attached by
1-6 linkages.

Cellulose is a polysaccharide made of long chains of β glucose molecules from which -OH groups stick out on both sides. These groups can form hydrogen bonds with neighbouring chains, thus building up a bundle of chains called a *micelle*.

Groups of micelles massed together make up *microfibrils* of 10–30 nm diameter – see Figure 17. In a plant cell wall these are laid down parallel to each other forming layers in an organic matrix. Successive layers being deposited at different angles, often interwoven like basketwork, provide a strong yet slightly elastic layer, permeable to water and solutes.

Carbohydrate, particularly glucose, is the respiratory substrate for most organisms. Carbohydrates also occur as gums and mucilages in plants where they may be a protection or a food reserve. In combination with proteins,

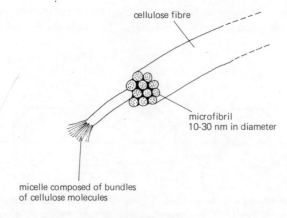

cellulose fibre

microfibril
10-30 nm in diameter

micelle composed of bundles
of cellulose molecules

Figure 17   The structure of a cellulose fibre

polysaccharides form *mucopolysaccharides* found in the mucus used as a lubricant by animals. The *chitin* of arthropod exoskeletons and many fungal cell walls is basically very similar to cellulose. Another important carbohydrate is the pentose sugar which, together with an organic base and one or more phosphoric acid molecules, forms a *nucleotide*. Nucleotides are the basic building blocks of the nucleic acids RNA and DNA (ribonucleic acid and deoxyribonucleic acid). Some nucleotides such as NAD and FAD, are vital hydrogen carriers in respiration (see chapter 2).

Proteins

Proteins contain carbon, oxygen and hydrogen, nitrogen and often sulphur and phosphorus. They are composed of amino acids, of which there are about twenty naturally-occurring types, with the basic structure shown below:

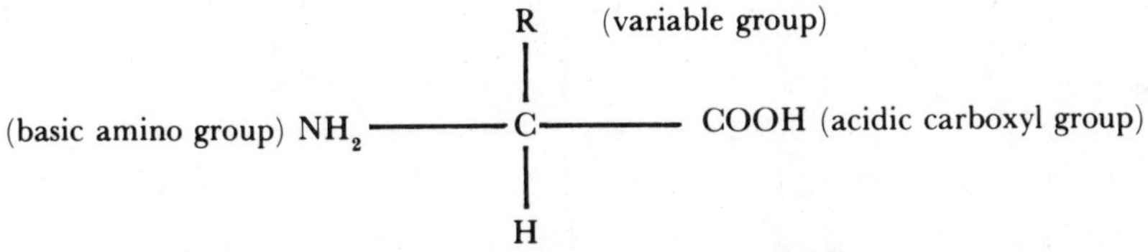

$$\text{(basic amino group) } NH_2 - \overset{\displaystyle \overset{R \quad \text{(variable group)}}{|}}{\underset{\displaystyle \underset{H}{|}}{C}} - COOH \text{ (acidic carboxyl group)}$$

The variable group may be only a single hydrogen atom as in glycine or in arginine, a larger amino acid.

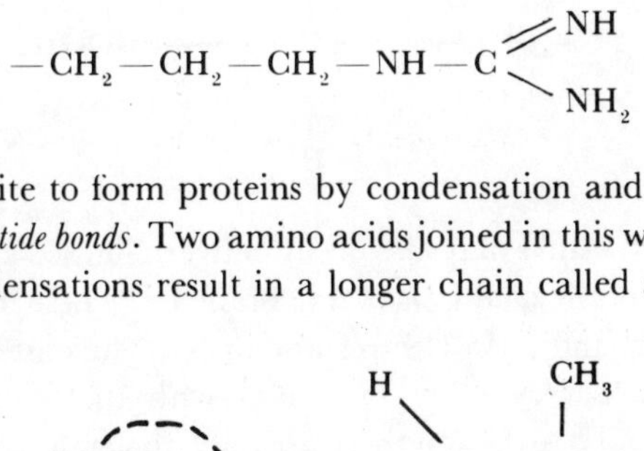

$$-CH_2-CH_2-CH_2-NH-C\begin{smallmatrix}\diagup NH \\[4pt] \diagdown NH_2\end{smallmatrix}$$

Amino acids unite to form proteins by condensation and the links between them are called *peptide bonds*. Two amino acids joined in this way make a *dipeptide* while further condensations result in a longer chain called a *polypeptide*.

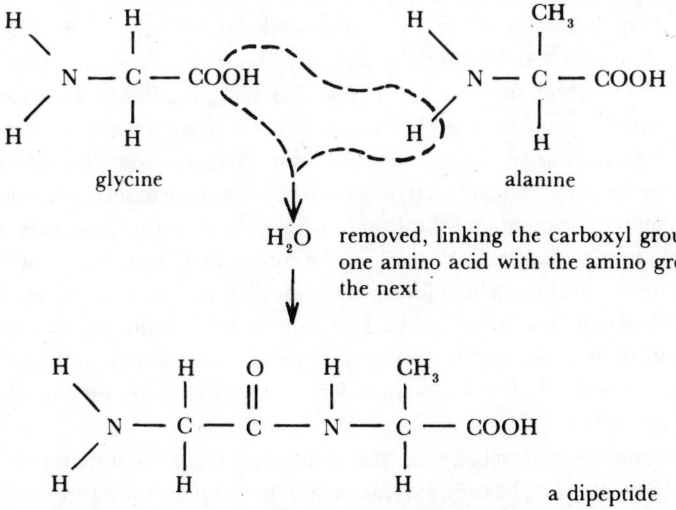

H_2O removed, linking the carboxyl group of one amino acid with the amino group of the next

a dipeptide

A typical protein consists not only of several polypeptide chains but also cross links at intervals. These may be by weak hydrogen bonds or very strong *disulphide links* provided by the sulphur-containing amino acid cysteine. The -SH group of one cysteine molecule can be joined to that of another by oxidation, producing a *disulphide S-S bond*:

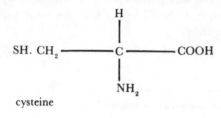

cysteine

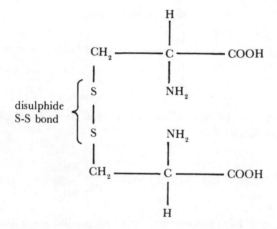

At a suitable pH cross links may also occur between ionised amino and carboxyl groups at the ends of the chains or of side branches. These ionise to NH_3^+ and COO^- respectively and form electrostatic or 'salt' linkages.

Most proteins are very large molecules with molecular weights in the hundreds of thousands. Although there are only about twenty amino acids, the number of ways in which they can be put together and cross-linked allows a vast diversity of types of protein. The external shape of a protein molecule may be either rounded – *globular protein*, or straight chains – *fibrous proteins*. The globular ones tend to be more biologically active like enzymes and hormones, whereas the fibrous ones tend to be tough, insoluble and to form the structural proteins of the body like the keratin of hair and the collagen of connective tissue. Many proteins have an internal spiral or helical form, first shown in keratin and called the α helix. In collagen it is a triple helix. The helices are crosslinked usually by hydrogen bonds so that a stable and unique three-dimensional configuration exists for each protein. This is an essential feature as we shall see for example in enzyme action.

The main function of protein is that it forms much of the cellular material, that is, the cytoplasm and membranes. It is rarely stored except in a few seeds and not normally used as a respiratory substrate except when carbohydrate and lipid sources have been exhausted. It is much more important as a stable structural component for enzymes, hormones, antigens etc. Sometimes the protein is combined with another substance, making a conjugated protein, the non-protein part being called the *prosthetic group*. For example the protein globin, combined with the pigment haem, forms the respiratory pigment haemoglobin.

By virtue of their large size protein molecules do not go into true solution but form *colloidal suspensions*. They diffuse very slowly and cannot diffuse across cell membranes; they can exist as either a semi-solid *gel* or a more hydrated liquid *sol*. The gelation probably involves the formation of cross-links which prevent the chains moving easily past each other. This ability is considered in more detail in chapter 14 dealing with the proteins involved in amoeboid movement and muscle action. The size of protein molecules provides a big surface area or interface with the surrounding medium and a large surface tension can develop. This has the effect of holding in place any molecules which touch the surface of the protein molecules, a process called *adsorption*. Adsorption seems to be important for maintaining the positions of molecules in cells and may be a factor involved in enzyme action.

The presence of basic amino groups and acidic carboxyl groups at the free ends and some side branches of polypeptide chains gives both acidic and basic properties to proteins. This allows them to combine with either acidic or basic substances in the construction of cellular materials. It also means that because the amino and carboxyl groups can ionise, and act as bases by picking up protons (NH_3^+), or as acids by donating protons (COO^-), proteins and amino acids are able to act as buffers in the fluids in and around the cell, reducing the effects of the minor changes in pH.

Autotrophs are able to synthesise protein but heterotrophs vary in their ability to build up amino acids and to convert them from one to another. In man for instance, there are ten amino acids (eight in an adult) which cannot be synthesised, or are synthesised very slowly, and must be taken in ready-made in the diet. They are called the *essential amino acids*, and proteins that contain them are *first class proteins*, usually of animal derivation, but also including soya bean protein. Other proteins, deficient in one or more essential amino acids, are referred to as *second class proteins* and include most plant proteins.

Lipids

The word *lipid* includes both fats and oils, fats being solid at room temperature (usually reckoned as 20°C) and oils being liquids. In its widest sense lipid is also used for other substances which are soluble in fat solvents like ether or chloroform. This would include such diverse substances as steroids – see p. 47 and carotenoids – see chapter 5.

True fats and oils are combinations of glycerol (propane-1, 2, 3-triol) and fatty acids (alkanoic acids). Three fatty acid chains attached to a molecule of glycerol constitute a *triglyceride*. The fatty acids which go to make up a triglyceride may be all the same or differ from each other. The formation of triglycerides involves condensation and the formation of an *oxygen* or *ester bond* between the glycerol and each fatty acid chain:

$$
\begin{array}{c}
H \\
|\\
H-C-OH \\
|\\
H-C-OH \\
|\\
H-C-OH \\
|\\
H
\end{array}
\qquad\qquad
\begin{array}{l}
H \\
|\\
H-C-O-OC-(CH_2)_n-R_1 \\
|\\
H-C-O-OC-(CH_2)_n-R_2 \\
|\\
H-C-O-OC-(CH_2)_n-R_3 \\
|\\
H
\end{array}
$$

glycerol   glycerol + three fatty acids = a triglyceride

two typical fatty acids:

$$
\begin{array}{c}
\quad\; O \;\; H \;\; H \;\; H \;\; H \;\; H \;\; H \;\; H \;\; H \;\; H \;\; H \;\; H \;\; H \;\; H \;\; H \;\; H \;\; H \;\; H \\
\quad\; \| \;\; | \;\; | \;\; | \;\; | \;\; | \;\; | \;\; | \;\; | \;\; | \;\; | \;\; | \;\; | \;\; | \;\; | \;\; | \;\; | \;\; | \\
HO-C-C-C-C-C-C-C-C-C-C-C-C-C-C-C-C-C-H \\
\quad\quad\; | \;\; | \;\; | \;\; | \;\; | \;\; | \;\; | \;\; | \;\; | \;\; | \;\; | \;\; | \;\; | \;\; | \;\; | \;\; | \;\; | \\
\quad\quad\; H \;\; H \;\; H \;\; H \;\; H \;\; H \;\; H \;\; H \;\; H \;\; H \;\; H \;\; H \;\; H \;\; H \;\; H \;\; H \;\; H
\end{array}
$$

stearic acid $C_{17}H_{35}COOH$ (saturated – having the maximum number of hydrogen atoms attached to the carbon atoms)

$$
\begin{array}{c}
\quad\; O \;\; H \;\; H \;\; H \;\; H \;\; H \;\; H \;\; H \quad\quad H \;\; H \;\; H \;\; H \;\; H \;\; H \;\; H \;\; H \\
\quad\; \| \;\; | \;\; | \;\; | \;\; | \;\; | \;\; | \;\; | \quad\quad | \;\; | \;\; | \;\; | \;\; | \;\; | \;\; | \;\; | \\
HO-C-C-C-C-C-C-C-C=C-C-C-C-C-C-C-C-C-H \\
\quad\quad\; | \;\; | \;\; | \;\; | \;\; | \;\; | \;\; | \quad\quad | \;\; | \;\; | \;\; | \;\; | \;\; | \;\; | \;\; | \\
\quad\quad\; H \;\; H \;\; H \;\; H \;\; H \;\; H \;\; H \quad\; H \;\; H \;\; H \;\; H \;\; H \;\; H \;\; H \;\; H
\end{array}
$$

oleic acid $C_{17}H_{33}COOH$ (unsaturated – having one or more double bonds between the carbon atoms)
(Stearic acid is octadecanoic acid)   (oleic acid is cis-octadec-9-enoic acid)

Plants appear to be able to synthesise their own fatty acids and triglycerides, but animals seem less able to do this. The human body for instance can synthesise most fatty acids with the exception of some unsaturated ones, particularly linolenic and linoleic acids. These are called the *essential fatty acids* but only very small amounts are required and they come mainly from seed and vegetable oils.

Like protein, lipid is an essential constituent of cytoplasm, in cell membranes and organelles. Fats yield more energy per gramme than carbohydrates do, and hence lipids provide a compact food store. In the mammalian body excess carbohydrate is converted to fat and stored under the skin and around certain organs, where it acts both as a food store and insulation. Fats and oils are also common food stores in seeds and spores where much potential energy can be packed into a small space.

In combination with phosphoric acid, lipid forms *phospholipid*, when one fatty acid molecule is replaced by a phosphate, often attached to an organic base as for example in lecithin. The phosphate makes that end of the molecule water soluble or hydrophilic, while the other end remains water repellant – hydrophobic. This probably accounts for the importance of phospholipids in cell membranes, since they help to bring together both water-soluble and fat-soluble substances.

Lecithin:

Waxes are basically similar to triglycerides but with the glycerol replaced by a higher or more complex alcohol. Their fatty acid chains are also more complicated than those of fats and the result is a tough lipid with a high melting point. They are found for instance as part of the protective covering of many animals and plants – often called *cuticle*, which helps to reduce the rate of water loss.

Steroids, while being soluble in fat solvents are quite different structurally from them, consisting of a basic plan of seventeen carbon atoms in four rings (see diagram following). Cholesterol is an important steroid of animal tissue. There are a number of derivatives of cholesterol with a wide range of functions in the mammalian body, including the oils of skin and hair, bile acids and many hormones, particularly the sex hormones of the gonads, and the adrenal cortex hormones. Vitamin D is also produced in the skin from a derivative of cholesterol under the influence of ultra violet light.

Shape of a typical steroid, consisting of four interlocking
rings of seventeen carbon atoms

cholesterol

Vitamins

Vitamins are sometimes called accessory growth factors. Unlike the other food types we have looked at, vitamins do not fall into a clearly-definable group. Instead they consist of a wide range of organic substances required in small amounts for the healthy metabolism of organisms. They vary in the ways in which they are involved in metabolism and the action of some of them is still only partially clear. Many are important coenzymes (see p. 58). The absence of a particular vitamin from an animal's diet is characterised by a specific *deficiency disease*, and it was often the symptoms of the disease which helped to elucidate the involvement of the vitamin in metabolism. Autotrophic organisms have the ability to synthesise the vitamins they require, whereas heterotrophs must obtain most of them ready-made from their food. Animals vary in their ability to manufacture vitamins; for example a form of vitamin D can be produced in human skin by the action of ultra-violet light on a steroid derivative, and most mammals, though **not** apes and man, can synthesise vitamin C. Table 1 shows the best known vitamins and gives some indication of the uses they are believed to have in body metabolism.

Mineral salts

It is usual to distinguish between minerals required in small amounts, the *major minerals* and those required only in minute amounts, and therefore called *trace elements*.

Table 2 lists the main mineral salts and their known uses in plants and animals.

The effects of various mineral deficiencies can be studied in plants using water culture solutions from which one mineral is omitted at a time, so that the effects of its absence can be studied. When plants or animals release waste products or die and decay under the influence of micro-organisms, the minerals they contained are released back into the environment.

Table 1   Vitamins

Vitamin	Solubility and stability	Food source	Results of deficiency
A an alcohol $C_{20}H_{30}O$	Fat soluble. Stable, not destroyed by normal cooking.	Fat of mammalian and fish livers, milk fat, eggs, carotene of carrots, green veg. e.g. lettuce, spinach, watercress.	Eye defects – xerophthalmia in children – inflamed cornea and conjunctiva; in adult, poor vision in dim light (vitamin A part of rhodopsin, the pigment of the rods). Slow growth rate in children, malformed bones and teeth, thickened skin and skin infections. Excess is toxic.
B_1 Thiamine (aneurin) $C_{12}H_{18}ON_4Cl_2S$	Water soluble. Destroyed above 120°C and absent from canned food.	Wholemeal, yeast, milk, eggs, peas, and beans.	Deficiency upsets respiration since active form of B_1 is coenzyme needed for oxidative decarboxylation of pyruvic acid. Deficiency disease is beri-beri, caused by eating rice without the embryo or pericarp (polished). Results are muscle wastage, paralysis, slow heart beat, gastro-intestinal disorders.
B_2 Riboflavin $C_{17}H_{20}N_4O_6$	Water soluble.	Milk, liver, kidney, egg white.	Deficiency causes inflamed skin around nose, ears, cracking at mouth corners, eye lesions. Forms part of hydrogen acceptors FMN and FAD used in oxidations.
Nicotinamide $C_5NH_4CO\,NH_2$	Water soluble. Present in maize in bound form unavailable to body.	Meat, liver, yeast, wheat germ.	Some can be synthesised in man from amino acid tryptophan so deficiency often linked with protein deficiency. Deficiency disease called pellagra (diarrhoea, dermatitis, mental disorders). Required for NAD and NADP in respiration.

Table 1 (contd)

Vitamin	Solubility and stability	Food source	Results of deficiency
B_{12} Cobalamine $C_{63}H_{90}O_{14}N_{14}PCo$	Water soluble. Only known vitamin with a metal atom.	Liver, kidney, meat, milk. Absent from plants so may be deficient in vegetarian diet.	Required for carbohydrate, fat and protein metabolism; also nucleic acid production. Necessary for red blood cell formation. In pernicious anaemia the vitamin is not absorbed because of lack of an intrinsic factor made by the stomach lining.
C Ascorbic acid $C_6H_8O_6$	Water soluble. Easily oxidised, usual cooking loses about half vitamin C. Sterilised food may be deficient.	Fresh fruit and vegetables, especially citrus fruit and blackcurrants.	Scurvy – haemorrhages caused when 'cement' joining cells of capillaries is defective and capillaries leak blood. Needed for collagen in bone and connective tissue. May help to give resistance to disease.
D_2 Calciferol $C_{28}H_{43}OH$ D_3 Cholecalciferol $C_{27}H_{43}OH$	Fat soluble. Made by UV irradiation of ergosterol in skin.	Fish liver oil, egg yolk.	Deficiency causes malformation of bone and dentine due to calcium and phosphate not being laid down in childrens' bones – rickets, or removal of these minerals from adult bones – osteomalacia, leading to easy fracture. May aid absorption of calcium from gut.
E Tocopherol (α, β, γ forms) α form: $C_{29}H_{48}O_2$	Fat soluble. Stable.	Wheat embryo oil, wholemeal, green leaves, milk, meat, egg yolk.	Absence leads to sterility in many mammals including rats, mice, monkeys, rabbits, dogs. Deficiency has not been shown in man. In other species deficiency leads to muscular weakness.
K Naphthaquinone derivative	Fat soluble. Related substance K_2 formed by bacteria in gut.	Green vegetables, tomatoes, pig liver.	If deficient, liver forms insufficient prothrombin so blood clotting is delayed. Common deficiency in newborn babies.

Table 2 Minerals (Based mainly on flowering plants and ourselves)

Mineral	Use in plants	Use in animals
Nitrates	Required for protein, nitrogenous bases and chlorophyll synthesis. Deficient plants are stunted and the older leaves are yellow.	Nitrogen obtained from protein of diet. Required for synthesis of protein and nitrogenous compounds.
Sulphates	Source of sulphur for some amino acids like cysteine. Deficient plants show yellow leaves (chlorosis) especially young leaves – sulphur not easily transported.	Obtained from protein for manufacture of sulphur-containing amino acids.
Phosphates	Source of phosphorus for protein, nucleic acids and ATP synthesis. Phosphates used as buffers in tissue fluids.	
	Lack causes brown areas on leaves which may turn dark blue-green.	Creatine phosphate and arginine phosphate required for contraction of vertebrate and invertebrate muscle respectively.
Calcium	As calcium pectate a part of plant cell walls. Required for some enzymes. Lack causes early death of root and stem meristems, hooked young leaves, stunted roots.	Present in milk, cheese, hard water. Adult humans need about 800 mg/day. Necessary for calcium phosphate of bones and teeth, for muscle contraction and nerve conduction, blood clotting. Absorption through ileum depends on adequate levels of bile salts and vitamin D in body.
Iron	For chlorophyll synthesis, cytochromes, many enzymes, the electron carrier ferredoxin. Lack causes yellowing of young leaves and eventual inhibition of cell division.	Found in red meat, liver, kidney, eggs, spinach. Adults need 15 mg/day for formation of haemoglobin in red blood cells and for cytochrome. Shortage leads to anaemia.
Magnesium	Part of chlorophyll molecule; many proteins; as enzyme activator. Lack causes reduced growth, short internodes leaves die early, no flowers.	For skeletons as magnesium carbonate. Magnesium ions activate enzymes, muscles and nerves of higher animals.
Potassium	Enzyme activator, osmotic regulator e.g. in guard cells. Lack causes reduced growth, mottled leaves, often bronzed and inrolled.	For cell division, protein synthesis, growth. Muscle and nerve function.

Table 2 (contd)

Mineral	Use in plants	Use in animals
Sodium	Role in plants uncertain. May be enzyme activator. Important in C_4 pathway plants see chapter 5.	Important cation in animal cells. Enzyme activator used with potassium and magnesium to maintain muscle and nerve function.
Chloride	Important anion for buffering and exchange of ions across membranes. Induced lack causes reduced growth, chlorosis, stunted roots.	For hydrochloric acid in gastric juice.
Boron (trace)	As borate, not activator or part of any known enzyme. May inhibit some enzymes and thereby act as regulator in these reactions. Lack causes meristem to breakdown, stem apex dies, flowers and fruit suppressed or malformed.	Widespread in very small amounts. May be concerned with carbohydrate transport.
Manganese (trace)	Growth factor and enzyme activator in plants and animals. Lack causes chlorosis and mottled leaves	Needed for bone development.
Copper (trace)	Part of some oxidase enzymes e.g. cytochrome oxidase. Lack in some fruit crops makes leaves become mottled and die, main shoots die, bark becomes rough and exudes gum. Cereal leaves roll up and go white.	Aids haemoglobin synthesis. Part of haemocyanin and some oxidase enzymes.
Zinc (trace)	Growth factor, may be involved in auxin metabolism (see chapter 13). In deficient plants, leaves and stems fail to elongate and expand.	Possible growth factor e.g. in rodents. Present in mammalian carbonic anhydrase. Required for insulin manufacture.
Molybdenum (trace)	As molybdates required for nitrogen fixation and nitrate assimilation, as enzyme activator. Deficiency shown by chlorosis between veins, death of leaf edges, no fruit set. Loss of leaf blade in cauliflower.	

DIETETICS — BALANCED DIETS AND ENERGY REQUIREMENTS

Dietetics is the study of diets and their regulation for people, taking into account their age, sex, occupation, state of health etc. The result should be a diet which is balanced in terms of food content and energy supplied. A balanced diet should contain:

(i)   correct proportions of carbohydrate, protein and fats;
(ii) enough energy for the particular person;
(iii) vitamins;
(iv) mineral salts;
(v)   water;
(vi) roughage.

Most normal diets are likely to be well-balanced, but the various types of food are not equally available all over the world. For example in underdeveloped countries, especially tropical ones, diets often contain much carbohydrate, particularly yam and cassava, but little protein. Adults need about one gramme of protein per kilogramme of body weight per day, but young growing children need three to four grammes per kilogramme body weight per day, otherwise they suffer from a protein deficiency called *kwashiorkor*. This disease appears when the child passes from the protein-rich diet supplied by its mother's milk to a largely carbohydrate diet of solid food. The symptoms include skin lesions, liver damage and lethargy and it may prove fatal during the first five years of life.

Malnutrition caused by lack of various vitamins in the diet results in the deficiency diseases described in Table 1. One example is the prevalence of pellagra in countries where animal products are largely absent from the diet and maize is the main vegetable constituent. In this case the absence of nicotinic acid could be partially avoided by growing some alternative cereal crops.

The energy value of foods is usually measured in joules and kilojoules. 4.2 joules is the amount of heat energy required to raise the temperature of 1 g of water by 1°C.; 1 kilojoule is equal to 1000 joules. The amount of energy contained in food is measured using apparatus called a *bomb calorimeter*. This apparatus allows the food to be burned completely to carbon dioxide and water, and the heat produced is transmitted to a known weight of water. The temperature of the water is noted at the start of the experiment, measured again at the end of the experiment, and the rise in temperature calculated. The heat to warm the water has come from the combustion of the food and gives some estimate of the energy that might be obtained from the food by the body. For example, 1 g of carbohydrate yields about 17.2 kJ; 1 g of fat 38.5 kJ and 1 g of protein 22.2 kJ. It is unlikely that the body's metabolism would be as efficient as this, but the measurement is useful for comparing the relative energy value of various kinds of foods.

The energy requirements of the human body can be determined by measuring its oxygen uptake under varying circumstances. The uptake of oxygen is an indication of the amount of oxygen being used to oxidise the food and provide energy. It is very difficult to produce any rules for energy requirements since people vary a great deal in their metabolic rate and the amount of physical activity that they undertake. In order just to stay alive i.e. maintain *basal metabolism*, about 7500 kJ/day is reckoned to be required for an average sized man and about 5850 kJ/day for a woman. *Basal metabolic rate* is usually estimated as 4.2 kJ per kg of body weight per hour. This increases to around 13 000 kJ/day for a man going about his normal daily activities and to about 16 500 kJ/day for a man doing heavy manual work.

It is a sobering thought that over half the world's population, particularly those in Asia and parts of South America, have an energy intake of less than 9240 kJ/day i.e. below the recommended minimum level for light work. Even allowing for lower rates for women and children this is still a very depressing figure. In contrast, the diets of the more industrialised countries are usually criticised for their high kilojoule intake – often in the form of excess carbo-hydrate, which tends to lead to obesity. Much of this carbohydrate is in the form of sugar, which also accelerates the rate of tooth decay in these countries. The sugar provides an ideal bacterial food that is broken down to organic acids and these attack the tooth enamel. There is evidence too, to link the high level of both animal fat and sucrose in the diet with coronary heart disease. There is also a tendency to eat much prepackaged dried and tinned food so that occasionally vitamins, particularly A, D and C may be deficient in the diet.

Water and its importance to life

In discussing the importance of various types of food it is sometimes forgotten that water makes up an essential part of a diet and is a fundamental requirement for all living cells. It is a major part of the bodies of most living structures. Human cells contain about eighty per cent water. Only in dormant structures such as seeds and spores or in tough skeletal materials is water scarce.

It seems very likely that life first evolved in watery surroundings and water has remained ever since the medium in which the chemical reactions of living things take place. Water is an excellent solvent. It is a *polar molecule*, the oxygen having a net negative charge and the hydrogens a net positive charge:

If a substance such as sodium chloride is released into water, the water attracts both the positive sodium ion and the negative chloride ions and tends to make them dissociate. The polarity of water molecules also tends to attract them together in small groups – the oxygen of one attracted to the hydrogen of the next. This is called *hydrogen bonding* and is a weak kind of bond but one which helps to keep organic molecules together.

Water has a high thermal capacity which means that a large increase in the temperature of the environment results in a comparatively small rise in the temperature of any water in the environment and if the temperature should drop it will drop more slowly in water than on land. Therefore, water provides a relatively stable environment without wide variations in temperature. In fact, water has a high boiling point for such a low molecular weight and, if this were not the case, it would have boiled off into space.

Surface tension, the force that makes the surface of a liquid contract so that it occupies the least possible area, is helped in water by the polarity of its molecules. Any molecules dissolved in water lower its surface tension and they tend to collect at the interface of the water and the air. This could have been important in the development of membranes, and is now important in the movement of water in and out of cells. The cohesive action of water molecules also helps to raise water up the vascular tissue of plants as we shall see in chapter 10.

Most liquids decrease in volume when they freeze and therefore increase in density and sink. Water, however, does the reverse. It increases in density and floats which means that the lower layers stay comparatively warmer and the organisms of these regions are to some extent protected from freezing.

Water is involved in all the metabolic processes of living things, such as digestion, photosynthesis, excretion, etc. It is a vital part of the transport systems of organisms from osmosis and transport across membranes to the large scale movements of blood, transpiration and translocation. In reproduction, water is required for most forms of gamete release and for embryo development. Water provides support in the form of turgor pressure, the transpiration stream and directly by giving buoyancy to aquatic organisms. Many of the senses of animals involve the use of water, particularly those of taste and smell. Water may also be used to regulate body temperature, by sweating and panting, in animals that maintain a constant temperature independent of their environment. Some of these processes will be examined in further detail in later chapters and the role of water will become more apparent. Even this brief list of its uses however, conveys some idea of the essential value of water to life on earth.

Roughage

Unlike the other items in our balanced diet, roughage is of no direct use in itself, since it is indigestible. It therefore provides solid material that stretches the walls of the intestine and stimulates them to contract and so push the food along. Insufficient roughage can cause constipation. In man much of the roughage comes from the cellulose of plant cell walls, which we are unable to digest, because we do not have any suitable digestive enzymes. Some animals such as rabbits have symbiotic bacteria in their appendix and colon which can digest cellulose to glucose and make some of this available to the animal.

Enzymes

There is only space here to mention the main characteristics of enzymes and to give some current ideas on their mode of action. A more detailed account will be found in *The cell concept*. Enzymes are organic catalysts, allowing chemical reactions to take place quickly at the temperature of living tissue. They control the rates and directions of chemical reactions permitting thousands of different kinds of reactions to proceed simultaneously in a microscopic cell.

The characteristics of enzymes

1   Enzymes are all complex protein molecules with high molecular weights.
2   They speed up chemical reactions. The speed at which an enzyme operates is indicated by the *turnover number*. This is the number of substrate molecules converted to end products per minute. One of the fastest known is catalase which converts hydrogen peroxide to water and oxygen and has a turnover number of six million.
3   Enzymes are inactivated or *denatured* by excessive heat. This is a change typical of protein, as for example when egg white sets on cooking – its molecular structure has been altered. Most enzymes have a Q_{10} of two up to about 40°C. (If the temperature is raised by 10°C the reaction goes twice as fast.) Above 40°C the reaction generally slows down and then stops at about 60°C. There must presumably be some heat resistant enzymes however, since certain blue-green algae can live in hot springs at temperatures of around 90°C.
4   Enzymes are sensitive to pH. Most function best at about neutral pH but some, particularly digestive enzymes have an optimum pH which is distinctly acid or alkaline. For example pepsin from the stomach of a mammal works most efficiently at a pH of 1.5 to 2.5, whereas trypsin from the duodenum has an optimum pH of around 8.5. Some enzymes have a wider pH tolerance, such as invertase which operates from pH 3 to 7.5. The varying pH probably affects the ionic state of the amino and carboxyl groups exposed at the ends or side chains of the protein. This could alter the distribution of electric charges on the surface of the enzyme, thereby denaturing it.
5   Enzymes are specific. They may be specific for a particular substance or for a particular chemical linkage, like the peptide bonds of a protein.
6   Many enzyme controlled reactions are reversible, the direction depending on the relative amounts of substrate and end products present. If there is much substrate A the reaction will proceed to B and C, but if these end products begin to accumulate the reaction will eventually reverse. $A \rightleftharpoons B + C$. In most biological situations, of course, the end products are likely to be in constant demand and therefore removed or altered very soon after production so that, *in vivo*, the reaction may not be reversible.

Theory of enzyme activity

The evidence of the effect of heat and pH on enzymes suggests that their configuration and charge may be important in the mechanism by which they work. This is supported by other evidence, such as the effect of increasing the substrate concentration while maintaining the enzyme concentration constant. The immediate result is likely to be that the reaction speeds up until a new 'plateau' is reached, at which point the enzyme is contacting the maximum number of molecules per unit time and no increase in available substrate can further speed up the process. This can only be done by increasing the enzyme concentration as well as the concentration of substrate.

It is suggested that enzyme and substrate together form an *enzyme-substrate complex*. Each enzyme molecule probably has a particular region on its surface, called an *active site*, which fits on to a part of the substrate molecule. This explains why the shape and the electrical charges on the enzyme molecule are so important. It is sometimes called the *'lock and key' hypothesis* (see Figure 18). Once

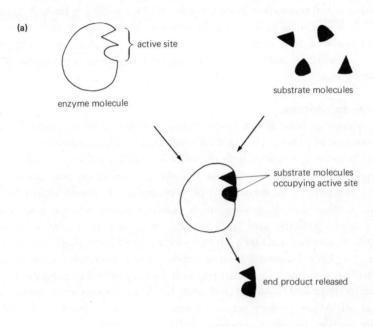

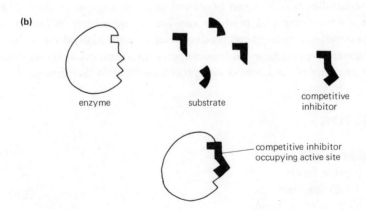

Figure 18 Enzyme action
(a) the 'lock and key' hypothesis
(b) the action of a competitive inhibitor

the end products have formed, the complex no longer fits together and therefore separates, exposing the active site again so that more enzyme-substrate complexes may form. Sometimes other activators or coenzymes are necessary to provide the right shape or charge for the enzyme. It may be a metal ion such as iron $^{++}$, manganese $^{++}$ or magnesium $^{++}$, which may help by providing positive charges.

Coenzymes include nicotinamide·adenine dinucleotide (NAD) which in the chemical reactions of respiration accepts hydrogen atoms transferred to it by dehydrogenase enzymes. This is why many of the vitamins of the B group are important in cell respiration, since nicotinic acid is required to make NAD and riboflavin is needed to produce flavin adenine dinucleotide (FAD).

Some enzymes need to be attached to a non-protein prosthetic group. For instance cytochrome oxidase, another respiratory enzyme has a prosthetic group containing iron.

Enzyme inhibitors

Some substances, instead of aiding enzyme-controlled reactions, actually slow them down or stop them. These are *inhibitors*. One type is a *competitive* or *reversible inhibitor* because it competes with the usual substrate for the active site of the enzyme (Figure 18). This implies that the configuration of the normal substrate and the competitive inhibitor must be very similar. It is well shown by the enzyme succinic dehydrogenase which usually oxidises succinic acid (butanedioic acid). Malonic acid (propanedioic acid) is very similar in its configuration to succinic acid and if it is in the vicinity it will slow down the reaction.

The other kind of inhibitor is non-competitive or irreversible since it attaches itself to the active site or some other region of the enzyme and remains there, thus altering its shape and making it impossible for the enzyme-substrate complex to form at all. Many poisons act as enzyme inhibitors in this way, including cyanide, carbon monoxide, mercury, arsenic and copper.

Not all enzyme inhibition is bad, however, since it is one way in which enzyme-controlled reactions can be slowed down or stopped in the cell. For instance accumulating end products can act as competitive inhibitors and prevent excessive amounts of end product being formed. Many drugs including the sulphonamides and some antibiotics operate in a similar way by combining with the enzymes of the bacteria and preventing their further growth.

QUESTIONS

1 Explain where and how
   (a) peptide bonds
   (b) disulphide links
   (c) ester (oxygen) bonds
   (d) glycoside bonds are formed.
2 What is the significance of each of the following facts?
   (a) Protein molecules form colloidal suspensions in water.

(b) Proteins have both acidic and basic properties.

(c) Fats yield more energy per gramme than carbohydrates.

(d) Water has a high thermal capacity.

(e) Malonic acid is a competitive inhibitor for succinic dehydrogenase.

5 Autotrophic nutrition

Only plants are capable of combining simple inorganic substances into complex organic ones capable of sustaining life. An organism which can carry out this method of nutrition is said to be autotrophic which means self-feeding. There are two types of autotrophic nutrition, chemosynthesis and photosynthesis.

Chemosynthesis is performed by some bacteria. The raw materials are carbon dioxide and water and the energy to combine them into organic compounds comes from the oxidation, during respiration, of various inorganic compounds. For example, the colourless sulphur bacteria, found in decaying organic material, oxidise hydrogen sulphide to sulphur and water. The energy released is used to build up organic molecules from carbon dioxide, while the sulphur is stored in the bacteria and may be oxidised at a future date if hydrogen sulphide becomes scarce. Even hydrogen can be used as a substrate by the hydrogen bacteria, which oxidise it, usually using nitrates and sulphates as oxygen sources. Some very important chemosynthetic bacteria are the nitrifying bacteria of the nitrogen cycle, which oxidise ammonia or nitrites to nitrates.

Photosynthesis occurs in plants containing chlorophyll, even if its green colour is obscured by other pigments as in some algae and bacteria. The process involves the formation of organic compounds, generally from carbon dioxide and water, using sunlight as an energy source, absorbed by the pigment. It may also be called *holophytic nutrition* which means completely plant-like feeding. Photosynthesis is vital as the means of making complex organic substances available to animals, hence the appearance of a photosynthesising plant at the beginning of virtually all food chains. During the chemical reactions of photosynthesis, oxygen is released into the atmosphere. This is essential to support the respiration of other organisms and to keep a balance between carbon dioxide and oxygen in our atmosphere.

THE RAW MATERIALS OF PHOTOSYNTHESIS

We know that the raw materials for photosynthesis are chlorophyll, carbon dioxide and water, in the presence of light and a suitable temperature. We can show the necessity for each of these in simple experiments using a destarched plant, i.e. one which has been kept in the dark for a minimum of twenty four hours immediately before the experiment. If at the end of the experiment starch is found in the leaves then it must have been produced during the course of the experiment, therefore photosynthesis must have taken place. To see if starch is present the leaf is first dipped into boiling water to kill the cells and burst the starch grains. It is then heated in methylated spirit which removes the chlorophyll and thus makes the result of the starch test visible. The decolourised leaf is rather stiff so it is preferable to dip it again in boiling water to soften it before spreading it out on a tile and covering it with iodine solution. Any parts of the leaf which contain starch will then turn blue-black, indicating that photosynthesis has occurred there.

Carbon dioxide

Carbon dioxide can be shown to be necessary for photosynthesis by using a destarched plant and enclosing two of its leaves as shown in Figure 19. The potassium hydroxide absorbs carbon dioxide so that leaf A is in a carbon dioxide-free atmosphere. The other flask around leaf B contains only water and is the control for the experiment. After about six hours in a well-lit position both leaves are tested for starch. The control leaf should give a positive result, while leaf A should have formed very little starch since it only had carbon dioxide available to it for a brief time. Although this experiment gives the result we might expect, it may be criticised on the grounds that it traps the gases around the leaf and introduces artificial atmospheric conditions, which may well affect the gas exchange of the leaf.

Light

The importance of light in photosynthesis may be demonstrated by covering a portion of a leaf of a previously destarched plant with a piece of black paper which shuts out the light. After exposing the plant to light for about six hours the leaf is tested for starch and this is found only where the light was allowed to reach the leaf surface, (see Figure 19). Again we are introducing an artificially enclosed environment around part of the leaf, hindering its gas exchange, and the absence of light may cause some of the stomata under the paper to close.

Water

The necessity for water is more difficult to show since it obviously cannot be removed from the plant without killing it, being an integral part of the plant's cells and involved in many other processes in the plant besides photosynthesis. One way to demonstrate the involvement of water in photosynthesis is to 'label' it, using water containing the heavy isotope of oxygen ^{18}O. This heavy oxygen can be traced through the plant and demonstrated to be evolved during photosynthesis, showing that the water has been used in the process.

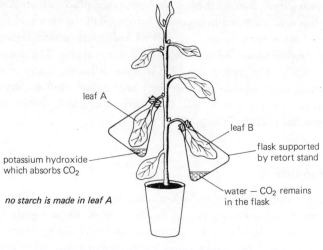

leaf A

leaf B

potassium hydroxide
which absorbs CO₂

flask supported
by retort stand

no starch is made in leaf A

water — CO₂ remains
in the flask

(a) to see if CO₂ is necessary

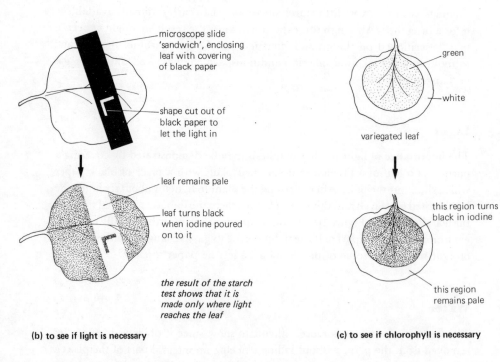

microscope slide
'sandwich', enclosing
leaf with covering
of black paper

shape cut out of
black paper to
let the light in

leaf remains pale

leaf turns black
when iodine poured
on to it

*the result of the starch
test shows that it is
made only where light
reaches the leaf*

(b) to see if light is necessary

green

white

variegated leaf

this region turns
black in iodine

this region
remains pale

(c) to see if chlorophyll is necessary

Figure 19   The conditions required for photosynthesis

Chlorophyll

The removal of chlorophyll from a leaf results in its death, so to show that it is necessary we make use of variegated leaves, in which chlorophyll is naturally absent from some parts. If a variegated plant is exposed to light and its leaves later tested for starch, the starch will only be found where chlorophyll was originally present in the leaf, as shown in Figure 19.

Temperature

Photosynthesis consists of a series of chemical reactions, each controlled by enzymes and, like all enzyme-controlled reactions, its rate is temperature dependent. It proceeds at its optimum rate at around 30°C with minor variations depending on the species. Below this level the rate rapidly falls off. Above 40°C however, photosynthesis soon stops since the enzymes, being proteins, are denatured.

MEASURING THE RATE OF PHOTOSYNTHESIS

An estimate of the rate of photosynthesis can be obtained by measuring either the uptake of carbon dioxide by leaves, or the evolution of oxygen. Figure 20 shows some apparatus which can be used to measure carbon dioxide uptake. A control apparatus without a green plant is used to measure the amount of carbon dioxide present in a known volume of air drawn through the apparatus. In the apparatus shown, the green plant will absorb some of the carbon dioxide passing it. Equal volumes of air are drawn through both sets of apparatus simultaneously. Then each solution of baryta water (barium hydroxide) is titrated against standard hydrochloric acid. The difference between the two titrations is the apparent uptake of carbon dioxide by the leaves and can be expressed in cm^3 CO_2 absorbed per hour/mm^2 of leaf surface or per gramme of fresh weight or dry weight of leaves. Of course this is only a measure of the *apparent rate of photosynthesis*, the experiment must be repeated with the plant container covered to exclude the light. This will give a measure of the carbon dioxide given out during respiration and it must be added to the first result if the *true rate of photosynthesis* is required. Since the amount of gas exchange carried out in respiration is small compared with that involved in photosynthesis it is often ignored.

The evolution of oxygen by aquatic plants can be measured by counting either the number of bubbles they produce per unit time, or by measuring the volume of gas produced. Suitable apparatus for each method is shown in Figure 20. It should be remembered however that the gas released is not entirely oxygen, but also contains carbon dioxide and nitrogen.

When the rate of photosynthesis is being measured it can also be compared under varying conditions of light, temperature etc. These factors which affect the rate of photosynthesis will be discussed later (see p. 16).

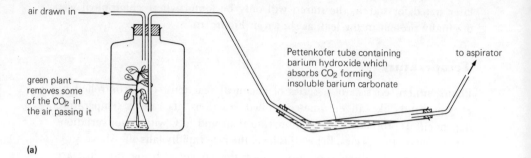

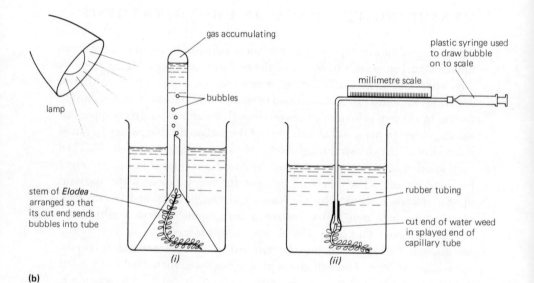

Figure 20 Measuring the rate of photosynthesis.
(a) Measuring the rate of carbon dioxide uptake by a green plant. The barium hydroxide is titrated against standard hydrochloric acid using phenolphthalein as indicator.
(b) Measuring the rate of bubbling by a water plant. The volume of gas released can be measured by the method shown in diagram (ii).

SITES OF PHOTOSYNTHESIS

The blue-green algae have their photosynthetic pigments on membranes dispersed in the cytoplasm but in other plants they are enclosed by membranes. In the photoautotrophic bacteria the containers are *chromatophores* and in other plants they are the *chloroplasts* found in leaves and green stems. The chloroplasts of many of the higher plants are able to move in the cytoplasmic streaming of the cell and may alter their position as the light intensity varies, becoming edge on to the direction of light if it is bright and side on if it is dim. (See Figure 21.) Many of the green algae are motile and can swim to orientate themselves with respect to light. Some even have photoreceptors which aid them to do so.

LEAF ANATOMY IN RELATION TO PHOTOSYNTHESIS

A vertical section through the lamina of a typical mesophyte leaf is shown in Figure 21, and illustrates how leaf structure is correlated with its functions as a photosynthetic organ. The leaf is flattened and very thin so it has a very large surface area to volume ratio and allows maximum exposure to light of the chloroplasts inside. Furthermore, the majority of the chloroplasts are found in the palisade mesophyll – the upper layers of the leaf.

The surface of the leaf, particularly on the underside, is pitted with small pores, the *stomata*, which allow gas exchange including the entry of carbon dioxide and the exit of oxygen. Inside the leaf is an extensive system of intercellular spaces providing an internal atmosphere in contact with large numbers of cells. The walls of these cells are more or less saturated with water, in which the incoming carbon dioxide dissolves or forms a weak solution of carbonic acid and enters the cells.

The many small veins of the leaf bring a supply of water and mineral salts, from the roots, in the xylem and carry away the manufactured food in the phloem.

THE STRUCTURE OF THE CHLOROPLAST

In higher plants the chloroplasts are usually disc-shaped biconvex structures about 5 μm in diameter as shown in Figure 22. Around the outside is a double protein/lipid unit membrane enclosing a protein/lipid *stroma*. This stroma appears to have no organised structure, but contains starch grains and enzymes which can catalyse the reduction of carbon dioxide. Embedded in the stroma are lamellae arranged one above the other and consisting of *grana* and *intergrana* regions. The grana are composed of a stack of protein and lipid layers with chlorophyll attached to the lipid molecules and carotenoids dissolved in the lipid. A typical chloroplast contains about sixty grana, each made up of about fifty lamellae. The grana are about 600 nm in diameter and on them the chlorophyll is believed to be arranged in granules previously called *quantasomes*. Each granule was thought to consist of about 230 molecules of chlorophyll, and to be the basic photosynthetic unit. Later work has indicated the presence of granules of two sizes which fit between each other but their exact functions are uncertain. Experiments have shown that separated lamellae will give off oxygen

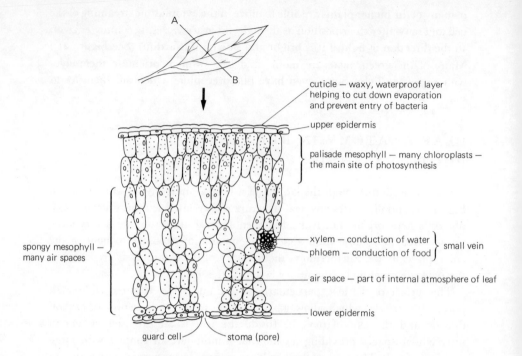

cuticle — waxy, waterproof layer helping to cut down evaporation and prevent entry of bacteria

upper epidermis

palisade mesophyll — many chloroplasts — the main site of photosynthesis

spongy mesophyll — many air spaces

xylem — conduction of water ⎤
phloem — conduction of food ⎦ small vein

air space — part of internal atmosphere of leaf

lower epidermis

guard cell   stoma (pore)

**part of section A — B through a leaf,
showing its adaptations for photosynthesis**

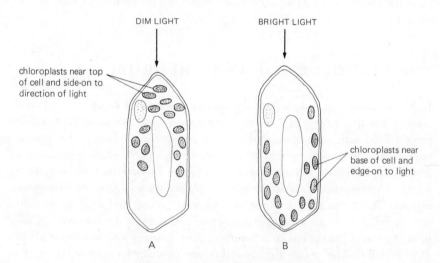

DIM LIGHT

BRIGHT LIGHT

chloroplasts near top of cell and side-on to direction of light

chloroplasts near base of cell and edge-on to light

A

B

changes in arrangement of chloroplasts in different light intensities

Figure 21   The site of photosynthesis in a leaf

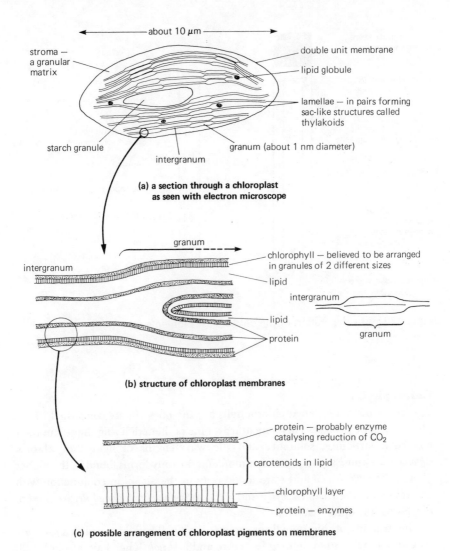

(a) a section through a chloroplast
as seen with electron microscope

(b) structure of chloroplast membranes

(c) possible arrangement of chloroplast pigments on membranes

Figure 22   The structure of a chloroplast

if brightly lit, suggesting that it is these membranes which are concerned in the chemical reactions of photosynthesis.

The chloroplast pigments

The existence of a number of pigments in green leaves can be demonstrated by grinding them up in a solution of acetone with a pestle and mortar and then separating the pigments by *paper chromatography*. Figure 23 shows a simple way in which this may be set up and the kind of results that may be obtained, using grass clippings or nettle leaves.

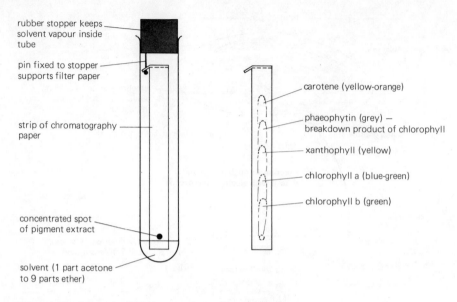

Figure 23   The separation of the chloroplast pigments

Chlorophylls

The green pigments called chlorophylls are the ones chiefly concerned in the photosynthetic process. There are at least nine of them differing slightly in their molecular structure, solubility and the wavelengths of light they absorb. *Chlorophyll a* and *b* are the most common and the only forms found in the higher plants. *Chlorophylls c, d* and *e* are found only in the algae, in conjunction with chlorophyll a. *Bacteriochlorophyll a* and *b* and the *chlorobium chlorophylls* are present in photoautotrophic bacteria.

The structure of chlorophyll a is shown on p. 69. The molecule has a *porphyrin ring* with a magnesium atom at its centre and a *phytol* (long chain alcohol) tail. The phytol chain is similar to carotenoid structure and could, like them, be derived from vitamin A.

Extracts of chlorophyll in organic solvents show absorption peaks at the blue-violet and red ends of the visible spectrum, as shown in Figure 24. If the rate of photosynthesis is recorded under monochromatic light of different wavelengths in succession, the photosynthetic activity of the plant can be measured for light of each colour. When the activity is plotted against the wavelength the result is an *action spectrum*, which, as Figure 24 shows, corresponds very closely to the absorption spectrum of chlorophyll extracts. This clearly suggests that chlorophyll is the pigment chiefly concerned with the absorption of light for photosynthesis.

The molecular structure of chlorophyll

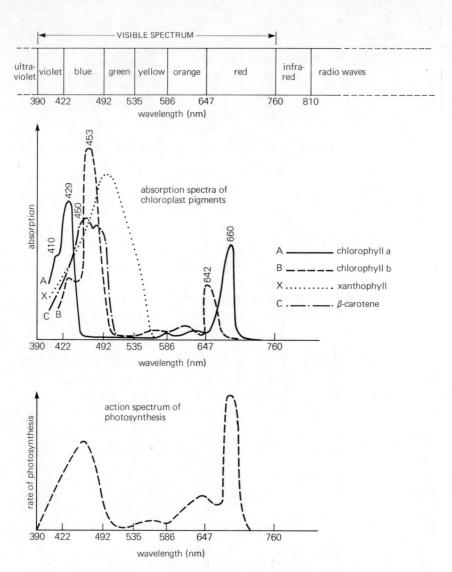

Figure 24   The role of the chloroplast pigments in light absorption

Carotenoids

Carotenoids are lipid compounds widely distributed amongst plants and animals. Hydrogen carotenoids (containing only carbon and hydrogen) are called *carotenes*; those that also contain oxygen are called *xanthophylls*. This group of pigments ranges in colour from yellow through orange and brown to purple.

Carotenoids are found close to chlorophyll in the chloroplast and the orientation of the two pigments on the lamellae seems to be important in photosynthesis. American plant physiologist T. Goodwin has suggested that the

β-carotene $C_{40}H_{56}$

chlorophylls and carotenoids may even be attached to the same protein, forming a complex which he has called *photosynthin*.

The role of the carotenoids in the chloroplast appears to be two-fold. They absorb light energy and transfer it to chlorophyll a and secondly they protect chlorophyll against photo-oxidation. Mutant algae lacking carotenoids have been shown to die when grown in the light because their chlorophyll oxidises in its presence.

Relation of pigment to habitat

It is noticeable, particularly amongst the algae, that the type of pigment present and the habitat of the plant are closely linked. Terrestrial plants and shallow water plants are green, absorbing red and blue light for photosynthesis. In deeper water red light is quickly absorbed and only the blue end of the spectrum penetrates. Here brown algae are found, with additional xanthophylls which absorb blue light. Deeper still the red algae become more common, absorbing mainly blue light, using pigments such as *phycoerythrin*.

THE PROCESS OF PHOTOSYNTHESIS

Put in very simplified form the photosynthetic process begins with the absorption of light energy by the chloroplast pigments and this energy is then used to split water. The hydrogen obtained from the water is used to reduce carbon dioxide, forming carbohydrate and the remaining oxygen is evolved as a waste product.

The evidence for light and dark reactions

Chemical reactions are affected by temperature; a $10°C$ rise will approximately double the rate. Photochemical reactions are not affected by temperature. Photosynthesis is affected by light **and** temperature as we have seen, suggesting both photochemical and chemical stages in the process. These stages are referred to as the *light* and *dark reactions* of photosynthesis. The light reaction can take place only in the presence of light, whereas the dark reaction can occur in light or darkness. It is worth noting, however, that photosynthesis is at its most efficient under a regime of alternating light and dark periods. It seems that the products of the light reaction accumulate faster in the light than they can be incorporated into the dark reaction, which is slower, and the alternating periods of light and darkness prevent a build up of these products.

Evidence for these reactions has come from work with isolated chloroplasts. In the light they accumulate energy-storing ATP and reduce a hydrogen acceptor NADP (nicotinamide adenine dinucleotide phosphate) a derivative of vitamin B. Oxygen is also evolved. If carbon dioxide is supplied to them the chloroplasts will carry out the synthesis of carbohydrate. In the dark the chloroplasts will also synthesise carbohydrates if supplied with ATP, $NADPH_2$ and carbon dioxide. Thus the following stages are suggested:

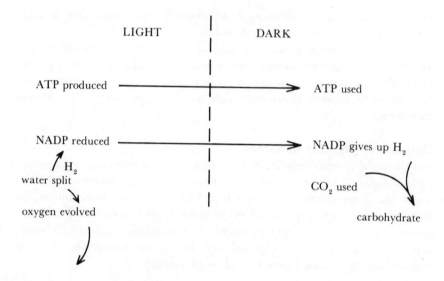

The light or Hill reaction

As we can see above, the light reaction consists of the photochemical splitting of water, providing hydrogen atoms for the reduction of carbon dioxide in the dark reaction and, secondly, the formation of an energy store in ATP, which can be used to power the dark reaction. The production of ATP by photochemical means is called *photophosphorylation*.

The light reaction begins with the absorption of light by chlorophyll. The behaviour of light in optical systems can only be explained by saying that light moves as waves, but many photochemical reactions, including photosynthesis, can only be explained by assuming light to be of a particulate nature i.e. a stream of tiny particles called *photons*. The energy possessed by one photon is a *quantum* and the energy value of quanta is inversely proportional to the wavelength of the light.

In a photochemical reaction the quanta strike electrons and transfer energy to them. When this happens to chlorophyll an 'excited' electron is ejected at a higher energy level than the normal ground state. The energy of these free electrons may be passed from one molecule of chlorophyll to another and from the carotenoids to chlorophyll a. This is called *resonance transfer* and requires the pigment molecules to be close together, hence the importance of the membrane structure of chloroplasts. This kind of behaviour has led to the comparison of the chloroplast to a semi-conductor unit.

If the electron merely lost energy and fell back into the chlorophyll molecule it would fluoresce. A chlorophyll extract shows a blood red fluorescence in reflected light. In an intact chloroplast, however, the electron is 'picked up' by one or more electron acceptors and the excess energy it possesses is available for use by the cell. The chloroplast is therefore acting as a transducer, making light energy available as chemical energy in the cell.

Cyclic and non-cyclic photophosphorylation

Photophosphorylation occurs in two forms, cyclic and non-cyclic. In *cyclic photophosphorylation* as shown below the excited electron is picked up by an electron acceptor such as vitamin K or by flavin mononucleotide (FMN), part of the vitamin B complex. From the first electron acceptor the electron passes to the cytochromes and thence back to chlorophyll. As the electron passes from each acceptor to the next, energy is released and used up in the synthesis of ATP. By the time the electron returns to the chlorophyll molecule it has lost all its excess energy and is back to its normal ground state. The process is cyclic because it requires no external supply of electrons, but it does of course need a supply of electron acceptors, of ADP and inorganic phosphate.

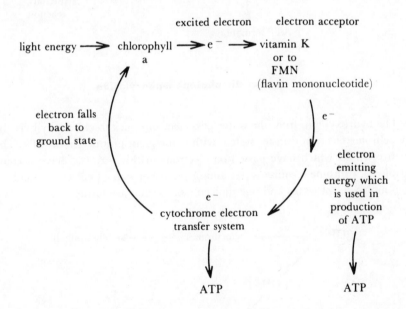

In non-cyclic photophosphorylation the excited electrons emitted by chlorophyll are picked up by an electron acceptor called ferredoxin. Water tends to dissociate spontaneously into hydrogen (H^+) and hydroxyl (OH^-) ions. Some of the H^+ ions from the water and the electrons from the ferredoxin combine to form hydrogen atoms. (A negative electron and a positive H^+ ion make one hydrogen atom.) These hydrogen atoms are taken up by the hydrogen acceptor

NADP which is then reduced. In its reduced state NADP enters the dark reaction of photosynthesis, providing hydrogen for the reduction of carbon dioxide. After passing on its hydrogen the NADP can be recycled and used again.

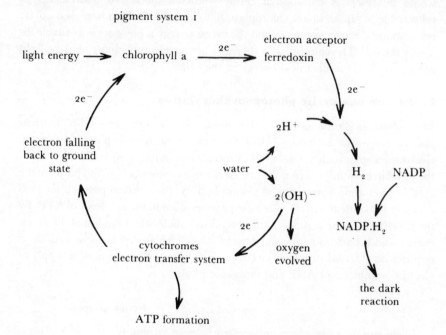

non-cyclic photophosphorylation

The hydroxyl ions from the water pass electrons back to chlorophyll via the cytochrome electron transfer system with consequent production of ATP. The hydroxyl ions which have passed on electrons in this way (i.e. have become oxidised), combine forming water and oxygen. For every four which combine two molecules of water and one molecule of oxygen are formed:

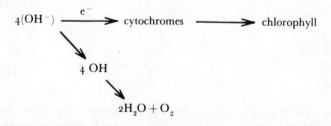

This process is non-cyclic, since hydrogen atoms are accepted by NADP and replaced from water.

It has been found that two pigment systems are involved in non-cyclic photophosphorylation and designated pigment system I (PS I) and pigment system 2 (PS 2). PS 2 gains electrons from water during hydrolysis and passes them to PS 1. PS 1 consists of chlorophyll a 683, P 700 and the carotenoids. PS 2 includes chlorophyll a 673, chlorophyll b and any phycobilins present. The numbers refer to the wavelength of light in nm at which the pigment shows maximum absorption.

The dark reaction or carbon pathway

The individual steps of the reduction of carbon dioxide and synthesis of carbohydrates were traced by Dr Melvin Calvin and his colleagues at the University of California, using a unicellular green alga called *Chlorella*. They caused algae in suspension to travel along a narrow tube at a known speed and injected carbon dioxide labelled with the radioactive isotope of carbon, ^{14}C. By varying the points at which the $^{14}CO_2$ was injected they could expose the cells to radioactive carbon for a known length of time, they then killed them rapidly in boiling methanol. Using chromatography and exposing the chromatogram to sensitive photographic film they were able to discover into what substances the ^{14}C had been incorporated. They found that after about five seconds exposure to $^{14}CO_2$ the radioactive carbon was mainly in a 3-carbon compound, – phosphoglyceric acid (PGA). After thirty seconds it was chiefly in two 3-carbon sugar phosphates, phosphoglyceraldehyde (PGAL) and dihydroxyacetone phosphate. Finally after about ninety seconds the carbon dioxide was incorporated into pentoses and hexoses.

The first step in this series of reactions was found to be the acceptance of carbon dioxide by a 5-carbon sugar phosphate called ribulose diphosphate as shown in Figure 25. When it accepts the carbon dioxide it becomes a 6-carbon compound which then splits, giving two molecules of a 3-carbon compound – phosphoglyceric acid. The next probable step is that the PGA is reduced by hydrogen, from the reduced NADP formed during the light reaction, using

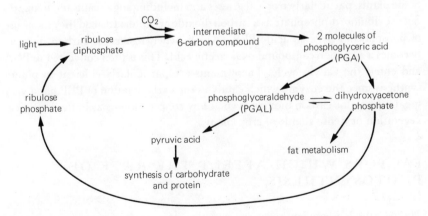

Figure 25   The carbon pathway

energy from the ATP also produced during the light reaction. The reduction of PGA results in the production of triose phosphate which can enter a number of pathways according to the requirements of the cell, to produce carbohydrates, lipids or amino acids.

In order to continue the Calvin cycle ribulose diphosphate must be reformed to accept more carbon dioxide. This is done from triose phosphate and fructose phosphate in a series of steps summarised in Figure 26.

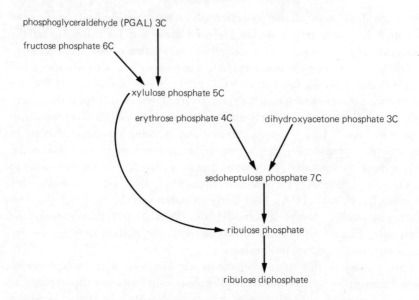

Figure 26   Regeneration of ribulose diphosphate

C₄ **Plants – the Hatch-Slack pathway**

Some plants, particularly tropical grasses and including sugar cane and maize do not use ribulose diphosphate as a carbon dioxide acceptor. Instead they make use of phosphoenol pyruvic acid (PEP), which, when it accepts carbon dioxide, becomes a 4-carbon compound oxaloacetic acid. This is then converted to PGA and enters the Calvin cycle. These plants are particularly efficient in photosynthesis since the enzyme which catalyses the carboxylation of PEP has a very great affinity for carbon dioxide even at low concentrations as in thick tropical vegetation or dense stands of crop plants.

FACTORS WHICH AFFECT THE RATE OF PHOTOSYNTHESIS

Photosynthesis is obviously a very complex process, involving a great many stages and substances. If any one of these slows down or is scarce then it may hold up the rest of the process and it is called a *limiting factor*.

Light

In general, increased light intensity increases the rate of photosynthesis until another factor, usually carbon dioxide, becomes limiting. At the usual carbon dioxide levels in the atmosphere the maximum photosynthetic rate is reached in many plants, at only quarter to half full sunlight. In shade species it may be considerably less.

Careful inspection of the leaves of many plants, particularly trees and shrubs will show that they shade each other as little as possible. This arrangement is called a *leaf mosaic*. It is obvious though that the lower leaves will suffer some shading effects and may not be photosynthesising at their maximum even in full sunlight. On the other hand, very high light intensity causes *solarisation*, the photo-oxidation of cell constituents, decolorisation of chlorophyll and ultimately even the death of the cells.

As the light intensity increases, a point is reached when the intake of carbon dioxide for photosynthesis exactly balances its output in respiration. This is called the *compensation point*. Further increase in light intensity will result in carbon dioxide being absorbed and oxygen evolved. (See Figure 27.)

Light also has indirect effects. Low light intensity leads to closure of the stomata, but experiments show little restriction of carbon dioxide entry as a result. High light intensity, however, usually results in a high transpiration rate

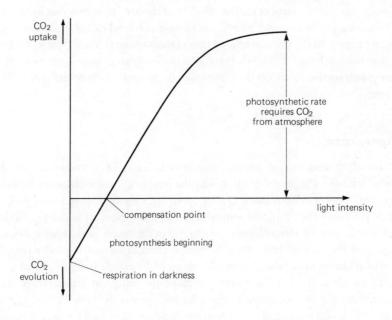

Figure 27   Relation between carbon dioxide uptake and evolution in photosynthesis and respiration. The intake of carbon dioxide for photosynthesis exactly balances its output in respiration at the compensation point.

and this may also lead to dehydration which has a significant effect on photosynthetic rates. Depending on the habitat of the plant many other factors could influence the amount of light available. These include the amount of exposure, the direction of slope of the land, atmospheric conditions such as fog, dust, humidity, also day length, and, in aquatic plants, the depth of the water.

Quality of light

We have already seen that the action spectrum for photosynthesis (p. 68) has peaks in the red and blue regions, yet the wavelengths available to a plant may vary in different habitats. Clouds, for instance, reduce the amount of red light reaching the ground. Under trees much of the red and blue light will be already absorbed by the leaves above. You may have noticed how green the light is in a wood. In water, however, the shorter wavelengths penetrate further, the red end of the spectrum soon being absorbed, hence the variety of pigments found amongst the algae and described on p. 71.

Carbon dioxide

At the beginning of the chapter we discussed the way in which the level of carbon dioxide remains relatively constant in the atmosphere at about 0.03% by volume. Under bright sunlight and a temperature of 20–25°C, with a plentiful supply of water, the amount of carbon dioxide in the atmosphere seems likely to be the limiting factor for most plants. Increasing the level of the gas up to 1% shows an increase in the photosynthetic rate of most species. Above this level the effect depends on the species. Often there is no corresponding increase in rate and in some plants such as tomatoes the leaves may begin to die as the carbon dioxide level rises.

Temperature

Since the dark reaction of photosynthesis is a series of enzyme-controlled reactions, it is not surprising that increasing the temperature speeds up the rate of the reaction. Photosynthesis has a Q_{10} of approximately two up to about 30°C, which is probably the optimum temperature for most plants for short periods (about 30 minutes). Rates at higher temperatures for longer periods soon begin to drop, probably due to enzyme destruction, accumulation of end products and limited availability of carbon dioxide. About 40°C the rate falls off rapidly as the enzymes are denatured. In temperate regions the range of temperature for photosynthesis for the majority of the plants is probably around 10°–35°C. Tropical species do not usually photosynthesise below about 5°C, whereas some conifers may continue to do so around freezing point.

Water

Less than 1% of the water absorbed by most plants is needed for photosynthesis, so it is not likely that its deficiency would affect the process directly. The indirect effects of water shortage however, are likely to retard photosynthesis, causing dehydration which will affect the structure of protoplasm and hence its metabolism. The important structural arrangement of the chloroplast is likely to be affected too. It was originally thought that water deficit closing the stomata would reduce carbon dioxide absorption, but there is much experimental evidence to suggest that even stomata appearing closed when viewed microscopically are still sufficiently open to admit the gas.

Mineral salts

Mineral salts are not directly involved as raw materials for photosynthesis, but shortage of either iron or magnesium affects the rate of chlorophyll production and hence, indirectly, the photosynthetic rate. Some ions, such as potassium and some trace elements, such as molybdenum, are also required, though the exact function of some of them is obscure.

Oxygen

It has been found that for some plants, such as wheat, the atmospheric concentration of oxygen (21%) slows down photosynthesis. It may be that the increased availability of oxygen speeds up the respiratory rate allowing it to compete more favourably with photosynthesis. Hydrogen carriers could also be reducing oxygen rather than carbon dioxide and thereby having a retarding effect. There is also evidence that oxygen limits the production of excited electrons from chlorophyll molecules. This would reduce the availability of hydrogen atoms for the dark reaction and of ATP for the energy requirements of the cells.

THE FATE OF THE PRODUCTS OF PHOTOSYNTHESIS

The triose phosphate formed by the dark reaction can pass along different pathways to form carbohydrates, proteins or lipids, according to the requirements of the cell, or it may be used as a respiratory substrate.

The carbohydrate pathway

The pathway from triose phosphate to starch, sucrose and cellulose is shown overleaf:

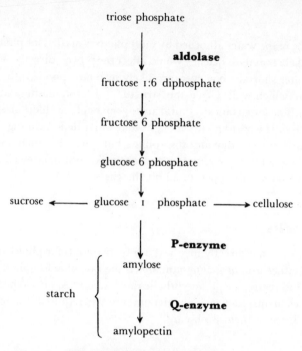

triose phosphate

aldolase

fructose 1:6 diphosphate

fructose 6 phosphate

glucose 6 phosphate

sucrose ← glucose 1 phosphate → cellulose

P-enzyme

amylose

starch {

Q-enzyme

amylopectin

The carbohydrate pathway

The first stage is the conversion of triose phosphate to fructose 1 : 6 diphosphate catalysed by aldolase. One phosphate is removed to form fructose-6-phosphate and the molecule is then rearranged giving glucose-6-phosphate. The phosphate is transferred from carbon 6 to carbon 1, resulting in the formation of glucose-1-phosphate. By removal of the phosphate and condensation of the sugar molecules, disaccharides such as sucrose and polysaccharides such as cellulose and starch may be produced.

Carbohydrate is usually passed around the body of the higher plants as sucrose in the phloem (see chapter 8). Arriving at its destination it may be used as a respiratory substrate in an actively growing region or stored, usually as starch an insoluble polysaccharide, in roots and stems, particularly perennating organs.

The pathway to protein

It is important to remember that not only carbohydrate is formed as a result of photosynthesis. In order to make protein, a source of nitrogen is required. For higher plants this is provided mainly by nitrate passing up through the xylem from the roots. The way in which it is incorporated into a protein is by no means clear, but the probable first step is its reduction to nitrite and then to hydroxylamine and possibly even to ammonia:

$$HNO_3 \rightarrow HNO_2 \rightarrow NH_2OH \rightarrow NH_3$$

nitrate nitrite hydroxyl- ammonia
amine

using nitrate and nitrite reductases and hydrogen donors such as reduced ferredoxin, NADH, NADPH, FAD, and molybdenum. ATP is also required to supply energy for the process.

The hydroxylamine or ammonia could then be taken up by α-ketoglutaric acid of the Krebs cycle, ultimately forming glutamic (2-aminopentanedioic) acid. Using glutamic acid as an initial donor of amino groups, a variety of amino acids could be built up by transaminase enzymes as seen in Figure 28.

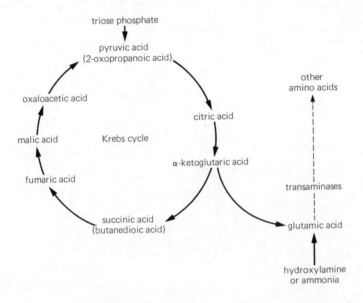

Figure 28   The pathway to protein

The proteins produced by such assemblages of amino acids could become part of the cytoplasm or nucleic acids of growing cells, or form enzymes or pigments.

The pathway to lipids

The synthesis of lipids requires the formation of glycerol (propane 1, 2, 3-triol) and fatty (alkanoic) acids, and their combination by condensation and the formation of ester bonds. Glycerol phosphate may be produced by the reduction of dihydroxyacetone phosphate, using $NADH_2$ as a hydrogen donor. The fatty acid chains begin with the combination of pyruvic (2-oxopropanoic) acid with coenzyme A making 'active acetate' or acetyl coenzyme A. (See Figure 29.) Acetyl coenzyme A carboxylase adds carbon dioxide to form malonyl coenzyme A, which can react with another molecule of acetyl coenzyme A, producing aceto-acetyl coenzyme A, releasing a molecule of carbon dioxide and a molecule of acetyl coenzyme A, which can then be recycled. By condensation and reduction a fatty acid residue is formed which can combine with more malonyl coenzyme A, adding by condensation and reduction two more molecules of carbon to the chain. By repeating the process fatty acid chains of varying length

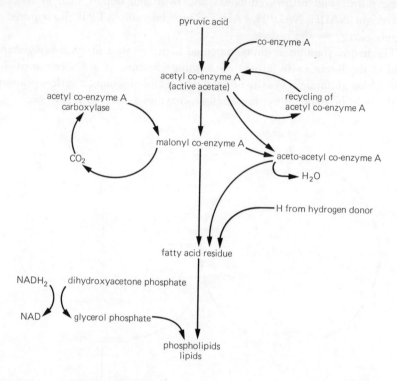

pyruvic acid

co-enzyme A

acetyl co-enzyme A
(active acetate)

acetyl co-enzyme A
carboxylase

recycling of
acetyl co-enzyme A

CO_2

malonyl co-enzyme A

aceto-acetyl co-enzyme A

H_2O

H from hydrogen donor

fatty acid residue

$NADH_2$ dihydroxyacetone phosphate

NAD   glycerol phosphate

phospholipids
lipids

Figure 29   The pathway to lipids

can be built up and finally combined with glycerol phosphate, either as phospholipids or true lipids.

Phospholipids are required for the construction of cell membranes, while lipids are often used as food stores, particularly as oil globules in seeds.

PHOTOSYNTHETIC BACTERIA

Some autotrophic bacteria are photosynthetic. They contain a pigment called *bacteriochlorophyll*, which is similar to the chlorophylls of other plants, except that it has the ability to absorb infra red light as well as the blue-violet end of the visible spectrum. The light energy absorbed by the pigment is used by the bacteria to split hydrogen sulphide. The hydrogen reduces carbon dioxide as a preliminary to the production of complex organic molecules, while the sulphur is sometimes deposited in the bacterial cells. The bacteria are called the green or the purple sulphur bacteria, depending on the type of bacteriochlorophyll they contain. They are found in the anaerobic conditions in the mud at the bottom of ponds and lakes where hydrogen sulphide is plentiful.

QUESTIONS

1 Give an illustrated account of the structure of
  (a) a green leaf
  (b) a chloroplast
  and explain how each is adapted to carry out its roles in photosynthesis.
2 Distinguish between cyclic and non-cyclic photophosphorylation.
3 Beginning from triose phosphate trace the pathways to
  (a) carbohydrate
  (b) fat and
  (c) protein.
4 Discuss the biological significance of the following facts:
  (a) green algae are not found in deep water;
  (b) in the light, isolated chloroplasts accumulate ATP, reduce NADP and give off oxygen; in the dark they will synthesise carbohydrates if supplied with ATP, $NADPH_2$ and carbon dioxide;
  (c) under normal conditions carbon dioxide is more likely to be a limiting factor for photosynthesis than either light or temperature.

6 Heterotrophic nutrition

Heterotrophic organisms are unable to manufacture their own food and must obtain it in organic form from their environment, by means of holozoic, saprophytic or parasitic nutrition. Holozoic nutrition is shown by the majority of animals and involves the eating of other animals and plants. Saprophytes include many fungi and bacteria which absorb their nutriment from the dead and decaying bodies of other organisms or from some other source of organic material such as human foods like jam or bread. Some animals and plants are parasites, feeding directly on the living tissues of other organisms.

Since holozoic animals take quantities of ready-made food into their bodies, they require a receptacle into which the food may be placed. Not all animals require this, as we shall see later in parasitic forms like the tapeworm for example, where already-digested food may simply be absorbed through the animal's body covering. The entry of food into the body is called *ingestion* and the food receptacle it enters is usually called a *gut* or *alimentary canal*. In it the food is *digested* to smaller molecules such as monosaccharides and amino acids, which can be more readily *absorbed* into the animal's body. Its use in growth and repair is called *assimilation* and it is also used, as we have already discussed, in the provision of energy by means of cellular respiration. Any parts of the food intake which cannot be digested during its time in the animal's body are eventually passed out of the body. This is called *egestion*.

The simplest type of food container for digestion is the *food vacuole*, as shown in Figure 30(a), formed by pseudopodia in amoeboid animals. There is usually no mouth or fixed point of ingestion and egestion. The pseudopodia merely enclose the food by flowing around it, digestive enzymes are secreted into the vacuole and the food is digested and absorbed. This is called *phagocytosis*. Any undigested material is simply left behind when the animal moves away. Figure 30(b) shows a slightly more complex condition in *Paramecium* where the food vacuoles follow a fixed pathway or *cyclosis*. Since in these examples the food is digested entirely within the cell, it is *intracellular digestion*, whereas digestion in a gut outside the cells is *extracellular*. In some animals digestion occurs in both forms. In *Hydra* for example, it is initially extracellular in a sac-like body cavity called the *enteron*; later, digestion continues intracellularly inside the cells of the endoderm or inner body layer, the cells of which have pseudopodia. In evolution extracellular digestion has gradually replaced intracellular digestion in importance as the gut has become more complex.

Hydra and many other simple animals have only one entry/exit point to the gut called a mouth and there is no anus. Figure 30 shows a range of digestive tracts of

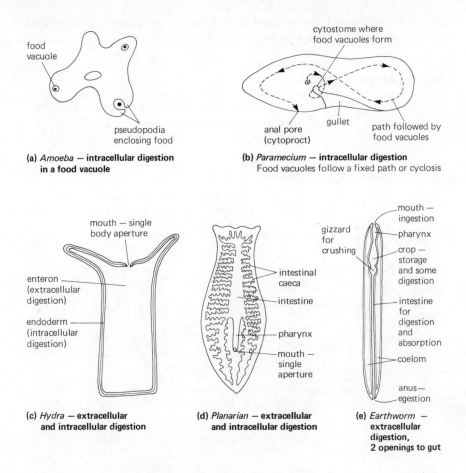

(a) *Amoeba* — **intracellular digestion in a food vacuole**

food vacuole

pseudopodia enclosing food

(b) *Paramecium* — **intracellular digestion**
Food vacuoles follow a fixed path or cyclosis

cytostome where food vacuoles form

anal pore (cytoproct)

gullet

path followed by food vacuoles

(c) *Hydra* — **extracellular and intracellular digestion**

mouth — single body aperture

enteron (extracellular digestion)

endoderm (intracellular digestion)

(d) *Planarian* — **extracellular and intracellular digestion**

intestinal caeca

intestine

pharynx

mouth — single aperture

(e) *Earthworm* — **extracellular digestion, 2 openings to gut**

mouth — ingestion

gizzard for crushing

pharynx

crop — storage and some digestion

intestine for digestion and absorption

coelom

anus— egestion

Figure 30   Possible stages in the evolution of the gut

increasing complexity. The platyhelminth planarian also has only one aperture to the gut but the intestine divides into three branches, each having many lobed *intestinal caeca*, ensuring that no part of the body is far from the digested food. The platyhelminths are triploblastic, acoelomate animals, having three body layers, ectoderm, mesoderm and endoderm, but no body cavity or coelom. In many animals the coelom is well-developed and separates the gut from the outer layers of the body, as shown by the annelid body plan Figure 30(e). The gut is tubular with a mouth and anus at opposite ends. Parts of the gut are modified for digestion and absorption, while the food is distributed by a blood circulatory system.

METHODS OF CAPTURING AND INGESTING FOOD

Many different feeding methods have evolved even in closely related animals. The mechanisms are commonly classified into three groups according to the type of food being ingested. *Microphagous* feeders ingest small particles, *macrophagous* feeders take in larger particles and some animals feed on *fluids or soft tissues*.

Microphagous feeders

Animals in this category are aquatic and often sedentary or sluggish. Their food is usually plankton and they feed almost continuously. (See Figure 31.)

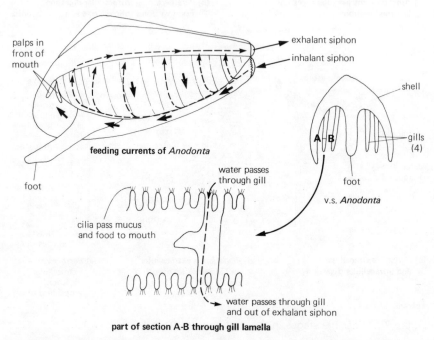

feeding currents of *Anodonta*

v.s. *Anodonta*

part of section A-B through gill lamella

(a) *Anodonta ciliary feeding — the broken lines indicate water entering inhalant siphon, passing through gill lamellae and leaving by exhalant siphon. Thick arrows show food trapped in mucus on gills and carried to mouth.*

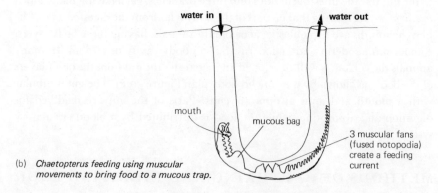

(b) *Chaetopterus feeding using muscular movements to bring food to a mucous trap.*

Figure 31 Some examples of microphagous feeding

Pseudopodia are used to engulf food in some Protozoa, such as *Amoeba* and also in some multicellular animals like Coelenterata and Turbellaria to ingest food particles from the gut. *Cilia* are used to provide currents of water bringing food particles to the mouth in a range of animals including ciliated Protozoa, sponges, some annelids, most lamellibranchs and some sea squirts. Sometimes sticky mucus accompanies the cilia helping to trap the food as in *Amphioxus*, a cephalochordate.

Some chironomid midge larvae and some gastropods, like *Crepidula*, use *mucus traps* and periodically ingest the mucus and any trapped food. In some Holothuria (sea cucumbers) the mucus covers tentacles which catch falling particles and transfer them to the mouth.

Muscular movements may be used to cause water currents to bring food particles to a filter. Some polychaetes, such as *Chaetopterus*, secrete mucus nets through which water is pumped by the animal's posterior appendages. About every fifteen minutes it ingests the net and trapped food. The whale bone whales and many fish use muscular contractions of the pharynx to set up feeding currents from which plankton can be filtered.

Setae (hairs) can be swept through the water, collecting small particles which are then transferred to the mouth in many aquatic Crustacea including *Daphnia*, copepods and barnacles.

Filter feeders can trap particles a few micrometres in diameter, while those trapped by mucus feeders are even smaller. Water snails and young tadpoles can even feed on the thin protein film at the water's surface, produced by decaying plants.

Macrophagous feeders

Detritus feeders are usually burrowing, sluggish animals continuously ingesting mud etc., from which they absorb any organic material and egest the rest. They include annelids like *Arenicola* – the lugworm, and earthworms, burrowing echinoderms, such as the heart urchin, and burrowing crustacea.

Boring and scraping: specialised mouthparts have evolved which scrape up particles of food, for example the radula of gastropods, a ribbon-like structure co ered in hooks, which rasp at the food. The ship worm, *Teredo*, which is actually a lamellibranch, rotates its two shell valves to drill into wood and then ingests the sawdust. It is one of the few animals that produces an enzyme, cellulase, which can digest cellulose. Termites also drill into wood using their jaws and contain in their intestines bacteria and a flagellate protozoan called *Trichonympha*, which can also digest cellulose, some of which is then available to the termite. This is a symbiotic relationship since it is of mutual advantage.

Seizing prey: some animals including most birds seize their prey and immediately swallow it whole without mastication. *Hydra* uses its nematocysts to

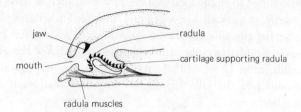

(a) *Longitudinal section through head of Helix, the snail. The hooked teeth of the radula rasp off food particles and scrape them on to the jaw. As the teeth wear away new ones are produced at the back.*

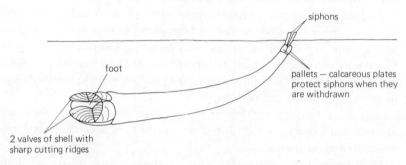

(b) *Teredo boring through wood. The adductor muscles rotate the two shell valves to act like a drill.*

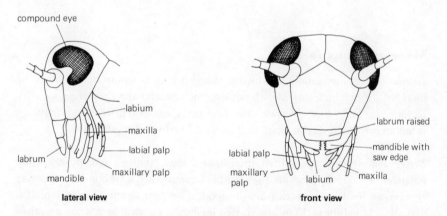

(c) *Periplaneta, the cockroach. An insect with masticatory mouthparts.*

Figure 32   Examples of macrophagous feeders

trap its prey then seizes it with its tentacles and puts it straight into its body. In many animals seizing the prey is followed by chewing. Vertebrates usually have toothed jaws and mammals have developed various types of teeth for different purposes. Masticatory mouthparts are also present in many arthropods, see

Figure 32(c). A few animals seize their prey and begin some digestion outside their bodies. The starfish for example, uses its tube feet in relays to pull open the shells of mussels. It then everts its stomach into the mussel, kills it, and partially digests it before inverting its stomach again, together with the contents of the mussel shell.

Fluids and soft tissues: animals living on liquid or soft food usually have pumping mechanisms for sucking the food into the body, and often have piercing mouthparts to get at the food. Those feeding on blood also produce an anticoagulant which prevents the blood clotting and blocking the mouthparts. Typical piercing and sucking mouthparts are present in hookworms, leeches, ticks and mites, while mouthparts for sucking only are seen in groups such as suctorian protozoans, Lepidoptera and Diptera. (See Figure 33.)

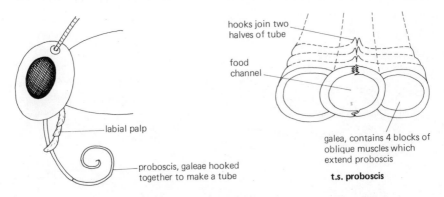

(a) *Butterfly head, side view and transverse section of proboscis, used for sucking nectar.*

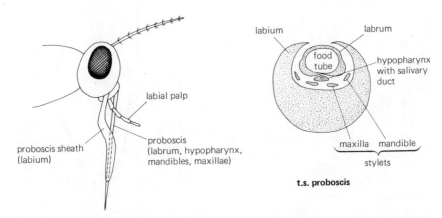

(b) *Piercing and sucking mouthparts of Anopheles mosquito. Stylets pierce the skin, labrum forms a sucking tube. The saliva of the female contains an anticoagulant because it sucks blood.*

Figure 33   Mouth parts for liquid food

TEETH

Teeth occur in all the vertebrate groups which possess jaws but only the teeth of mammals vary in appearance and function at different points along the jaws. This is the *heterodont* condition, unlike the *homodont* condition of other vertebrates where all the teeth are similar and usually cone-shaped. Mammalian teeth are formed in two sets, a first *milk* or *deciduous dentition* followed by a second *permanent set*. This is the *diphyodont* condition, whereas in other vertebrates the teeth are continuously replaced.

Mammalian teeth

Each tooth is formed by á thickening of ectoderm called the *enamel organ*, containing *ameloblasts*, which produce enamel, and a *mesodermal dental papilla* consisting of *odontoblasts*, which secrete dentine (see Figure 34). The teeth are

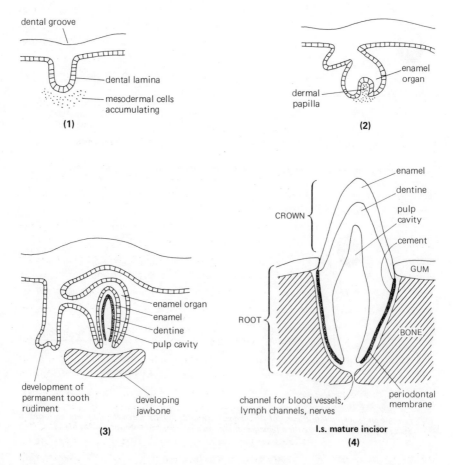

Figure 34   Structure and development of mammalian tooth

formed as a line of thickenings, the dental lamina in the mouth epithelium, and gradually extend down into the mesoderm as they grow. The *enamel* of the outer part of the tooth is the hardest tissue in the body and consists of rods of mineral salts embedded in keratin fibres laid down at right angles to the surface of the dentine and in wavy lines, helping to minimise the risk of the tooth enamel splitting under the impact of chewing. Inside the enamel is *dentine*, a slightly softer material containing fibres of the protein, collagen, running through a calcified matrix, and odontoblast fibres inside fine dentinal tubules. At the centre of the tooth is a *pulp cavity* containing blood capillaries and sensory nerve fibres which supply the odontoblasts. Most teeth stop growing at a certain size, but herbivores' teeth usually grow continuously, being constantly worn away by the food. These teeth retain a very wide opening to the pulp cavity called a *persistent pulp* so there is a good blood supply throughout life. In teeth with a fixed period of growth the pulp cavity becomes constricted, when that required size is reached, by the downward growth of the roots.

Holding the tooth in its socket in the jaw is *tooth cement*, a form of modified bone. In herbivores it extends between the ridges of enamel and forms part of the grinding surface. The relative rates of wear of the enamel, dentine and tooth cement mean that the herbivore's teeth are virtually self-sharpening (see Figure 35). Between the cement and the tooth socket are collagen fibres, forming the *periodontal membrane*, by which the tooth is fixed, and which allows it to flex slightly without breaking. The numbers and types of teeth in a dentition vary according to the diet and two examples are shown in Figure 35.

THE ALIMENTARY CANAL IN MAN (Figure 36)

Most of what we know about the mammalian gut and its associated glands is derived from studying the human gut, so we shall use that as an example of the typical mammalian condition.

In the mouth, or *buccal cavity*, food is chewed and mixed with saliva. The three pairs of *salivary glands* are compound tubular glands. The *parotids* below the ear and opening on the inside of the cheek, the submaxillary under each side of the lower jaw and the *sublingual* beneath the tongue. The glands are stimulated when food is seen, smelt, or enters the mouth, and are innervated by sympathetic nerves and the chorda tympani (a branch of the seventh cranial nerve – see p. 117).

Saliva is a watery solution of neutral pH containing sodium chloride and phosphates and carbonates of calcium, potassium and magnesium. It moistens and lubricates the food with mucus, facilitating tasting and swallowing. It also contains an enzyme, *salivary amylase* (ptyalin), which converts cooked starch (starch grains with their coat of amylo-pectin broken up) to maltose and glycogen, and uncooked starch to dextrins. After mastication the tongue moulds the food against the roof of the mouth forming it into a ball or *bolus*. A 'flap' called the *epiglottis* closes off the entrance to the trachea, the soft palate or *uvula* closes off the internal openings to the nose and the food is swallowed through the pharynx

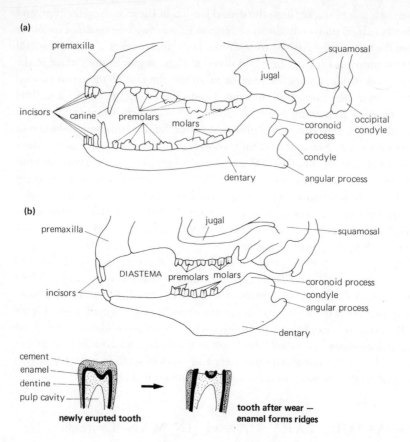

(a)

premaxilla

squamosal

jugal

incisors

canine premolars molars

coronoid
process

occipital
condyle

condyle

dentary

angular process

(b)

premaxilla

jugal

squamosal

DIASTEMA premolars molars

coronoid process

incisors

condyle

angular process

dentary

cement
enamel
dentine
pulp cavity

newly erupted tooth

**tooth after wear —
enamel forms ridges**

Figure 35   (a) Dog teeth: a typical carnivore. Formula $i\frac{3}{3}c\frac{1}{1}p\frac{4}{4}m\frac{2}{3}=42$.
The last upper premolar cuts down outside the first lower molar. These are the
carnassial teeth used for slicing flesh from bones.

(b) Rabbit teeth: a typical herbivore. Formula $i\frac{2}{1}c\frac{0}{0}p\frac{3}{2}m\frac{3}{3}=28$.

The diastema allows separation of freshly cut vegetation from that being chewed at
the back of the mouth. The ridges on the cheek teeth are caused by differential wear
as shown above.

into the oesophagus. The swallowing reflex is controlled by the medulla
oblongata of the brain and briefly inhibits breathing so that choking is avoided.

The food is forced down the oesophagus by the contraction of its circular and
longitudinal muscles, called *peristalsis*. At the entrance to the stomach the
circular *cardiac sphincter* muscle dilates and admits the food. The stomach wall
produces gastric juices in response to the sight, smell and taste of food, aided by
innervation via the vagus nerve. The gastric flow is maintained by the
production of a hormone, *gastrin*, produced by the epithelium of the pyloric
region of the stomach and which passes through the bloodstream and back to the
gastric glands.

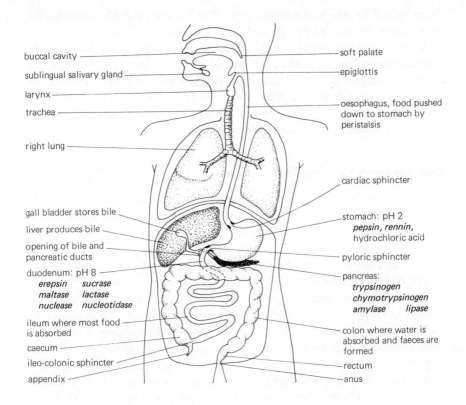

Figure 36   Alimentary canal of man (enzymes in italics)

Two types of cell produce the gastric juice inside deep pits in the stomach wall. *Oxyntic cells* secrete hydrochloric acid giving the juice a pH of 1.5 to 2. Inside these cells the enzyme carbonic anhydrase catalyses the formation of carbonic acid from carbon dioxide and water. The carbonic acid then dissociates into bicarbonate ions (HCO_3^-) and hydrogen ions (H^+). Sodium chloride in the cell also dissociates and the hydrogen and chloride ions combine to form hydrochloric acid which is then released from the cells. The other type is the *chief* or *peptic cell* which produces *pepsinogen*, an enzyme precursor that, in the presence of hydrochloric acid, is activated to *pepsin* and hydrolyses proteins to polypeptides. These cells also secrete *pro-rennin* which in its active form *rennin*, coagulates the soluble milk protein *caseinogen* to insoluble *casein*. Rennin is probably absent from adults, but is important in babies where milk forms the bulk of the diet and is more easily digested in this coagulated form.

The acid provides a suitable pH for the enzymes and kills bacteria entering with the food and drink. It also begins the digestion of sucrose to glucose and fructose and the breakdown of nucleo-proteins to nucleic acid and protein. The cells of the upper part of each gastric pit secrete mucus and this, together with the hormonal control of gastric secretion, helps to protect the stomach lining from digestion and formation of a gastric ulcer. The hormone should ensure that the juice is only released when food is there to absorb it.

As well as the circular and longitudinal muscles present along the rest of the length of the gut, the stomach has oblique muscles (see Figure 37). These cause a pendular swinging movement when they contract and help to mix the stomach contents and the gastric juice. After one to two hours in the stomach the food has a semi-fluid consistency and is called *chyme*. It is released in small amounts through the *pyloric sphincter* into the duodenum.

Digestion in the small intestine

The small intestine is about seven metres long in man and consists of a straight *duodenum* and a coiled *ileum*. Opening into the duodenum is a combined duct formed from the union of the bile duct and pancreatic duct. The ileum is supported by a mesentery attached to the posterior wall of the abdomen and containing branches of the mesenteric artery and vein.

The wall of the small intestine has the usual four layers as shown in Figure 37. Its inner surface has folds, the *valvulae conniventes*, which help to slow down the passage of food. All over the surface of the folds are tiny finger-like projections called *villi* – about twenty to forty per square millimetre which, together with the folds provide a large surface area for digestion and absorption of food. (See Figure 38.) The villi also contract and sway, thus contacting more food.

The duodenum receives digestive juices made by the liver, pancreas and the intestinal wall. The liver cells produce *bile* which is stored in the *gall bladder* and released as required down the *bile duct* to the duodenum. It is a yellowish-green watery fluid of pH 8 containing bile salts, bile pigments, mucin and cholesterol. It contains no enzymes but its alkalinity helps to neutralise the acid chyme entering the duodenum and aids the activity of enzymes in the pancreatic and intestinal juices. The bile salts, chiefly *sodium glycocholate* and *sodium taurocholate*, help to emulsify fats, breaking them up and providing a larger surface area for digestion. The pigments *bilirubin* and *biliverdin* are excretory products formed during the breakdown of old red blood cells by the liver. In the large intestine bacterial action converts them to *stercobilin* which is partially responsible for the colouring of the faeces. The *mucin* acts as a lubricant, but the *cholesterol* is probably another excretory product with no specific function. It is kept in solution by the bile salts and, if they drop below a certain concentration, the cholesterol comes out of solution forming gall stones in the bile ducts. Under normal conditions the cholesterol is believed to be converted by bacteria in the large intestine to *coprosterol* and is egested with the faeces.

Pancreatic juice is colourless with a pH about 8.8, due to the sodium bicarbonate present. It also contains two enzyme precursors, *trypsinogen* and *chymotrypsinogen*, which are only activated when they contact the enzyme enterokinase produced in the intestinal juice. The delay in activating them ensures that these protein-digesting enzymes do not digest the pancreatic duct as they pass along it. In their active forms *trypsin* and *chymotrypsin* digest proteins to polypeptides. Pancreatic juice contains an *amylase* similar to that in saliva, which

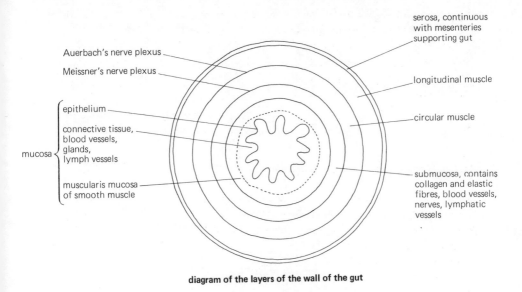

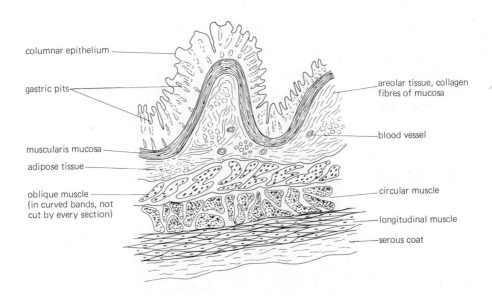

diagram of the layers of the wall of the gut

l.s. part of cardiac region of stomach (oblique muscles absent from pyloric region) x 50

Figure 37   Structure of the layers of the gut wall

continues the digestion of starch to maltose. Also present is a fat-digesting enzyme, *lipase*, which hydrolyses fats to glycerol and fatty acids.

The intestinal juice or *succus entericus* is a watery solution of pH about 8.3. Its

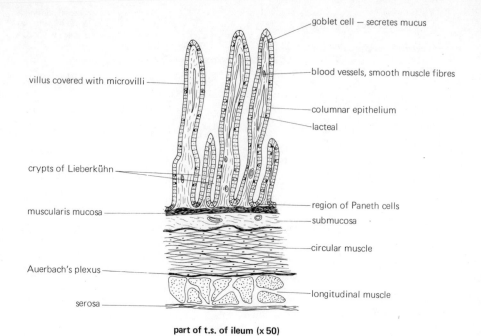

goblet cell — secretes mucus

villus covered with microvilli

blood vessels, smooth muscle fibres

columnar epithelium

lacteal

crypts of Lieberkühn

region of Paneth cells

muscularis mucosa

submucosa

circular muscle

Auerbach's plexus

longitudinal muscle

serosa

part of t.s. of ileum (x 50)

villi which can move and contact food

network of capillaries inside villus carries away monosaccharides and amino acids

crypt of Lieberkühn

lacteal into which glycerol, fatty acids and fat droplets pass

arteriole

Paneth cells which secrete enzymes

venule

circular muscle

Brunner's gland (duodenum only) secretion helps to protect lining

longitudinal muscle

stereogram of part of duodenum

Figure 38   Structure of the small intestine

enzymes are produced by *Paneth cells* lining pits in the intestinal wall, called the *crypts of Lieberkühn* (see Figure 38). These enzymes include a number of peptidases formerly grouped together as what was thought to be a single enzyme, *erepsin*.

These various peptidases hydrolyse polypeptides to amino acids, thereby completing the digestion of protein. Also present are a number of carbohydrases; *sucrase* (invertase) converts sucrose to glucose and fructose; *maltase* converts maltose to glucose; and *lactase* converts lactose to glucose and galactose. *Nuclease* and *nucleotidase* are responsible for the hydrolysis of nucleic acids.

The crypts of Lieberkühn are found throughout the small intestine but in the duodenum is an additional type of gland called *Brunner's gland*, which secretes an alkaline fluid containing mucus. This presumably helps to maintain the correct pH for digestion and also protects the lining layer of cells.

Peristalsis and hydrolysing enzymes reduce the food to a fluid called *chyle*. The peristaltic waves travel at about 2 cm sec^{-1} and constrictions also occur and disappear at intervals, helping to mix the food. *Auerbach's nerve plexus* between the longitudinal and circular muscles controls peristalsis. For clarity it has been necessary to deal with each enzyme in turn, but in fact, of course, digestion is a continuous and simultaneous process. The control of the small intestine secretions involves at least three known hormones. When acid food arrives in the duodenum, hormones are released by the duodenal wall into the blood. One hormone, *cholecystokinin*, causes the gall bladder to contract and release bile down the bile duct. Another, *secretin*, stimulates production of bile and of pancreatic juice, while a third, *pancreomysin*, stimulates enzyme production by the pancreas. The touch of food on the intestinal mucosa seems to be the trigger for succus entericus secretion.

Absorption

Very little absorption of food occurs in the stomach, mainly water and glucose. The bulk of absorption takes place in the ileum when the food has been digested to molecules of hexose sugars, amino acids, glycerol and fatty acids, which are small enough to pass through the gut wall. In man, and other mammals, absorption is aided by the large surface area provided by the villi and their covering of *microvilli* a few ten thousandths of a millimetre long. The provision of additional surface area for absorption is seen in other animal groups too, such as the gut caeca of platyhelminths and insects, the typhlosole of an earthworm or the spiral valve in the intestine of a dogfish.

In mammals carbohydrates are absorbed chiefly as monosaccharides. Experiments have shown however, that glucose and galactose are absorbed more rapidly than fructose, and pentoses are taken in still more slowly. Obviously simple diffusion is not a sufficient explanation, especially as absorption sometimes occurs against a high concentration gradient, indicating active transport across the membrane. Glucose and galactose may enter faster because they are immediately phosphorylated by phosphatase enzymes in the cells lining the gut, and hence a very steep concentration gradient is maintained.

Amino acids and monosaccharides entering the villi are rapidly transferred to the network of blood vessels and transported away. These capillaries ultimately drain into the *hepatic portal vein*, which carries the food to the liver.

Some fat is absorbed as glycerol and fatty acids which are passed into channels in the villi called *lacteals*. These are part of the lymphatic system which eventually drains into the blood through the thoracic duct at the junction of the left jugular and subclavian veins (see chapter 7). The lacteals also receive tiny particles of fat about 0.5 μm in diameter, produced by a combination of hydrolysis by lipase and emulsification by the bile salts. These would presumably clog the fine capillaries of the villi. Some fatty acids appear to be absorbed combined with the bile salts which are then recirculated via the bloodstream to the liver. Absorption of vitamins, inorganic salts and water also occurs in the small intestine directly, without any necessity for prior digestion. The mineral salts vary considerably in their rate of uptake, sodium, potassium and chloride ions being quickly absorbed, magnesium, nitrate and sulphate ions entering much more slowly. Fat-soluble vitamins such as A, D, and K pass with the fat into the lacteals. Absorption of water is mainly by osmosis since the gut contents gradually become hypotonic to the blood.

The food spends three to four hours in the small intestine before passing through the *ileo-colonic sphincter* into the large intestine.

The large intestine

The large intestine is about one and a half metres long and divided into a caecum and appendix, rectum and anal canal. The *caecum* is large in diameter and has a blind-ending appendix projecting from it. In some herbivores, such as the rabbit the caecum and appendix are important as sites of cellulose digestion by symbiotic bacteria, but in man it does not have this function and indeed may sometimes trap food which putrefies and causes inflammation, resulting in appendicitis. The *colon* has three regions, the ascending, transverse and descending limbs. It bends round at the *sigmoid flexure* to become the *rectum*, leading to the anus which is closed by a sphincter muscle.

The wall of the large intestine has the usual four layers but no villi, though mucus-secreting glands are present and there are large patches of lymphoid tissue which presumably eliminate bacterial toxins. The main function of the large intestine is the absorption of water so that the contents gradually become more solid and consist of insoluble waste materials referred to collectively as *faeces*. These vary in content with the diet, but may contain undigested roughage, dead cells from the gut lining, living and dead bacteria, unwanted mineral salts, including iron, calcium and magnesium, usually as phosphates, stercobilin from the bile salts, hydrogen sulphide, ammonia and *indole* and *skatole* – products of amino acid breakdown responsible for the offensive smell. Surprisingly the water content may still be as high as sixty to seventy per cent.

Faecal movement along the gut is slow, usually in powerful waves particularly when more food is taken in. This gives time for water absorption and mineral salt secretion. Faeces may take from fourteen hours to three days or more to pass to the rectum and their arrival there stimulates *defaecation* (egestion). This is a partly voluntary process using the abdominal muscles and diaphragm and relaxing the sphincter muscle, and partly involuntary due to strong contractions of the rectum.

Assimilation

Assimilation is the incorporation of food into the body for growth and repair. In a mammal the nutrients absorbed from the gut are brought to the liver which stores, changes or re-directs them as required. Amino acids are needed for growth, repair and secretion but the intake is generally much higher than is necessary and neither proteins nor amino acids can be stored in the body. They must be used or altered immediately by one of three processes: deamination, transamination or amide formation. These processes are particularly rapid in the liver and kidney.

In *deamination* the amino group (NH_2) is removed from the amino acid in the form of ammonia probably by oxidation, but the ammonia is highly toxic and is converted into less poisonous urea (carbamide) (see chapter 10). *Transamination* is the transference of amino groups between amino acids to make another kind. All the non-essential amino acids can be made in this way, but the essential ones must be taken in ready made in the diet. *Amide formation* results in the synthesis of the amide glutamine from the amino acid glutamic acid and ammonia, catalysed by the enzyme glutaminase. The glutamine molecules act as a store of amino groups which can later be used for transamination, or the ammonia can be removed from the amide and used to neutralise excess acids produced during metabolism in the kidney.

The residue of the amino acid after the amino group has been removed by any of these three processes is called a *keto acid* (oxo acid). About sixty per cent of keto acids are *glucogenic*, that is, they can be converted to glucose and enter carbohydrate metabolism. They include alanine, glycine and glutamic acid. Another group of amino acids is *ketogenic* because they form ketone bodies during their oxidation to carbon dioxide and water. They include tyrosine and phenylalanine. The fate of the remaining amino acids such as valine and tryptophane is not known.

Carbohydrate metabolism revolves around the maintenance of a steady level of glucose in the blood. This is kept to approximately 0.1 g per 100 cm^3 regardless of the level of sugar in the diet and is a very important aspect of homeostasis. The level is maintained by the interconversion of glucose and glycogen, the latter being formed mainly in the liver and muscles. A rise in blood sugar level results in increased production of *insulin* from the β *cells* of the *islets of Langerhans* in the pancreas (see Figure 40). The effect of insulin is to accelerate the conversion of glucose to glycogen so that the blood sugar level falls again. If the level drops too low, *somatotropin* (growth hormone) from the pituitary stimulates the α *cells* of the islets of Langerhans to produce *glucagon*. This hormone facilitates the conversion of glycogen to glucose and the level will rise again.

Glycogen is synthesised from glucose-1-phosphate in the presence of a co-enzyme called *uridine triphosphate* (UTP) and derived from the pyrimidine uracil found in RNA. The UTP reacts with glucose-1-phosphate to form uridine diphosphate glucose (UDPG) and inorganic phosphate which can combine with more glucose. The enzyme UDPG transglycolase then fits the glucose molecules together in a straight chain linked by 1-4 bonds. UDP is set free as the chain forms and converted back into UTP by ATP molecules. For each addition of a glucose molecule to the chain two ATP molecules are required, one to form more glucose-1-phosphate, the other to make more UTP. The cyclic nature of this process is shown below:

glycogen synthesis

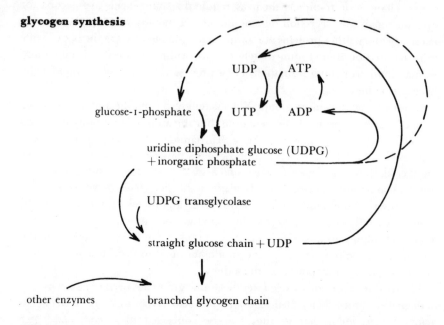

The final stage in glycogen synthesis is the build up by various enzymes of the straight glucose chains into a long branched chain.

Not all the glycogen stored comes from glucose, however, some comes from the residues of deaminated amino acids and some may be formed from other products such as glycerol. If the intake of carbohydrate is excessive the glycogen storage capacity of the liver (about 100 g) and muscles (about 300 g) may be exceeded and the additional carbohydrate is then converted to fat for storage. The fat-storage regions of the body include the connective tissues under the skin, and in many organs and the mesenteries that support them. *Adipose tissue* is a collection of cells in which fat accumulates. The fat forms a large globule in the cell pushing the nucleus and cytoplasm to the periphery. The fat is usually transported as droplets to the storage cells but then redistributed as needed in the form of water-soluble phospholipids.

The conversion of carbohydrate to fat begins with its breakdown to pyruvic (2-oxopropanoic) acid which is then decarboxylated by coenzyme A to 'active acetate'. A series of coenzymes synthesise the reduction of the active acetate to various fatty acids. These are finally combined with glycerol produced from dihydroxyacetone phosphate to form fats for storage. In chapter 5 (p. 81) some of the coenzymes believed to be involved are shown.

Modifications of the gut in herbivorous mammals

Cellulose makes up a large part of the diet of a herbivore and is very resistant to digestion so herbivores tend to have longer guts than carnivores and the food remains there longer. Some cellulose is digested by *autolysis*, that is the digestion of the cell walls by enzymes released on the death of the cells, but most of it is carried out by symbiotic bacteria at some point along the gut.

In cows for example, food is swallowed into a complicated four-chambered stomach (see Figure 39). It first enters the *rumen* and *reticulum* where bacteria and ciliates digest the cellulose and release fatty acids which the host can use to build up glycogen. The food is then regurgitated and chewed and finally swallowed into the *psalterium* and then the *abomasum* in which gastric glands and

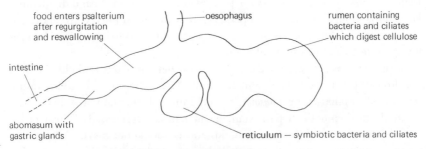

food enters psalterium after regurgitation and reswallowing

oesophagus

rumen containing bacteria and ciliates which digest cellulose

intestine

abomasum with gastric glands

reticulum — symbiotic bacteria and ciliates

the four-chambered stomach of a sheep

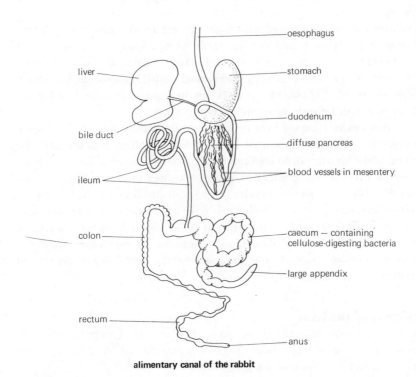

oesophagus

liver

stomach

duodenum

bile duct

diffuse pancreas

blood vessels in mesentery

ileum

colon

caecum — containing cellulose-digesting bacteria

large appendix

rectum

anus

alimentary canal of the rabbit

Figure 39   Modifications of the gut in herbivores

enzymes are present. Food may take seven to ten days to pass through the gut of cattle.

THE ACCESSORY GLANDS OF THE GUT

The mammalian liver

The liver is the largest gland in the body and lies directly under the dome of the diaphragm so that when it contracts the liver is squeezed and blood is helped to circulate through it. It is covered with peritoneum attached to the diaphragm by peritoneal ligaments, and by folds of peritoneum to the stomach and duodenum. The liver is subdivided into five lobes, each of which is supplied with small *cystic ducts* along which bile can pass to the gall bladder, under the right central lobe, or down the bile duct to the duodenum.

The liver receives oxygenated blood from the hepatic artery and blood rich in food from the hepatic portal vein. Inside the liver, these vessels divide into a network of capillaries or *sinusoids*, which ramify throughout the tissue and eventually drain into the hepatic vein, in which products released by the liver are carried away. In the walls of the sinusoids are occasional phagocytic *Küpffer cells*. These are part of the reticulo-endothelial system and responsible for destroying old red blood cells, bacteria and any foreign matter passing through the sinusoids.

The liver itself is composed of small liver cells, each with a prominent nucleus and a store of glycogen and fat. The cells form a spongy network around interconnecting spaces or lacunae, through which the sinusoids pass. Between the liver cells are even finer intercellular channels called *bile canaliculi*, into which the cells secrete bile. These fine channels join up into progressively larger ducts and eventually drain into the cystic ducts.

In microscopic section the liver tissue frequently appears lobular (see Figure 40) but this is an effect produced by variations in blood pressure between branches of the hepatic portal vein and those of the hepatic vein. The pig's liver, however, is divided into lobules by connective tissue continuous with that of a layer called *Glisson's capsule* just under the peritoneum. Between the lobules are the *interlobular vessels* – arterioles from the hepatic artery and factors (branches) of the hepatic portal vein, while in the centre of each lobule is the *intralobular vessel*, a factor of the hepatic vein. The blood drains across the lobule from the interlobular vessels through the sinusoids to the intralobular vessel and eventually out of the liver.

Functions of the liver

The liver has numerous functions, many of which are concerned with the metabolism of food and have been discussed in this chapter. A summary of the more important liver functions is given below:

1 carbohydrate metabolism and regulation of blood sugar level;
2 deamination and transamination of amino acids, amide formation;

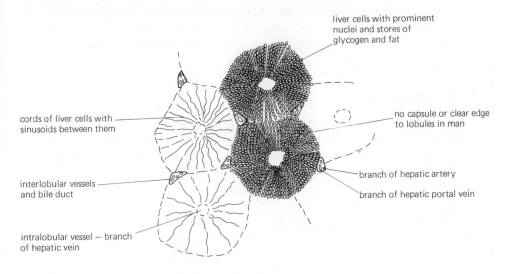

liver cells with prominent nuclei and stores of glycogen and fat

cords of liver cells with sinusoids between them

no capsule or clear edge to lobules in man

interlobular vessels and bile duct

branch of hepatic artery

branch of hepatic portal vein

intralobular vessel — branch of hepatic vein

t.s. liver of man (x 50) (diagrammatic, lobules are rarely very clear)

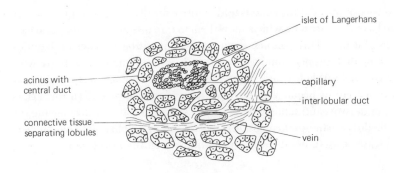

islet of Langerhans

acinus with central duct

capillary

interlobular duct

connective tissue separating lobules

vein

t.s. part of pancreas of man (x 60) (diagrammatic, acini less distinct in microscope preparations)

Figure 40   Histology of the liver and pancreas

3   fat metabolism;

4   secretion of bile;

5   storage of iron released from the breakdown of old red blood cells;

6   storage of vitamins A and D and B_{12} the anti-anaemic principle;

7   manufacture of plasma proteins including those used in blood clotting;

8   like other organs the liver produces heat by its active metabolism and this is subsequently distributed by the blood;

9   defence by the cells of Küpffer removing old red blood cells, bacteria etc.;

10   detoxication. This includes the breakdown of ammonia from deaminated

amino acids into less toxic urea via the ornithine cycle (see chapter 10); the destruction of hormones therefore limiting their period of effectiveness; and modification of drugs and alcohol prior to their excretion by the kidney.

The pancreas

The pancreas in man is a soft cream-coloured organ twelve to fifteen centimetres long, lying between the stomach and duodenum. It is composed of secretory cells arranged in sacs called *acini* or *alveoli* around a central duct (see Figure 40). Patches of alveoli are grouped together into lobules by connective tissue. The cells of the alveoli secrete pancreatic juice into the central ducts which join up and eventually form the pancreatic duct.

Scattered at intervals among the alveoli are small masses of cells called the islets of Langerhans which are ductless or endocrine glands and secrete the hormones insulin and glucagon directly into the blood.

CARNIVOROUS PLANTS

Carnivorous or insectivorous plants feed autotrophically using their green leaves but also have modifications which allow them to trap insects so that they also feed heterotrophically. This enables them to live in nitrogen-deficient habitats augmenting their supply from insect protein. In Britain sundew and butterwort are found on heathlands and bladderwort in ponds. Each has a trap that produces a scent or nectar attractive to insects (see Figure 41). In the Venus flytrap, butterwort and sundew the traps are modified leaves which enclose the insect. Bladderwort traps them inside little sacs and the pitcher plant has pitcher-shaped leaves containing digestive juices into which the insects fall.

SAPROPHYTES

Saprophytes feed on dead animals and plants and include many bacteria and fungi. They secrete a range of enzymes through their body surfaces on to the food where extracellular digestion occurs. The soluble food is then absorbed into the saprophyte's body. These organisms are particularly important in promoting the decay of dead animal and plant material so that the elements locked up in it can be recycled.

PARASITES

Parasites feed on the living tissues of plants and animals. Many bacteria and fungi are parasitic causing a variety of plant and animal diseases which are discussed in chapter 16.

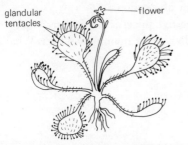

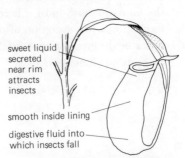

glandular tentacles — flower

Drosera — sundew. The sticky tentacles trap insects and the leaf folds over to secure them.

sweet liquid secreted near rim attracts insects

smooth inside lining

digestive fluid into which insects fall

Nepenthes — a pitcher plant. Trapped insects are digested inside modified leaves.

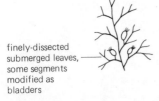

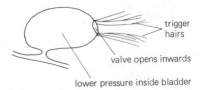

finely-dissected submerged leaves, some segments modified as bladders

trigger hairs

valve opens inwards

lower pressure inside bladder

Utricularia — bladderwort. Hairs inside bladder absorb water and reduce pressure inside. Crustacean touches trigger hairs and is swept inside, where it probably decays by bacterial action.

Figure 41   Carnivorous plants

There are even a few parasitic flowering plants such as *Cuscuta*, the dodder and *Lathraea*, toothwort. Neither contains chlorophyll and each feeds by sending out growths which penetrate the hosts' vascular tissues. Dodder species are parasitic on a range of plants, including gorse and nettles, while toothwort parasitises the roots of beech and hazel.

Animal parasites vary a good deal in the closeness of their association with the host, some merely visiting it for food like a mosquito, others remaining with the host and feeding at intervals like a flea, and some like tapeworms and flukes being internal parasites which never leave the host. The adaptations they show for feeding vary accordingly, from the biting and sucking mouthparts of some insects to the absence of mouthparts, or even a gut, in some internal parasites (like the tapeworm, which absorbs digested food all over its surface). A variety of animal and plant parasites are reviewed in *The diversity of life*.

QUESTIONS

1   Survey the methods of food capture and ingestion shown by invertebrates.
2   Compare and contrast the dentition of the dog and the rabbit. How is each adapted for its diet?
3   What are the functions of bile?

4 Trace the stages in the digestion of (a) protein (b) starch, from its entry into the human mouth until it is ready for absorption.
5 Explain how the secretion of the digestive juices is controlled.
6 Describe the gross structure and histology of the mammalian liver. What are its principal functions?

7 Transport in animals

During the course of evolution, as animals became more highly organised, larger and more active, increasingly efficient circulatory mechanisms were required to transport respiratory gases, nutrients, and the products of metabolism from one part of the body to another. Several different kinds of circulatory mechanism can be recognised.

1 *Intracellular transport* In most protozoans and in many, if not all, metazoan cells cytoplasmic streaming supplements diffusion as a means of moving substances around inside the cell.

2 *Movement of external medium* In some animals, notably sponges and coelenterates, the water in which they live serves as the transport medium and is moved about inside the body by ciliary, flagellar or muscular activity.

3 *Fluid in body cavity circulated by body movement* In some animals, for example nematodes, the fluid in the coelom or pseudocoelom (the body cavity) is the main transport medium. This fluid flows past all the tissues and organs, propelled by contraction of the body wall muscles. In other groups such as echinoderms, annelids and chordates this method supplements other mechanisms.

4 *Movement of fluid in an open circulatory system* In most arthropods and many molluscs the transporting fluid, *haemolymph*, is pumped by a muscular heart through vessels into tissue spaces or *sinuses*, collectively called the *haemocoel*, and thence back to the heart. The haemocoel is not derived from the coelom, but develops from the embryonic blastocoel. The true coelom is restricted to small cavities around certain organs. The heart of animals with an open circulatory system is usually only weakly contractile and blood flow is generally assisted by contractions of body wall muscles. In insects, alary muscles attached to the heart contract to expand the heart and so help draw blood in from the haemocoel (see Figure 42).

5 *Movement of fluid in a closed circulatory system* In most annelids, cephalopod molluscs (octopus and squid), and vertebrates, the transporting fluid, *blood*, is circulated in a system of closed tubes or vessels of varying diameter, by one or more muscular hearts. In contrast to the situation in open circulatory systems, the fluid that bathes the cells, the *tissue fluid*, although derived from the transporting fluid (blood), is distinct from it. In vertebrates the tissue fluid is returned to the blood vascular system through another system of vessels – the *lymphatic system*.

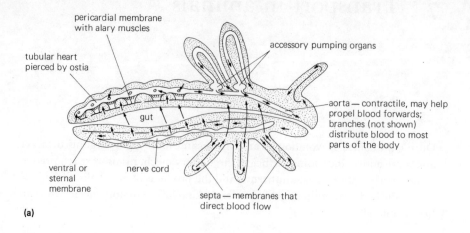

pericardial membrane
with alary muscles

accessory pumping organs

tubular heart
pierced by ostia

gut

aorta — contractile, may help
propel blood forwards;
branches (not shown)
distribute blood to most
parts of the body

ventral or
sternal
membrane

nerve cord

septa — membranes that
direct blood flow

(a)

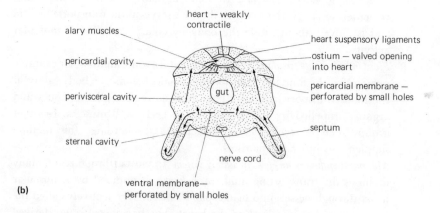

heart — weakly
contractile

alary muscles

heart suspensory ligaments

pericardial cavity

ostium — valved opening
into heart

perivisceral cavity

gut

pericardial membrane —
perforated by small holes

sternal cavity

septum

nerve cord

(b)

ventral membrane —
perforated by small holes

Figure 42 The open circulatory system of an insect. Shaded areas represent haemocoel. Arrows indicate direction of blood flow.

(a) Diagrammatic side view. Blood flows forwards in the heart and enters the haemocoel via branches of the aorta. It then flows backwards to re-enter the heart through the ostia. The various membranes, sternal, pericardial, etc., help direct blood flow through the tissues. Accessory pumping organs, where present, are generally concerned with maintaining blood flow in the appendages (wings, legs, antennae).

(b) Diagrammatic transverse section. When the alary muscles contract, the resulting expansion of the heart causes blood to pass in from the haemocoel through the ostia. The subsequent contraction of the heart propels blood forwards; valves prevent blood flowing out through the ostia. The contraction of the alary muscles also alters the position of the pericardial membrane. The resulting pressure changes encourage blood flow from the perivisceral cavity into the pericardial cavity, and from the sternal cavity into the perivisceral cavity.

A closed circulatory system has certain advantages over an open system. The blood pressure and velocity of circulation are generally much higher in closed circulations. The size and activity of animals with an open system are thought to be limited by the sluggishness of blood flow. Insects would seem to be an exception in that they have an open system and yet are highly active, but it should be remembered that they do not rely on the circulatory system for the transport of respiratory gases. Another advantage of a closed system is that blood flow to certain parts of the body can be reduced by the constriction of blood vessels, *vasoconstriction*. This means that a greater volume of blood can be diverted to areas of special need, for example, to muscles when action is required, or to the intestine to collect the products of digestion after a meal.

In the circulatory mechanisms described above you will observe that during the course of evolution the role of transporting fluid has passed from the water that surrounds the animal to special complex tissues like blood which, although largely composed of water, also contain cells that increase the fluid's transporting capacity as well as serving a protective function.

MAMMALIAN BLOOD

Composition

Blood consists of a suspension of blood cells or *corpuscles* together with cell fragments, the *platelets* or *thrombocytes*, in a yellowish, watery medium called *plasma*. There are two main types of corpuscle; red corpuscles or *erythrocytes*, and white corpuscles or *leucocytes*. In the descriptions of blood cells that follow, all the estimates of cell number refer to human blood. An adult man has five to six litres of blood in his body; a woman has, on average, one litre less.

Erythrocytes serve for the transport of the respiratory gases. They are minute, biconcave discs (see Figure 43) formed principally in the red marrow of the sternum, ribs and vertebrae. During their formation they lose their nuclei (this does not happen in the other vertebrate classes). The cytoplasm of erythrocytes is packed with molecules of the red, iron-containing pigment, *haemoglobin*. This pigment greatly increases the oxygen-carrying capacity of the blood. The biconcave shape of erythrocytes increases their surface area to volume ratio and greatly speeds up gas exchange between the cells and the surrounding plasma.

There are between four and a half and six million erythrocytes in each cubic millimetre of human blood. This number varies according to factors like altitude (people living at high altitude may have as many as eight million erythrocytes per mm^3) and the individual's state of health (people with severe anaemia tend to have a low red cell count).

Erythrocytes are produced and destroyed at a high and continuous rate. They live for about four months after which they are destroyed by phagocytic cells in the liver and spleen. These organs retain the iron for use in the manufacture of fresh haemoglobin. It has been estimated that between one and two million erythrocytes are destroyed every second. Obviously the rate of production must

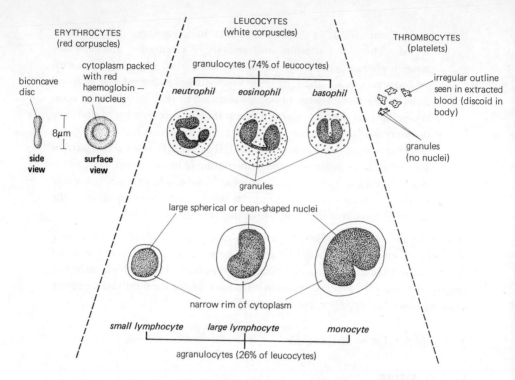

ERYTHROCYTES
(red corpuscles)

biconcave
disc

cytoplasm packed
with red
haemoglobin —
no nucleus

8µm

side
view

surface
view

LEUCOCYTES
(white corpuscles)

granulocytes (74% of leucocytes)

neutrophil   *eosinophil*   *basophil*

granules

large spherical or bean-shaped nuclei

narrow rim of cytoplasm

small lymphocyte   *large lymphocyte*   *monocyte*

agranulocytes (26% of leucocytes)

THROMBOCYTES
(platelets)

irregular outline
seen in extracted
blood (discoid in
body)

granules
(no nuclei)

Figure 43   Mammalian blood corpuscles (all drawn to same scale)

normally keep pace with red cell breakdown. Indeed, in certain circumstances, for example after severe blood loss, erythrocytes can be produced at four or more times the rate of destruction.

Leucocytes are concerned with fighting disease. They are generally larger but less numerous than erythrocytes. There is approximately one leucocyte for every six hundred erythrocytes. Two main types of leucocyte can be distinguished; *granulocytes* and *agranulocytes* (see Figure 43). Granulocytes are formed in the bone marrow. They have an irregular shape, granular cytoplasm and a lobed nucleus. Three types – *neutrophils, eosinophils* and *basophils* – are distinguished on the basis of the different staining properties of their granules. The most abundant of these, the neutrophils are phagocytic; they ingest bacteria and dead or damaged cells. Far less is known about the other two types. Eosinophils increase in certain allergic conditions such as hay fever and asthma while basophils increase in certain types of inflammation. The significance of these increases is yet to be discovered.

Most agranulocytes are produced in the lymph nodes and spleen by the division of cells derived from bone marrow. They have a large, spherical or bean-shaped nucleus bordered by a rim of non-granular cytoplasm. Two main types are recognised, *lymphocytes* (the more abundant of the two) and *monocytes*. The former are involved in antibody production while the latter are phagocytes.

Thrombocytes play a vital role in blood clotting. They are cytoplasmic fragments of large blood cells, *megakaryocytes*, produced in the bone marrow. There are between 250 000 and 500 000 platelets in each mm³ of blood.

Plasma

Plasma consists of water (approximately ninety per cent) and a variety of dissolved substances. The most important constituents are:

plasma proteins – albumin, globulin and fibrinogen
food – glucose, other monosaccharides, amino acids and fats
excretory material – urea and other nitrogenous compounds
ions – notably sodium, chloride, potassium, phosphate, calcium, sulphate and bicarbonate.

In addition, hormones, small amounts of respiratory gases, vitamins and enzymes are also present.

Functions of mammalian blood

The main functions of blood are the transport of substances around the body, distribution of heat, defence against disease and blood loss, and maintenance of a stable internal environment.

Transport

The blood transports a variety of substances around the body.

1 The products of digestion are carried from the capillaries in the intestine to the liver where the sugar content is regulated (p. 99), after which the soluble foods, as well as vitamins and minerals derived from the food, are carried to the cells.

2 Excretory materials such as urea and uric acid are carried from the tissues or organs where they are formed to the organs where they are removed (excreted).

3 Hormones are carried from the endocrine organs where they are made to the target organs whose activities they affect.

4 Respiratory gases are transported between the respiratory organs and the respiring cells. Oxygen is carried from the lungs to the tissues, while carbon dioxide is carried from the tissues to the lungs.

Oxygen transport

Human arterial blood contains about twenty volume per cent (percentage volume) of oxygen. Approximately 0.3 per cent is carried in physical solution and the rest is carried in loose association with the respiratory pigment haemoglobin, as *oxyhaemoglobin*. Haemoglobin readily associates with oxygen in regions of high oxygen tension (concentration) such as occur at the respiratory surface (the lungs). Equally important, oxyhaemoglobin readily *dissociates*, giving up its oxygen, in the regions of low oxygen tension that prevail in the tissues.

$$Hb + O_2 \underset{\text{low } O_2 \text{ tension}}{\overset{\text{high } O_2 \text{ tension}}{\rightleftharpoons}} HbO_2$$

haemoglobin   oxyhaemoglobin

Haemoglobin is made up of a pigment, *haem*, combined with a protein, *globin*. Haem consists of a porphyrin ring linked to an atom of ferrous iron. Oxygen combines loosely with the ferrous iron without oxidising it to the ferric state (such a reaction would not be readily reversible).

Haem

All vertebrates possess haemoglobin but the type of haemoglobin varies from species to species. The various haemoglobins differ in their globin component. The protein part of the molecule affects many of its properties, perhaps most importantly its affinity for oxygen, that is, how readily it combines with oxygen. Within a given species several types of haemoglobin may be present, either at the same time or at different stages in the life cycle. For example, in man, adult haemoglobin differs from foetal haemoglobin, which it replaces shortly after birth.

The affinity of haemoglobin for oxygen can be determined by exposing a solution of deoxygenated haemoglobin to a gradually increasing oxygen tension and then measuring the proportion of haemoglobin which is in the oxygenated state (HbO_2) at each tension. The relationship between oxygen tension and the percentage of HbO_2 produces a characteristically s-shaped graph known as the *oxygen dissociation* or *oxygen equilibrium curve* (see Figure 44). This graph reveals that oxygen is taken up rapidly at low oxygen tensions, but at higher tensions the rate of absorption slows down and approaches the one hundred per cent saturation level very slowly. Ideally, the oxygen tension at which the pigment is fully saturated with oxygen should correspond with the oxygen tension at the respiratory surface, so that the pigment is used efficiently and does not leave that

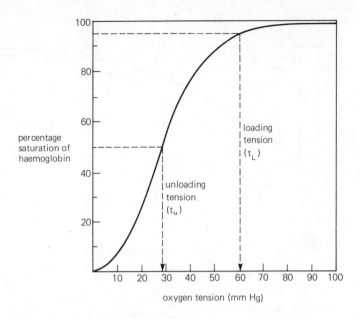

Figure 44   An oxygen equilibrium curve

surface only partially saturated, or loaded, with oxygen. In practice, the maximum operating capacity of the pigment is unlikely to be more than ninety-five per cent of the saturation level (because the oxygen tension needs to be so much higher if total saturation is to be achieved). The tension at which the pigment can become ninety-five per cent saturated is accordingly called the *loading tension*.

The oxygen equilibrium curve can be analysed in the reverse direction, to find out how decreasing oxygen tension affects the saturation of the pigment. This will show how the pigment gives up oxygen (dissociates). Viewed in this way, the curve reveals the ease with which dissociation takes place. Below the loading tension a small drop in oxygen tension results in the release of a large amount of oxygen from the pigment. The tension at which only fifty per cent of the pigment is oxygenated is known as the *unloading tension*, because at this tension the pigment will give up nearly half its oxygen load. The unloading tension should correspond with oxygen levels encountered in the tissues.

It is not simply fortuitous that the loading and unloading tensions of a particular pigment coincide with the environmental and tissue tensions in which it operates. The pigments have evolved to fit these requirements. The adaptive nature of respiratory pigments is revealed in the oxygen equilibrium curves of the three different haemoglobins shown in Figure 45. The haemoglobin of *Arenicola*, the lugworm, has a very high affinity for oxygen – it is ninety five per cent saturated at a very low oxygen tension (about 13 mm Hg). This ensures that the lugworm's blood can become saturated in the conditions of low oxygen availability that prevail in its environment. Lugworms live in burrows in the sand where, at low tide, the oxygen tension falls to about 13 mm Hg.

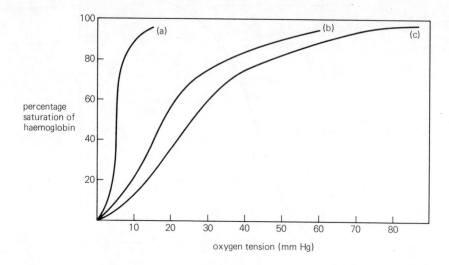

Figure 45   Oxygen equilibrium curves of;
(a) the lugworm, *Arenicola*
(b) human foetal haemoglobin
(c) human adult haemoglobin

The curve for human haemoglobin is to the right of that for *Arenicola* showing that it has a lower affinity for oxygen. This is to be expected in a creature that lives in an environment where oxygen is plentiful. The curve for human foetal haemoglobin is to the left of the curve for adult haemoglobin showing that it has a higher affinity for oxygen. This situation ensures that oxygen can be transferred easily from maternal blood to foetal blood at the placenta. Incidentally, the muscles of vertebrates contain a pigment called muscle haemoglobin or *myoglobin*. The curve for this pigment lies to the left of the curve for 'blood' haemoglobin so that oxygen is easily transferred from the blood to the muscle pigment.

The affinity of a pigment for oxygen varies with temperature, carbon dioxide tension and other factors. Increasing temperature and increasing carbon dioxide tension both decrease the pigment's affinity for oxygen and so shift the curve to the right. The effect of increased carbon dioxide concentration is known as the *Bohr effect*. The significance of this effect is that in regions of high carbon dioxide tension oxygen is given up to the tissues more readily.

Haemoglobin is not the only respiratory pigment. Information about the nature, distribution and oxygen-carrying capacity of haemoglobin and some other important pigments is summarised in Table 3.

Carbon dioxide transport

In man the blood can carry as much as 50 volume per cent of carbon dioxide. Only 2.5 volume per cent is carried in physical solution, so other mechanisms are obviously involved. Carbon dioxide can combine with the amino groups of

Table 3 Respiratory pigments and oxygen capacities of some different bloods

Pigment	Chemical Nature	Colour	Site	Animal	O_2 volume per cent
Haemoglobin	protein (globin) + haem	red	corpuscles	mammals birds reptiles amphibians fish	15–30 20–25 7–12 3–10 4–20
			plasma	some annelids, some molluscs	1–10 1–6
Haemocyanin	protein + copper	blue	plasma	some molluscs, crustaceans	1–5 1–4
Chlorocruorin	protein (not globin) + haem	green	plasma	some annelids	9
Haemerythrin	protein + iron	reddish-violet	plasma	some annelids	2

amino acids and proteins, including haemoglobin, forming *carbamino compounds*. About one fifth of the total carbon dioxide is carried in this way. Most of it however, is transported as bicarbonate ions. In regions of high carbon dioxide tension, the formation of bicarbonate ions takes place as follows. Carbon dioxide dissolves in the plasma and diffuses into red corpuscles. In these cells and in the plasma a small amount of carbon dioxide combines with water to form carbonic acid. This reaction would normally proceed very slowly but the corpuscles contain an enzyme, *carbonic anhydrase*, which catalyses the formation of carbonic acid. The latter dissociates to form bicarbonate and hydrogen ions.

$$CO_2 + H_2O \underset{\text{anhydrase}}{\overset{\text{carbonic}}{\rightleftharpoons}} H_2CO_3 \rightleftharpoons H^+ + HCO_3$$

Simultaneously, as oxygen is given up to the tissues, haemoglobin dissociates from the cations, mostly potassium ions, with which it was previously associated. (Deoxygenated Hb is a weaker acid than oxygenated Hb and so has less attraction for cations.) The haemoglobin anions then combine with some of the hydrogen ions from the carbonic acid forming haemoglobinic acid (H.Hb).

Because of the carbonic anhydrase, bicarbonate ions are at a higher concentration inside the cells than in the plasma. As bicarbonate ions are readily diffusible they quickly pass into the plasma. The necessary ionic balance within the corpuscle is restored by the entry of chloride ions from the plasma. Cations in the plasma, chiefly sodium (the most abundant cation), balance the bicarbonate ions entering the plasma. This whole sequence of events, summarised in the diagram below, takes its name from the movement of chloride ions, and is called the *chloride shift*. In the low carbon dioxide tensions at the respiratory surface, the whole process is reversed, and carbon dioxide is released into solution in the plasma.

The chloride shift

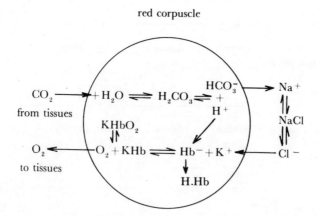

Distribution of heat

Heat is generated largely as a result of cellular respiration. It follows then, that most heat is generated in the most metabolically active tissues, notably the liver and muscles. Blood carries this heat to all parts of the body. The homeostatic mechanisms responsible for maintaining a constant body temperature are described in chapter 9.

Defence

The blood is involved in three defence mechanisms – *clotting*, *phagocytosis* and the *immune response*. The latter two are discussed in chapter 16 on disease.

Clotting

A clot is a plug of protein fibres and blood cells that forms to close damaged blood vessels thereby reducing blood loss and excluding potentially harmful micro-organisms. The essential feature of clot formation is the conversion of the soluble plasma protein, *fibrinogen*, into the insoluble fibrous protein, *fibrin*. A network of fibrin fibres forms across the wound, in which blood cells become entangled. If the clot is external it dries and hardens to form a scab.

At least twelve factors are known to play a part in the conversion of fibrinogen to fibrin. When a vessel is damaged, platelets stick to areas of vessel wall denuded of endothelium (see p. 118). They also release phospholipid which, together with a tissue factor released by the damaged vessel, initiates the clotting sequence. These substances combine with various factors in the blood to produce the enzyme *thrombokinase* (thromboplastin). This enzyme catalyses the formation of another enzyme, *thrombin*, from the inactive enzyme precursor, *prothrombin*. In the presence of calcium ions, thrombin converts fibrinogen into fibrin. The clotting sequence is outlined in Figure 46. Vitamin K, long known to be essential for normal blood clotting, is required for the formation of prothrombin and two of the plasma factors involved in thrombokinase formation.

The large number of stages in the clotting process is thought to be a safety device, reducing the risk of unnecessary clot formation. The latter does occur in the condition known as thrombosis.

Maintenance of a stable internal environment
The protective mechanisms described above, and in chapter 16 on disease, clearly help to maintain the constancy of the internal environment. The transporting role of the blood is no less important, providing as it does the means whereby all the cells in the body are rapidly provided with the substances they need to maintain themselves. It also removes substances the cells do not require with equal rapidity.

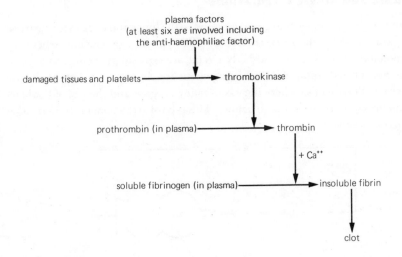

Figure 46   The clotting sequence

The plasma proteins have a special homeostatic role to play by contributing to the colloid osmotic pressure of the blood which helps to control blood volume and water balance in the body. They also act as buffers helping to minimise changes in the pH of the blood.

MAMMALIAN CIRCULATION

The basic plan of mammalian circulation is shown in Figure 47. Blood is pumped by the heart along *arteries* to *capillaries* and then returned to the heart by *veins*.

Capillaries are microscopic vessels that receive blood from the smaller arteries (*arterioles*) and deliver it into the smaller veins (*venules*). They form dense networks in all the tissues and organs of the body. It has been estimated that there are rather more than 60 000 miles of capillaries in an adult man. The exchange of respiratory gases, nutrients, and waste and metabolic products between the blood and the tissues takes place through the capillary walls. These offer little resistance to the passage of materials as they consist of a single layer of cells, the *endothelium* (see Figure 47).

Arteries convey blood from the heart under high pressure, and their walls are very thick to contain this pressure. They have an outer fibrous coat which confers strength and protection, a thick middle layer consisting of circularly arranged involuntary muscle and elastic fibres, and a lining of endothelial cells (see Figure 47). The diameter of arteries and arterioles can be altered by contraction and relaxation of the muscle layer.

Venous blood pressure is much lower than arterial pressure and the walls of veins, although comprising the same layers as artery walls, are much thinner. Veins also differ from arteries in that they have pocket valves at intervals in their walls which permit blood to flow only towards the heart (see Figure 47).

Double and single circulations

In Figure 47 you can see that blood is passed to the lungs and back to the heart on a separate circuit – the *pulmonary circuit*. This type of arrangement, where the pulmonary circuit and general body circuit are separate, is known as a *double circulation*. The advantages of this arrangement are obvious if we compare it with the circulation of a fish where the gas exchange organs and the rest of the body are on the same circuit (see plan below). This type of arrangement is described as a *single circulation*.

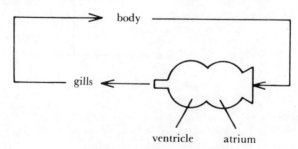

single circulation of a fish

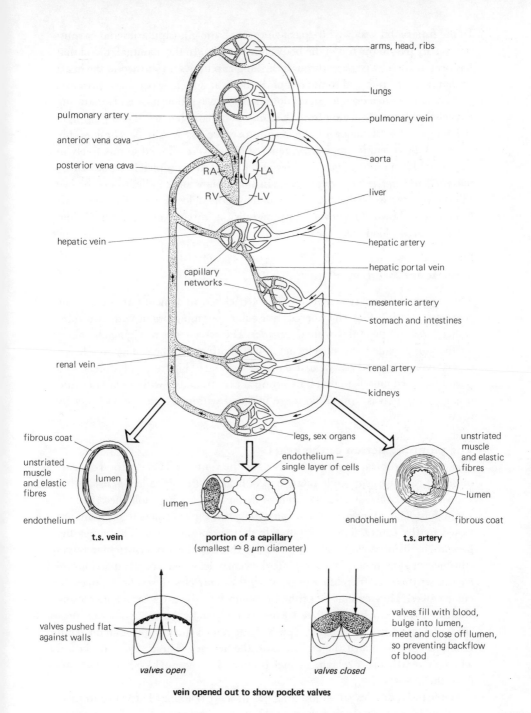

Figure 47 Plan of mammalian circulation and structure of the three main vessel types. Arrows show the direction of blood flow. Shaded portions represent deoxygenated blood and unshaded portions represent oxygenated blood. A = atrium, V = ventricle, L = left, R = right.

In the fish, blood is slowed by passage through the gill capillaries and so must necessarily pass to the rest of the body rather slowly. In the mammal, blood that has been slowed by passage through the lung capillaries is returned to the heart so that it can be pumped to the rest of the body at a high velocity and pressure.

Associated with a double circulation there is always some means of separating oxygenated blood returning from the lungs and deoxygenated blood passing to the lungs. The efficiency of the respiratory process would be considerably impaired if oxygenated and deoxygenated blood were allowed to mix freely in the heart. In mammals the two sides of the heart are completely separated by *interatrial* and *interventricular septa*. Even in amphibians and reptiles where the two sides of the heart are only partially divided by septa, folds in the walls of the heart have been shown to prevent any significant mixing of oxygenated and deoxygenated blood (see *The diversity of life*, p. 168).

The Heart (see Figure 48)

The mammalian heart lies in the thorax enclosed in a membranous sac, the *pericardium*. It is a four-chambered, muscular, pumping organ with two thin-walled *atria* and two thick-walled *ventricles*. The atria act as receiving chambers for the pump while the ventricles act as distributing chambers. The muscle is a special type of striated muscle called *cardiac muscle* (see Figure 49). It differs from normal striated muscle in that it can contract continuously without fatigue, and it is *myogenic*, that is, contractions are initiated within the muscle itself not by nerves.

The pumping action of the heart

The two atria contract simultaneously as do the ventricles. Contraction of heart muscle is called *systole*, while relaxation of heart muscle is called *diastole*. Atria and ventricles contract in turn so that while the atria are in systole the ventricles are in diastole, and vice versa. During *atrial systole* the entrances to the veins are closed by the contraction of the muscle that surrounds them. The increasing pressure in the atria eventually forces blood through the atrioventricular valves (the bicuspid and tricuspid valves) into the ventricles which are relaxing. During *ventricular systole* the increasing pressure in the ventricles closes the atrioventricular valves. They cannot be pushed through into the atria by the increasing ventricular pressure because they are held in position by the taut tendinous cords (heartstrings). Eventually blood is pushed out of the ventricles through the semilunar valves that guard the entrances to the arteries. These valves are closed when the ventricles are relaxing, which prevents backflow of blood into the heart from the arteries.

While the ventricles are contracting the atria are relaxing. The vein entrances open and blood is drawn into the heart by the reduced pressure in the atria. The pressure changes that accompany the filling and emptying of the heart are shown and explained in Figure 50; these should be studied carefully.

The sequence of events just described is called the *cardiac cycle*. During this cycle the sound of the atrioventricular valves closing, followed slightly later by

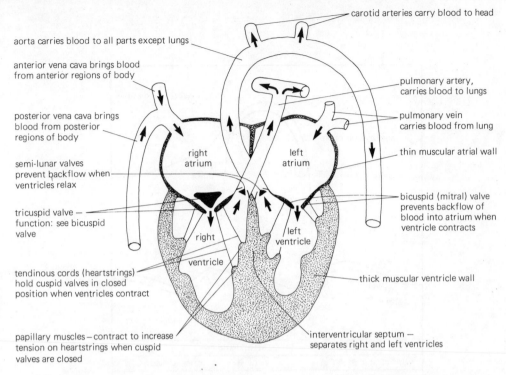

carotid arteries carry blood to head

aorta carries blood to all parts except lungs

anterior vena cava brings blood from anterior regions of body

pulmonary artery, carries blood to lungs

posterior vena cava brings blood from posterior regions of body

pulmonary vein carries blood from lung

right atrium

left atrium

thin muscular atrial wall

semi-lunar valves prevent backflow when ventricles relax

bicuspid (mitral) valve prevents backflow of blood into atrium when ventricle contracts

tricuspid valve — function: see bicuspid valve

right ventricle

left ventricle

tendinous cords (heartstrings) hold cuspid valves in closed position when ventricles contract

thick muscular ventricle wall

papillary muscles — contract to increase tension on heartstrings when cuspid valves are closed

interventricular septum — separates right and left ventricles

Figure 48   Diagram of a longitudinal section through a mammalian heart. Arrows show the direction of blood flow.

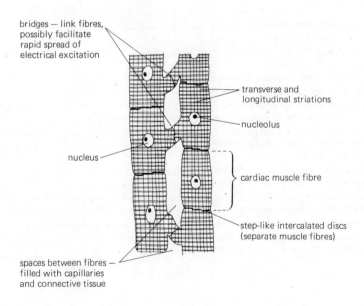

bridges — link fibres, possibly facilitate rapid spread of electrical excitation

transverse and longitudinal striations

nucleolus

nucleus

cardiac muscle fibre

step-like intercalated discs (separate muscle fibres)

spaces between fibres — filled with capillaries and connective tissue

Figure 49   Cardiac muscle in longitudinal section (× 1000)

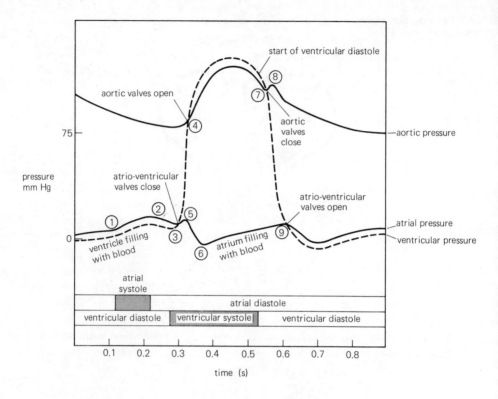

Figure 50   Recordings of pressure changes in the aorta, the atrium and the ventricle during the cardiac cycle (based on the data obtained from the dog).

Start of *atrial systole* lasts about 0.1 second. Increased atrial pressure gives impetus to filling of ventricles

2   Start of *atrial diastole* – causes drop in atrial pressure

3   Start of *ventricular systole*

3–4   Ventricular pressure exceeds atrial pressure, causing atrio-ventricular valves to close. Ventricular pressure goes on increasing steeply as contraction continues

4 · Ventricular pressure exceeds aorta pressure and so pushes open the aortic (semi-lunar) valves. This allows blood to flow into the aorta which increases aortic pressure

5   Short-lived increase in atrial pressure caused by ventricular contraction which bulges the atrio-ventricular valves into the atrium. Why are the valves not pushed open into the atria by ventricular contraction?

5–6   Atrial pressure drops as atrium continues to relax

6   Atrial pressure starts to rise as it fills with blood from the veins

7   Pressure in relaxing ventricle falls below aortic pressure causing aortic valves to close

8   Aortic pressure increases as distended artery wall regains its shape – in so doing pushing blood along the artery away from the heart. Why does the aortic pressure then fall?

9   Pressure in relaxing ventricle falls below atrial pressure causing atrio-ventricular valves to open. This allows the rapid filling of the ventricles from the atria

the sound of the semi-lunar valves closing, together make up the *heart beat*. Thus, there is one heart beat for each cardiac cycle. The human heart beats about seventy times per minute although this rate may be more than doubled during strenuous activity.

Heart rate is inversely related to body size. This is to be expected as small animals have higher metabolic rates than large animals. The elephant has a resting heart rate of about twenty five beats per minute while the tiny shrew's resting rate is about six hundred beats per minute.

Initiation of heart beat

The heart receives two nerves (see Figure 51), the *accelerans*, a sympathetic nerve, and a branch of the *vagus*, a parasympathetic nerve. (The terms sympathetic and parasympathetic are explained in chapter 11.) If these two nerves are severed the heart will continue to beat rhythmically for some time, demonstrating that nerve impulses do not initiate contraction. In fact, as already mentioned, contraction of the heart is initiated within the heart muscle itself. A region of fine muscle fibres in the wall of the atrium called the *sino-atrial node* (SAN) or *pacemaker* (see Figure 51) sends out regular pulses or waves of electrical excitation that pass through the heart muscle causing it to contract. The electrical excitation passes through the atria to another node, the *atrio-ventricular node* (AVN), and then spreads rapidly along the *Purkinje tissue*. These tracts of fine muscle fibres pass down through the interventricular septum and fan out into the ventricle walls. Once the wave of excitation has passed, the cardiac muscle relaxes. It is now possible to correct abnormalities of heart rhythm by the implantation of a battery-operated artificial pacemaker.

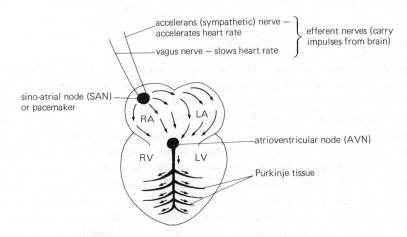

Figure 51 Diagram showing how electrical excitation generated in the pacemaker spreads to other parts of the heart. The nerves shown modify the activity of the pacemaker.

The nerves that pass to the heart do, of course, serve a purpose. They modify the activity of the pacemaker. Impulses passing to the heart along the vagus slow the heart rate while impulses arriving via the accelerans speed up heart rate. Adrenalin, the hormone released in response to fear or anger, has the same effect on heart rate as sympathetic stimulation. Several advantages of this double innervation and antagonistic control of heart rate are apparent. A 'brake' and an 'accelerator' make possible a much quicker, and much more delicate, adjustment of rate than either could alone.

Maintenance of blood flow

The pumping action of the heart provides the main motive force responsible for blood flow, but it is assisted by several other mechanisms. Arteries are distended as blood is forced into them, following which, the elastic recoil of the artery walls pushes blood into the next part of the artery, which becomes distended in its turn. Blood cannot pass back towards the heart as more blood is constantly being pushed along from behind by the contraction of the ventricles. The rhythmical distension and return to shape of the arteries keeps time with the heart beat, and can be felt as a *pulse* wherever an artery passes close to the body surface, for example, at the wrist and temple.

In veins there is little pressure to force blood along. The partial vacuum created in the thoracic cavity during inspiration, and the reduced pressure in the relaxing atria, both help to draw blood along veins and back to the heart. When muscles contract they squeeze the veins running through or alongside them, in so doing pushing blood towards the heart: pocket valves in the veins (see Figure 47) prevent blood being squeezed back, or flowing back, away from the heart. Finally, blood return from regions above the heart is assisted by gravity.

Exchange at the capillaries

Blood entering the arterial end of a capillary network has a high hydrostatic pressure (approximately 40 mm Hg), which tends to force water and small solutes out of the vessel. This is opposed by the colloid osmotic pressure of the blood (approximately 25 mm Hg), which tends to draw water and small solutes into the vessel. As the hydrostatic pressure exceeds the osmotic pressure, water, ions and molecules are forced out through the capillary walls. These are fairly freely permeable. The fluid that leaves the capillaries bathes the tissues and is called *tissue fluid*. It resembles plasma in its composition but has a lower plasma protein content. It was previously supposed that plasma proteins were too large to pass out of the capillaries, but experiments with dogs have revealed that approximately half of the plasma proteins pass out of the blood during the course of twenty-four hours. The same series of experiments also revealed that about sixty per cent of the plasma volume passes out of the capillaries in twenty-four hours. The tissue fluid mediates exchange between the blood and the cells: oxygen and nutrients pass from the blood to the cells via the tissue fluid, while waste materials and secretory products move in the opposite direction.

At the venous end of the capillary network the hydrostatic pressure has fallen to about 15 mm Hg and no longer exceeds the osmotic pressure, so there is a net movement of water and small solutes back into the capillaries. There is however a greater total leakage from the capillaries than return flow. The surplus fluid is collected up by small vessels with fairly freely permeable walls, the *lymph capillaries*. These unite to form large lymph vessels which ultimately empty into the venous system.

Flow through the lymphatic system is maintained by pocket valves and muscle activity, as in veins. At intervals in the lymphatic system there are swellings called *lymph nodes*. These consist of fixed phagocytic cells and lymphocytes held together by connective tissue. They act as bacterial filters and, in cases of infection, often become swollen.

Regulation of blood pressure

Blood pressure must be maintained within certain limits. A fairly high blood pressure is needed for the efficient functioning of organs such as the lungs and the kidneys, but if the blood pressure is too high these same organs, and others, will be damaged.

Blood pressure is monitored by sensitive stretch receptors in the walls of the *carotid sinuses* and the aortic arch (see Figure 52). The carotid sinuses are bulbous swellings of the external carotid arteries. The stretch receptors send impulses along nerves to centres in the medulla concerned with control of heart rate and blood vessels, the *cardiovascular centres*. The frequency of impulses transmitted to the brain varies according to the arterial pressure. If arterial pressure is low, the impulse frequency is low, and vice versa. If the impulse frequency is higher than normal, impulses are sent from the medulla to the heart, causing it to slow, and to the peripheral vessels, causing vasodilation (the muscle walls relax expanding the lumen of the vessels). These two responses reduce cardiac output and lower peripheral resistance to blood flow, thus reducing blood pressure and restoring it to normal. Lower than normal blood pressure is countered by increased heart rate and vasoconstriction. Figure 52 summarises the way that pressure receptors, medullary centres and effector mechanisms combine to regulate blood pressure.

QUESTIONS

1 Distinguish between the following types of circulatory system:
   (a) single and double
   (b) open and closed.
2 Outline the events that take place during ventricular systole. Give full details of the pressure changes involved.
3 Explain how the heart beat is initiated and regulated.
4 Describe the sequence of events that is initiated when:
   (a) a blood vessel is damaged
   (b) blood pressure rises above its normal level.

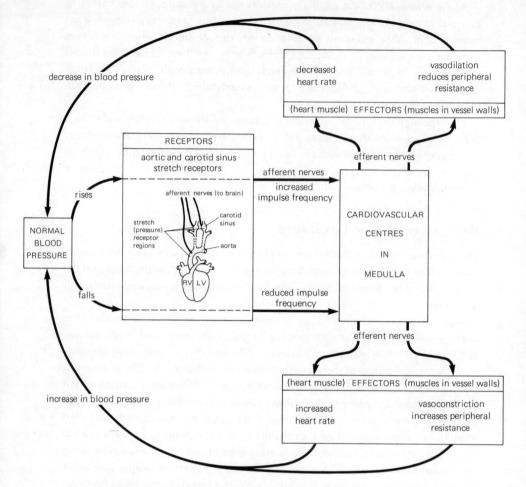

Figure 52   The control of blood pressure

5   Explain the meaning of the following terms:
   (a) respiratory pigment
   (b) oxygen equilibrium curve
   (c) loading tension.

8   Transport in plants

Water, mineral salts and organic substances circulate only by diffusion from cell
to cell in the simplest plants. In ferns, gymnosperms and angiosperms however,
circulation also occurs through special tube-like vascular tissues; phloem carries
organic substances and xylem transports water and minerals.

WATER RELATIONS OF PLANT CELLS

The kinetic energy of water molecules causes them to move in and out of plant
cells along concentration gradients caused by variations in the contents of the cell
sap. The ability of the water molecules to move is modified by bonds, formed
between them and with various solutes. The diffusion of water through a semi-
permeable membrane is termed osmosis and occurs from a less concentrated to a
more concentrated solution, theoretically until equilibrium is reached. In
practice, this is unlikely to arise in the intact plant, because much of the
circulation of water is in response to concentration gradients maintained by the
active transport of metabolites in and out of cells, so the membrane is really
selectively permeable.

The greater the concentration of the cell sap the higher its osmotic pressure or
osmotic potential will be, but water movement depends not on the actual osmotic
pressure but on the difference between the osmotic pressures of adjacent cells.
This difference in osmotic potential is called the *diffusion pressure deficit* or *water
potential* of the cells (denoted by ψ, the Greek letter pronounced psi). As the
water potential draws water into a cell the vacuole and cytoplasm begin to press
outwards against the cellulose cell wall. The pressure exerted is called *turgor
pressure* and will increase until the cellulose cell wall is unable to stretch any
further. The wall itself then begins to exert an inward *wall pressure*. At this point
the cell cannot take up any more water. It is fully turgid and its water potential
has dropped to zero. Therefore it can be said that:

$$\text{DPD} = \text{OP} - \text{TP}$$

DPD	=	OP	−	TP
(diffusion pressure deficit or water potential)		(osmotic potential)		(turgor pressure)

and when DPD = O   OP = TP.

In contrast, when water is lost from a cell its water potential increases and its
turgor pressure decreases. As the cell contents cease to press against the cell wall
the cell becomes flaccid and if many cells are in this condition that part of the

plant begins to wilt. Continued loss of water causes the protoplast to shrink away from the cell wall and may cause irreversible damage. If this extreme loss of water is caused by the cell being surrounded by a solution of higher osmotic pressure, then the cell is said to be *plasmolysed*, and the external solution occupies the spaces where the protoplast has shrunk away from the cell wall. Water relations of cells are discussed further in chapter 6 of *The cell concept*.

Turgor or hydrostatic pressure provides much of the support for non-woody plants, but some vascular plants also contain mechanical or supporting tissues such as *collenchyma* and *sclerenchyma* (see Figure 53). Collenchyma has cellulose cell walls, thickened at the corners or at some points in the walls, but retaining its living contents. Sclerenchyma has walls thickened with lignin and no living contents. Its cells may be long spindle-like *fibres* or short, almost isodiametric, *sclereids*. Fibres are often found associated with vascular tissue, while sclereids may act as supporting struts in leaves e.g. *Hakea*. (See Figure 53.)

WATER RELATIONS OF INTACT FLOWERING PLANTS

Water enters the root hairs of land plants, passes up through the stems and is lost through the leaves and stems by evaporation. This water loss is called *transpiration* and the passage of water through the plant is called the *transpiration stream*. (See Figure 54.)

Uptake of water by the roots

Most water absorption occurs in the root hair zone, each root hair consisting of a fine outgrowth from a cell of the outer piliferous layer of the root, a few millimetres back from the tip. Collectively they provide a very large surface area in close contact with the soil particles. Water passes from the soil into the root hairs along a water potential gradient because the root hair sap contains sugars and other solutes and is more concentrated than soil water. This passive osmotic absorption of water will continue as long as the cell sap is more concentrated than the surrounding soil water.

From the root hair the water passes across the cortex of the root to the xylem (see Figure 54(b)). It may move by diluting the contents of each parenchyma cell in turn and then passing on to the next by osmosis, but it has also been suggested that the water could move through the fine protoplasmic connections, *plasmodesmata*, from one cell to the next or through the cellulose cell walls between the cells. In many species the endodermal cells of the absorbing region develop a thickening of waxy, waterproof suberin, initially internally on their radial walls – the *Casparian strip* – (see Figure 55). This may force water to pass through the protoplasts of the cells rather than through their walls and so regulate the movement of water into the xylem. Water probably enters the xylem by active secretion from the surrounding living cells and a *root pressure* is built up, forcing water a short distance up the stem. Root pressure can be demonstrated by

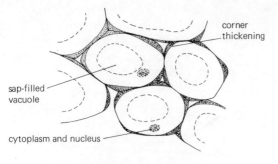

corner thickening

sap-filled vacuole

cytoplasm and nucleus

t.s. angular collenchyma from stem of *Cucurbita pepo* **(marrow) (x 1600)**

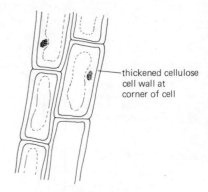

thickened cellulose cell wall at corner of cell

l.s. collenchyma from *Cucurbita pepo* **stem (x 600)**

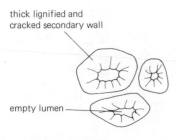

thick lignified and cracked secondary wall

empty lumen

sclereids from the flesh of a pear (x 100)

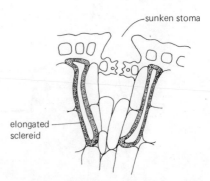

sunken stoma

elongated sclereid

sclereids supporting the leaf in *Hakea* **(x 100)**

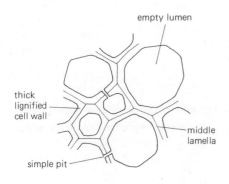

empty lumen

thick lignified cell wall

middle lamella

simple pit

t.s. fibres from maize stem (x 400)

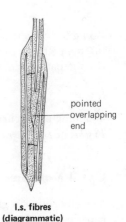

pointed overlapping end

l.s. fibres (diagrammatic)

Figure 53   Supporting tissues of angiosperms

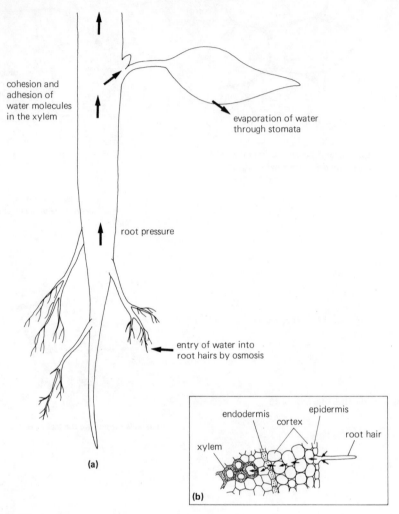

cohesion and
adhesion of
water molecules
in the xylem

evaporation of water
through stomata

root pressure

entry of water into
root hairs by osmosis

(a)

endodermis   epidermis
        cortex
                                root hair
xylem

(b)

Figure 54   The transpiration stream
(a) the pathway of water through the plant
(b) the pathway of water across the root

attaching a mercury manometer to the cut end of the stem of a well-watered
Fuschia or *Hydrangea* plant. Pressures of one to two atmospheres can be recorded.

Uptake of ions

Salt absorption is greatest within a few millimetres of the apex of a root and
experiments with excised tissue show a link between the respiratory rate of the
tissue and salt uptake. Both are speeded up by raising the temperature, and
suppressed by respiratory poisons or by lowering the oxygen tension. It is likely

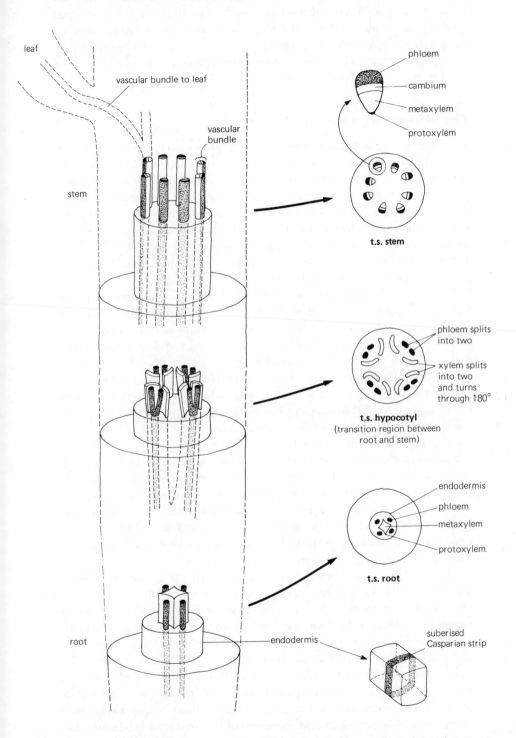

Figure 55 Typical arrangement of vascular tissues in dicotyledon root and stem

that different mechanisms operate for different ions but in general it seems that anion uptake is an active process linked with respiration, while cations enter passively and so maintain the cells' electrical balance. Some cations however, like potassium, may be actively passed in by specific carrier molecules. Again, the endodermis and stelar parenchyma may be regulating the rate of absorption into the xylem. See also chapter 6 of *The cell concept*.

The passage of water up the stem

Stems which have been killed, either by taking up poisons such as picric acid, or by heating encased in a steam jacket, are still capable of transpiring. This indicates that the movement of water up the stem occurs through non-living cells i.e. the xylem. Cut stems immersed in a solution of dye, such as eosin, absorb the dye and subsequent sectioning and microscopic examination reveals that the xylem higher up the stem has been stained. Furthermore, stems placed in fatty solutions draw in the fat blocking the lumina of the xylem elements. Transpiration then ceases, showing that water normally passes through the xylem tubes and not through their cell walls.

The *vessels* and *tracheids* of the xylem offer little resistance to water movement. Both have lignified walls and no living contents when mature. Vessels are composed of a series of cells called *vessel elements* arranged end to end. As they mature their cellulose cell walls become impregnated with impermeable lignin and their living contents die. Their end walls break down, leaving a continuous tube and at numerous points in their walls are thinner regions called *pits*. Here, there is only the cellulose primary wall through which water can easily pass from one cell to another. Often the pits are *bordered*, having a projecting lignified rim. There may also be a central plug of lignin called the *torus*, which may help to regulate lateral movement of water. (See Figure 56.)

Tracheids offer much more resistance to water flow because they retain their end walls which taper and overlap each other. The oblique end walls and also the lateral walls have pits. Angiosperm xylem contains both vessels and tracheids, but gymnosperms have only tracheids. Xylem may also contain supporting fibres and xylem parenchyma, which acts as a food store in which starch accumulates towards the end of the growing season, and is used up by cambial activity the next spring.

The actual mechanism by which water moves up the xylem appears to involve the *adhesion* of the water molecules to the sides of the xylem tubes. Water always tends to adhere to the sides of a container and narrow tubes show this particularly well since there is a large surface area of the tube in contact with the water. The rise of the water will be ultimately limited by its own weight. Water molecules are also mutually attracted to each other and *cohere*, so as water is lost by evaporation from the mesophyll cells of the leaf, a pull is exerted on water in the xylem of the leaf veins. This pull is transmitted back down the stem to the roots and, as a result, water is dragged up the stem. During rapid transpiration, the network of water columns in the xylem of the stems and leaves may have such a strong pull exerted on it that it comes under tension (negative pressure),

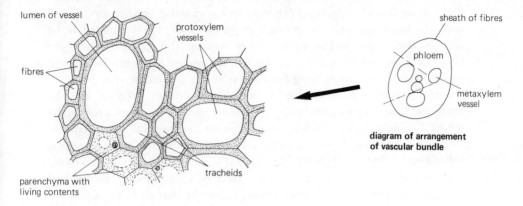

t.s. part of primary xylem from vascular bundle of maize stem (x 500)

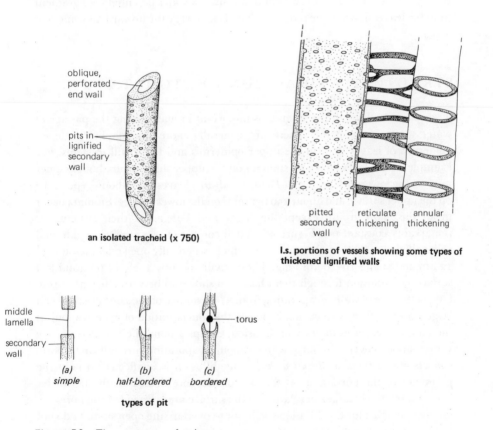

an isolated tracheid (x 750)

l.s. portions of vessels showing some types of thickened lignified walls

types of pit

Figure 56   The structure of xylem

and shrinks. Because the water adheres to them, the xylem walls are pulled inwards and the whole diameter of the stem shrinks. Sensitive recorders called *dendrographs* can be used to measure diurnal variations in the diameter of tree trunks, caused by changes in the rate of transpiration.

When a branch is cut, the sap inside disappears when the water columns break. If the branch is then enclosed in a pressure chamber and pressure exerted until the sap reappears, the pressure required to do this is assumed to be approximately equal to the original xylem tension. This technique has given results of from five to eighty times normal atmospheric pressure in different species, the higher figures being from desert plants and halophytes.

Although cohesion and adhesion together with root pressure may be important in causing water to move up the stem, there are some criticisms of the theory. For instance, water columns under tension in glass capillaries collapse at the slightest vibration, but in plants the xylem columns conduct water regardless of bending by the wind. Secondly, theoretically, the introduction of air bubbles into the water columns should interrupt the flow, yet plant stems broken and then placed in water do not usually wilt. It may be that air locks stop at the perforated end walls of vessels and that if necessary water can pass round them through the vessel walls. There is also of course, a water potential (ψ) gradient from the leaves down to the roots which will encourage the upward movement of water.

STRUCTURE AND ACTION OF STOMATA

Transpiration through the stomata is important in maintaining the passage of water through the plant. There are generally more stomata in the lower epidermis of leaves than in the upper epidermis and fewer still in stems. For example, apple leaves have no stomata on the upper surface but about 400 per mm² on the lower surface; bean (*Phasiolus vulgaris*) leaves have about 40 per mm² on the upper surface and about 250 per mm² on the lower surface. Stomata occur in all the plant groups except the Algae and Fungi and their structure is remarkably constant (see Figure 57). Each consists of two modified epidermal cells called *guard cells*, enclosing a pore, which, when fully open may measure 3–12 μm across and 10–40 $\bar{\mu}$m long. They usually occupy 1–2% of the total leaf surface yet diffusion through them has been shown to be very efficient – up to 60% of the rate of water evaporating from a free surface of the same area. Over a large water surface evaporation increases the concentration of water vapour in the air and decreases the rate of diffusion, except around the perimeter of the water vapour cover. Similarly water vapour evaporating through small pores collects above them as *diffusion shells*, but diffusion is unaffected around the perimeter of the pores and, as the size of the pore decreases, the perimeter becomes relatively larger in relation to the surface area. Provided the pores are far enough apart for the diffusion shells not to overlap, the open stomata do not form a barrier to diffusing water vapour. (See Figure 57(c).)

The stomatal mechanism

The opening and closing of stomata involves variations in water content of the guard cells, which have thicker cell walls next to the pore than next to the

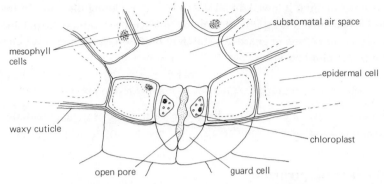

mesophyll cells

substomatal air space

epidermal cell

waxy cuticle

chloroplast

open pore

guard cell

(a) perspective view of stoma and surrounding cells (x 2700)

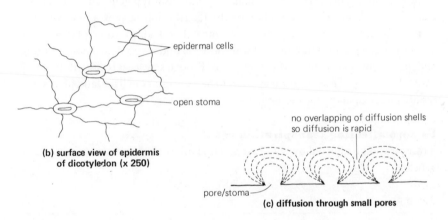

epidermal cells

open stoma

(b) surface view of epidermis
of dicotyledon (x 250)

no overlapping of diffusion shells
so diffusion is rapid

pore/stoma

(c) diffusion through small pores

Figure 57   The structure and functioning of stomata

surrounding epidermal cells. When they are full of water (turgid), their thin walls stretch more than the thick ones, causing the two cells to curve away from each other and open the pore (see **Figure** 57(a)). As they lose water and their turgor pressure drops, the guard cells become straighter and close the pore.

Unlike other cells of the epidermis, guard cells contain chlorophyll and photosynthesise so that sugar accumulates in them during daylight. It was thought that the sugar raised the concentration of the guard cell sap, drawing in water from the surrounding epidermal cells by osmosis. Very little sugar is produced however, and this does not therefore explain the rapidity of the opening.

Experiments have shown that, for most species, illumination causes an increase in pH accompanied by opening, whereas darkness promotes a lower pH and closure of the stomata. One hypothesis to account for this is that, during darkness, carbon dioxide accumulates in the saturated intercellular spaces of the leaf, forming carbonic acid and lowering the pH inside the leaf. This causes the sugar in the guard cells to be converted to starch, which is osmotically inactive, so their osmotic potential is lowered and they lose water, closing the pore. In the light the carbon dioxide is rapidly used up in photosynthesis, raising the pH and favouring the conversion of guard cell starch to glucose-1-phosphate, probably by the enzyme phosphorylase:

$$\text{starch} + \text{inorganic phosphate} \quad \overset{\text{pH 7}}{\longrightarrow} \quad \text{glucose-1-phosphate}$$

The glucose-1-phosphate is osmotically active, raising the osmotic potential of the cells and causing them to absorb water and become turgid, opening the pore.

Effects of transpiration

Before the absorption of salts was shown to be mainly an active process, transpiration was believed to be responsible for it. Now it is generally agreed that transpiration is merely responsible for the distribution of salts along with the water. Similarly there is no clear evidence that transpiration prevents the overheating of plants. High rates of transpiration and water deficit cause wilting and, in extreme cases, the death of the plant. Protein synthesis is also inhibited by water deficiency. Transpiration appears to be a necessary evil for land plants, the disadvantages balancing the benefits.

Factors affecting transpiration rates

Transpiration is affected by both external and internal factors as shown in Table 4 below:

Table 4

External factors	*Internal factors*
1 Vapour pressure deficit. The greater the difference between water vapour pressure inside and outside, the greater the rate. 2 Temperature/humidity. At constant temperature, decrease in humidity increases the rate; at constant humidity, increased temperature increases the rate. 3 Wind velocity. Wind blows away diffusion shells and flexes leaves and stems. 4 Light intensity. Light causes stomata to open and therefore increases rate. 5 Soil water content. Dehydration causes closure.	1 The ability of cells to retain water. 2 Stomatal control, especially near opening and closing times.

TRANSLOCATION OF SOLUTES

The green leaves and stems are the photosynthetic sites of the plant, where food is manufactured. It must then be transported or translocated in solution to all parts of the plant through the phloem, providing a source of energy, materials for growth and in some places a food store. The direction of translocation is mainly downward from the leaves to the roots but may also be upward and lateral to growing leaf buds, flowers and fruits. The direction may also vary with the time of year and age of the plant.

Phloem structure

In an angiosperm, phloem consists of *sieve tubes* and *companion cells* and varying amounts of parenchyma and fibres (see Figure 58). Sieve tubes develop from a linear series of cells called *sieve tube elements*. They are nucleate when young and

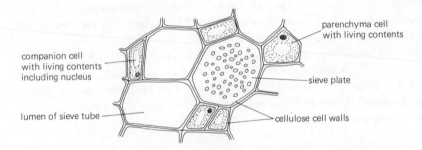

t.s. part of phloem of *Helianthus annuus* **(sunflower) stem (x1700)**

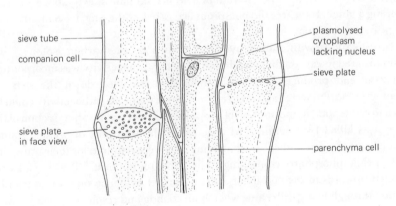

l.s. part of phloem of *Helianthus annuus* **stem (x1700)**

Figure 58   The structure of primary phloem in a dicotyledon

have cytoplasm containing plastids and *slime bodies* – rounded masses of protein. They have cellulose cell walls and the end walls between adjacent elements develop pores in groups called *sieve plates*, with fine protoplasmic strands passing through the pores from one element to the next. Beside each sieve tube element is a companion cell with a prominent nucleus and dense cytoplasm, strands of which pass through into the adjacent element. Sieve tube elements and companion cells are developed side by side as a result of longitudinal division of a meristematic cell. Gymnosperms have *sieve cells* which are not regularly arranged end to end, and have less elaborate sieve plates.

At maturity the nuclei, plastids and slime bodies of the sieve tube elements disintegrate, leaving only cytoplasm and nucleoli. The companion cells keep their nuclei and also have many mitochondria, so the companion cell and sieve tube element may form a single functional unit in which energy and nuclear control are provided by the companion cell. The functional life of sieve tubes is relatively short, only a few days in the protophloem. In most woody species, after one season, the cytoplasm disintegrates in the sieve tubes, ending their functional life and plugs of a carbohydrate called *callus* form in the sieve plates. Where secondary growth occurs, the older phloem layers are gradually crushed and may become lignified, being eventually cut off from the rest of the stem by the development of bark from a *cork cambium*.

Phloem parenchyma generally stores starch but probably also provides energy for the active secretion of nutrients into the sieve tubes at the source (photosynthetic site) and their removal at the sink (a meristematic region or storage organ). The phloem ray cells are concerned mainly with food storage and lateral transport of nutrients.

The evidence for transport in the phloem

The first evidence for transport of nutrients in the phloem came from tree ringing experiments in which the bark and outer tissues were removed down to the xylem. Organic compounds were found to accumulate slowly above the ring causing a bulge. If the tree did not sprout leaves below the ring, it eventually died from root starvation.

Investigations with radioactive tracers such as the carbon isotope (^{14}C) administered in carbon dioxide, showed that the radioactivity was incorporated into the end products of photosynthesis and travelled down the stem. If photographic film were exposed to cut sections of stem, the radioactivity could be seen to correspond to the position of the phloem. However, if a short section of the stem was killed by treatment with hot wax, the transport of organic solutes ceased at that point, indicating that living cells were required for their transport. Meanwhile phosphates containing radioactive phosphorus ^{32}P were still conducted upwards in the non-living xylem. Further evidence supporting translocation through living cells came when both cooling and respiratory poisons were found to inhibit the flow, whereas supplying additional ATP to leaves accelerated it.

Aphids have been used to investigate the contents and rates of flow in sieve tubes. The aphid inserts its mouthparts into a sieve tube to feed and if it is then cut away the sieve tube contents continue to exude from the mouthparts and can be collected. Analysis of these exudates has shown mainly sucrose, a few oligosaccharides like raffinose and stachyose, amino acids, amides and a few minerals, varying little with species or age.

The volume of exudate produced is about 5 mm^3 hour^{-1} and calculations indicate that this represents a flow of about 1 m hour^{-1} through the sieve tube. Speeds estimated using radioactive tracers are much slower, about 10–100 cm hour^{-1} depending on the species. Different substances appear to move at different rates. These speeds are still much too fast for diffusion, for example, the downward movement of sucrose through the phloem is about 40 000 times faster than the rate of its diffusion through water.

Factors affecting the rate of translocation

1 *Temperature*. It is difficult to separate temperature effects from their influence on other physiological processes but it seems that increased temperature increases translocation rates up to a maximum of about 35°C, probably by affecting the enzymes involved in the secretion and removal of sucrose from the tubes.

2 *Light*. Translocation to the roots is greatly enhanced in the dark in those plants studied.

3 *Metabolic inhibitors*. Hydrogen cyanide, 2-4 dinitrophenol (DNP) etc., inhibit carbohydrate translocation.

4 *Concentration gradients*. Carbohydrate always seems to move from regions of higher concentrations to regions of lower concentration.

5 *Mineral deficiencies*. Boron seems to be important in forming an ionisable complex with sucrose which then passes more easily through cell membranes. It also appears to slow down the enzymatic conversion of glucose-1-phosphate to starch thus keeping more sugar available for translocation.

6 *Hormones*. Cytokinins, IAA and gibberellins (see chapter 13), appear to at least partially control translocation, probably by their effects on metabolic rates at the source and sink.

Mechanisms of translocation

It is now generally agreed that solutes enter and leave sieve tubes by active transport, but it is by no means certain how they travel through the tubes. One suggestion is Münch's *mass flow hypothesis*. He postulates a passive flow of solutes along a turgor pressure gradient from a region of high concentration of solutes in the leaves to a region of lower concentration in the roots. Figure 59(a) shows apparatus for demonstrating mass flow. Osmometer A contains a higher concentration of solute and therefore it will develop a higher turgor pressure as water flows into it from the reservoir. This will cause water to flow from A to B, passively carrying the solute with it. The hydrostatic pressure built up in B will force water out of it back into the reservoir from which it could again enter A. If we had some way of keeping up the concentration in A then the circulation would continue indefinitely. In the living plant A is represented by the leaf cells

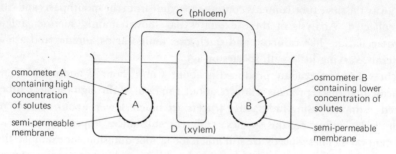

osmometer A
containing high
concentration
of solutes

semi-permeable
membrane

C (phloem)

osmometer B
containing lower
concentration of
solutes

semi-permeable
membrane

D (xylem)

(a) Münch's hypothesis of mass flow

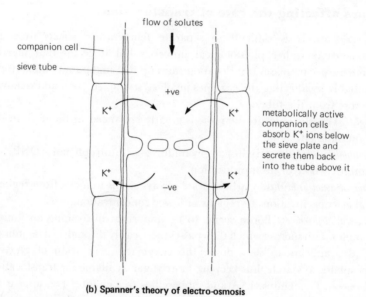

flow of solutes

companion cell

sieve tube

+ve

K^+

K^+

metabolically active
companion cells
absorb K^+ ions below
the sieve plate and
secrete them back
into the tube above it

K^+

K^+

−ve

(b) Spanner's theory of electro-osmosis

Figure 59   Mass flow and electro-osmosis. From Richardson, M., *Translocation in Plants* Studies in biology 10 (Arnold); after Spanner, D. C., *J. of Exp. Bot.* 9, 332–342 (1958).

supplying sugars and B by the plant cells receiving them. The connecting link C is the phloem carrying water and solutes while the recirculation of water through the reservoir is represented by the xylem. Continuous flow would be possible as long as the leaves continued to produce sugars. This theory does not show why living cells are necessary for translocation or explain why factors affecting metabolic rate also affect translocation speeds, unless one assumes that these only alter the rate of entry and exit to the seive tubes and not flow through them. It would however, explain why liquid exudes under slight pressure from phloem when bark is cut or from aphid mouthparts. There is also good evidence for concentration gradients of sugars in the phloem especially in trees. Mass flow does however require high turgor pressure especially to cause flow through the sieve plates. D. C. Spanner proposed the *electro-osmotic theory* in which mass flow occurs down the sieve tube and is then assisted across the sieve plate by electro-osmotic mass flow (see Figure 59(b)). He suggests that the sieve plates become polarised due to potassium ions being taken up on one side of the plate and secreted on the other side by the companion cells. This would produce an electrical gradient through the pores and cause unidirectional flow through them. It would explain the requirement for living cells and the fact that potassium ions are found in sieve tubes at the appropriate concentration.

One objection to the mass flow theory is that bidirectional movement of solutes through the phloem has been shown. It is possible however, that these occur through separate sieve tubes and along different concentration gradients to separate sinks e.g. from higher leaves to growing buds and from lower leaves to developing roots.

The other major theory is that of *protoplasmic streaming*, occurring round each sieve tube element and through the pores from one element to the next. This would account for the requirement for living contents and would allow bidirectional flow, even in the same sieve tube. Protoplasmic streaming has been observed in some sieve tubes but not all.

Other theories for phloem transport include *interfacial spreading*, in which solute molecules are adsorbed on to the surface of membranes or filaments, lowering their surface tension, and spread rapidly along them as long as the molecules are removed at the ends.

No one theory fits all the known facts of phloem transport but combinations of active transport, mass flow and protoplasmic streaming comply with most of them.

QUESTIONS

1 With the aid of diagrams, describe the structure of a stoma of a dicotyledon. Explain the series of events which are believed to lead to the opening of the stoma. Why is water loss so great from stomata even though the pores are so small?

2 Explain how osmosis, root pressure, cohesion and adhesion of water molecules and evaporation from the leaves are all believed to contribute towards the maintenance of the transpiration stream.

3 Summarise the evidence that movement of water up the stem occurs through the xylem.

4 What is the evidence for and against
(a) Münch's hypothesis
(b) protoplasmic streaming, as the mechanisms involved in translocation through the phloem?

9 Homeostasis and temperature regulation

HOMEOSTASIS

The cells of multicellular animals are surrounded by tissue fluid which forms the *internal environment* of the body. Claude Bernard, a French physiologist, was one of the first people to recognise the vital importance of maintaining a stable internal environment. In 1847 he wrote 'la fixité du milieu interieur est la condition de la vie libre'. By this he meant that if the internal environment can be kept constant in the face of changing external conditions, the animal will be free from the necessity of living in habitats where the conditions remain within the narrow confines consistent with life.

Cannon, an American physiologist, first used the term 'homeostasis' (from the Greek meaning 'staying the same') to describe the maintenance of internal stability. Originally, the term was only applied to the very carefully regulated conditions in birds and mammals, but it is now generally accepted that all organisms, even the most primitive unicells, employ some regulatory mechanisms to maintain differences between themselves and their surroundings, and can therefore be said to exhibit a degree of homeostasis. Thus, we should perhaps think of homeostasis as a characteristic of all living organisms, but one that has increased in efficiency during the course of evolution, conferring a greater degree of independence from the environment.

In mammals the main homeostatic processes or mechanisms regulate the following features of the internal medium, usually by adjusting their level in the blood from which the tissue fluid is derived (many of these mechanisms are described in other chapters):

(i) water and ion content – see chapter 10;
(ii) food materials, especially glucose, the main energy source – see p. 99;
(iii) respiratory gases – see p. 32;
(iv) excretory materials – these usually toxic substances must be removed before they reach a dangerous level; see chapter 10.

In addition, blood pressure (p. 125) and body temperature are maintained at a more or less constant level.

Most, if not all, homeostatic control mechanisms are *self-adjusting*, since fluctuations in the feature being regulated trigger the appropriate corrective mechanisms. They are also described as *negative feedback* mechanisms, meaning that the corrective mechanisms reverse, or negate, the effects of the original change. For example, a rise in the level of glucose in the blood brings into effect mechanisms that reduce the blood glucose level and so restore it to normal. Homeostatic mechanisms involve sensors or receptors that detect the change in level, effectors that correct the level, and a coordinating centre (see chapter 11).

A generalised homeostatic mechanism

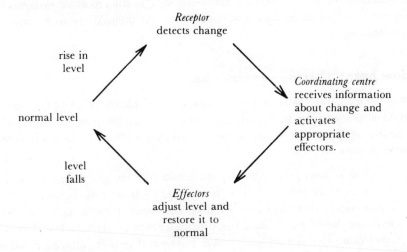

Receptor
detects change

rise in
level

Coordinating centre
receives information
about change and
activates
appropriate
effectors.

normal level

level
falls

Effectors
adjust level and
restore it to
normal

Homeostasis in cells is discussed in chapter 7 of *The cell concept*.

TEMPERATURE REGULATION

Protoplasm can only survive in a fairly narrow temperature range, between 0°C and 45°C. At temperatures below 0°C most cells are irreparably damaged by the formation of ice crystals; above 45°C, lack of oxygen (which is in greater demand at high temperatures), denaturation of enzymes, and the disruption of the lipid element in membranes, can all contribute to heat death. There are, however, exceptions. Many insect larvae can survive freezing and thawing and, at the other extreme, the blue-green algae that live in hot springs can survive in temperatures around 90°C.

Animals living on land are subjected to much greater temperature fluctuations than are aquatic animals; water heats up and cools down more slowly than air. Accordingly, many terrestrial animals have developed a variety of behavioural and physiological mechanisms which enable them to maintain their body temperature within a preferred range.

Traditionally, animals are divided into *homeotherms* and *poikilotherms* according to their ability to regulate body temperature. Poikilotherms (all invertebrates, fish, amphibia and reptiles) have a body temperature that varies with the temperature of the surroundings (the *ambient temperature*), while homeotherms (birds and mammals) maintain a fairly constant and high body temperature irrespective of the ambient temperature. In fact, many so-called poikilotherms maintain a remarkably constant body temperature (at least during the day). The desert lizard keeps its body temperature at around 37°C by basking in the sun to warm up, and retreating into the shade to cool off. The term *ectotherm* is used to describe animals like the lizard that gain heat by absorption from their surroundings (externally), while animals like birds and mammals that generate their body heat internally are called *endotherms*. The latter also make use of behavioural mechanisms, such as moving into burrows to avoid extremes of temperature, but these play a subsidiary role to internal thermoregulatory mechanisms.

How homeotherms conserve heat

Most homeotherms maintain a core temperature within the range 35°C to 42°C. As this is somewhat higher than the air temperature in most terrestrial habitats, it is hardly surprising that various responses have evolved to reduce heat transfer to the environment.

1   The loss of heat from the body surface can be reduced by lowering the temperature of the surface, thereby reducing the temperature gradient. This is achieved by constricting the arterioles that supply the skin capillaries, thus reducing the volume of blood (the distributor of heat) at the body surface. In some cases, special *shunt vessels* link arterioles and venules, allowing blood to by-pass the skin capillaries (see Figure 60).

2   Hair or feathers can be raised by the contraction of their erector muscles. This increases the thickness of the insulating layer of air trapped between the hair or feathers and the skin.

3   Sweating is inhibited to reduce heat loss by evaporation.

4   If the mechanisms described above are inadequate, additional heat can be generated by involuntary muscle twitches or shivering, and by increased metabolism of other tissues, notably the liver. Such measures can only be used on a short-term basis. The reason for this is fairly obvious. A high rate of metabolism creates a high food demand, but in cold conditions food is often scarce and so the animal cannot afford to increase its metabolism for extended periods. Consequently, in long cold spells many animals migrate or hibernate. During hibernation most mammals continue to regulate their body temperature, but at a lower level than normal, usually a few degrees above 0°C, while the metabolic rate is reduced to between one twentieth and one hundredth of its normal level.

Apart from the physical and chemical responses described above, certain structural (anatomical) features also help to conserve heat, for example, the insulating layer of dermal fat. This layer varies in thickness according to the habitat and, in many species, the season. On average, the insulation provided by dermal fat in Arctic mammals is nine times greater than that in tropical mammals.

Certain new-born mammals have pads of special *brown fat*, also commonly found in hibernators. This fat has been likened to an electric blanket – a justifiable analogy, for, when extra heat is required, heat production in the fat

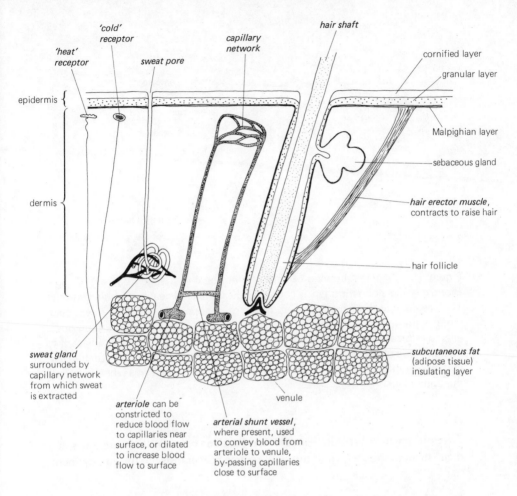

epidermis {

dermis {

'heat' receptor

'cold' receptor

sweat pore

capillary network

hair shaft

cornified layer

granular layer

Malpighian layer

sebaceous gland

hair erector muscle, contracts to raise hair

hair follicle

subcutaneous fat (adipose tissue) insulating layer

sweat gland surrounded by capillary network from which sweat is extracted

arteriole can be constricted to reduce blood flow to capillaries near surface, or dilated to increase blood flow to surface

venule

arterial shunt vessel, where present, used to convey blood from arteriole to venule, by-passing capillaries close to surface

Figure 60   Diagrammatic section through mammalian skin showing the structures involved in temperature regulation

cells is 'switched on', either by impulses passing down sympathetic nerves, or by the hormone noradrenalin.

The arrangement of blood vessels passing to the extremities can also help in heat conservation. The veins that return cooled blood to the body core generally lie next to the arteries that supply the extremities with warm blood, thus allowing heat exchange between the two. This means that blood cooled by passing through the extremities is warmed before re-entering the body core. The efficiency of this exchange is increased by the counter-current flow of venous and arterial blood (see Figure 61). In animals with special heat conservation problems, such as whales and porpoises, the vein that returns blood from the flipper is much-branched and wrapped around the artery, thereby greatly increasing the area of contact between the two vessels. This 'heat-transfer' arrangement benefits the animal in another way; the low temperature of the

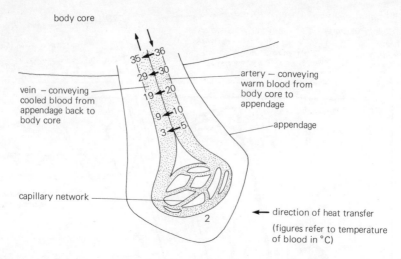

body core

vein – conveying
cooled blood from
appendage back to
body core

artery – conveying
warm blood from
body core to
appendage

appendage

capillary network

← direction of heat transfer

(figures refer to temperature
of blood in °C)

Figure 61   Diagram showing counter-current heat exchange in an appendage.
Blood passing along the artery is cooled by the transfer of heat to the adjacent vein.
This means that the temperature at the tip of the appendage will be low, which
reduces the temperature gradient between the appendage and its surroundings,
and so reduces heat loss. Blood passing along the vein is continually adjacent to
arterial blood of a slightly higher temperature. This ensures maximum heat transfer,
and blood returns to the body core only slightly cooler than it was when it entered
the appendage.

extremities will reduce the temperature gradient between the extremities and
their surroundings, which in turn will reduce heat transfer to the environment.

How homeotherms lose excess heat

1   Vasodilation increases blood flow to the skin, and a greater volume of blood is
returned to the body core in superficial veins (veins lying near the surface)
rather than in deeper lying ones. This aids heat loss from the surface by
convection and radiation.
2   Sweat secretion is increased, leading to increased evaporative heat loss. Each
cubic centimetre of water evaporated from the skin involves the loss of about
2.5 kJ of body heat. Of course, sweat is only of value as a cooling mechanism if
there is adequate water and salt available for replacement, and if the relative
humidity of the air around the body is such as to allow evaporation.
3   The evaporative heat loss from the respiratory tract can be increased by
panting. This is especially important in homeotherms like the dog, where
sweat glands are few in number or absent. Birds employ a similar mechanism,
rapidly oscillating the floor of the mouth and throat (gular flutter) to increase ·
evaporative heat loss.

Animals living in hot, dry conditions must restrict evaporation, and have developed a range of adaptations in order to do this. At one extreme is the camel, which can tolerate large diurnal variations in its body temperature, and can also withstand a much greater degree of dehydration than most other animals. At the other extreme, the kangaroo rat avoids high temperatures by staying in deep burrows during the day, only emerging at night to feed. Incidentally, this animal is especially remarkable in its ability to survive on a diet of dry seeds without drinking. It obtains a little free water from the seeds it eats, while the rest is obtained from the oxidation of food materials. (You will recall that water is one of the end-products of respiration.)

Homeostatic control of body temperature in mammals

Thermoreceptors (actually separate heat and cold receptors) are found in the skin, certain veins, the spinal cord and the hypothalamic region of the brain. It seems that information from all these receptors converges on the *temperature control centres* in the hypothalamus. There are two discrete areas in the hypothalamus, an anterior *heat loss centre* and a posterior *heat production and conservation centre*. The way in which these centres control body temperature is summarised in Figure 62. The anterior centre seems to be activated primarily by an increase in hypothalamic temperature, although it can be inhibited by impulses from peripheral (skin and venous) cold receptors. This contrasts with the posterior centre, which seems to be activated by the peripheral cold receptors, and inhibited when the heat loss centre is active. Information from the central and peripheral receptors is conveyed to the conscious centres of the brain resulting in an awareness of temperature which may lead to behavioural responses such as seeking shade, or putting on an extra jumper.

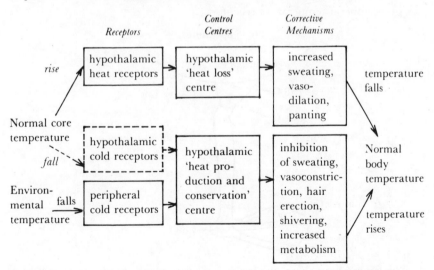

Figure 62 An outline scheme of the mammalian temperature control system. The evidence for the existence of hypothalamic cold receptors is contradictory. The interactions between the hypothalamic and peripheral receptors are not shown, but they are briefly described in the text.

ADVANTAGES AND DISADVANTAGES OF HOMEOTHERMY

Homeothermy has enabled birds and mammals to exploit habitats, such as the polar regions, that are too cold for terrestrial poikilotherms. It has also enabled them to develop the nocturnal habit to a greater extent than most poikilotherms (other than insects), since at night, when the temperature falls, most poikilotherms become cold and inactive (torpid).

On the other hand, getting rid of excess heat in hot dry regions is very difficult for homeotherms, which no doubt explains the relatively small numbers of homeotherms in such regions. In addition, homeothermy is metabolically expensive, requiring large amounts of food; a reptile, for example, is able to survive on one-tenth the food required by a similarly-sized mammal.

QUESTIONS

1 Explain the meaning of the following terms:–
   (a) homeostasis
   (b) negative feedback control mechanism.
2 Distinguish between the following pairs of terms:–
   (a) homeotherm and poikilotherm,
   (b) ectotherm and endotherm.
   Explain why aquatic poikilotherms have not developed the same range of thermoregulatory mechanisms as terrestrial poikilotherms.
3 Describe the part played by the following in thermoregulatory control:–
   (a) the hypothalamus,
   (b) peripheral temperature receptors.

4

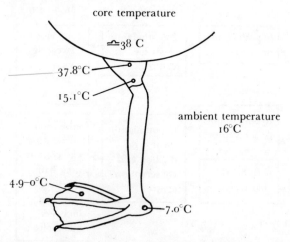

core temperature

≃38 C

37.8°C

15.1°C

ambient temperature
16°C

4.9–0°C

7.0°C

The figure above shows the leg of an arctic seagull. Explain why different temperatures are recorded in different parts of the leg. How does this arrangement benefit the animal?

10 Excretion and osmoregulation

Excretion, the elimination of metabolic waste products, is a vital homeostatic process. The main excretory materials in animals are carbon dioxide and water from respiration, and nitrogen-containing wastes derived from the breakdown of surplus protein. In certain circumstances these materials may perform useful functions; for example, an animal living in hot dry conditions normally uses metabolic water to maintain its body's water balance.

The way in which carbon dioxide is eliminated has already been discussed, so here the regulation of water and nitrogenous waste will be investigated. It is convenient to deal with these two processes together as they are interrelated. Nitrogenous waste is usually eliminated in aqueous solution, and, as a result, in many animals, the same organs are involved in both processes.

NITROGENOUS EXCRETION

The biochemical details in mammals are best known and are described here. Amino acids derived from cell replacement, together with those taken in surplus to the body's requirements, cannot be stored and so are transported to the liver. There, the nitrogen-containing amino group is removed (deamination), and the carbon-containing residue, a keto acid, either enters the respiratory pathway at the appropriate point (see p. 17), or undergoes conversion into a storage material. Deamination can be summarised as follows:–

$$R.CH.NH_2COOH + \tfrac{1}{2}O_2 \rightarrow R.CO.COOH + NH_3$$
$$\text{amino acid} \qquad\qquad \text{keto acid} \qquad \text{ammonia}$$

Ammonia is a highly toxic compound and must either be removed from the body rapidly or converted into a less toxic compound, usually *urea* (carbamide) or *uric acid*. All three compounds are normally present in the wastes of animals but their proportions vary according to the type of habitat. Animals are classified according to which of the three compounds predominates in their excreta; those that excrete mainly ammonia are called *ammonotelic*, those excreting mainly urea are called *ureotelic*, and those excreting mainly uric acid are *uricotelic*.

Ammonotelism (exhibited by marine and freshwater invertebrates, bony fish, and larval and permanently aquatic amphibians).

Because of ammonia's high toxicity, ammonotelism is only encountered in animals living in environments where there is abundant water for its rapid removal. Ammonia is highly soluble and diffuses out rapidly through any permeable surface in contact with the water; for example in bony fish (teleosts) most of the nitrogenous waste is lost as ammonia through the gills.

Ureotelism (exhibited by mammals and most adult amphibians).

Urea is less toxic than ammonia and so can be retained in the body for limited periods before removal. It is also more soluble than ammonia, which means that less water is required for its elimination. This is of course, an important consideration in terrestrial animals.

Urea is produced by a cyclic process called the *urea* or *ornithine cycle*. This was first elucidated by Sir Hans Krebs, the biochemist whose name is associated with the final aerobic pathway (see chapter 2). Urea is split away from the amino acid arginine, leaving the amino acid ornithine. This reaction is catalysed by the enzyme arginase. The purpose of the remainder of the cycle is to regenerate arginine from ornithine by the incorporation of ammonia. The main stages in the cycle are set out below.

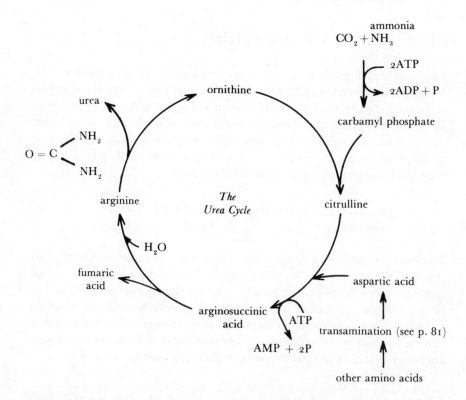

As you can see, the cycle is driven by energy derived from ATP; four high-energy phosphate groups are detached from ATP for each turn of the cycle.

Uricotelism (exhibited by terrestrial insects, molluscs, birds and most reptiles).

The formation of uric acid is even more complex than that of urea; essentially, the amino acids glycine and glutamic acid, together with the sugar ribose, are incorporated into a nucleotide, and this is then broken down to yield uric acid. Like ureotelism, the excretion of uric acid is an adaptation to water conservation. Since uric acid is virtually insoluble in water it is non-toxic and very little water is required for its elimination. Birds excrete a thick paste of uric acid crystals while insects are more efficient at extracting water and so excrete solid pellets of uric acid.

It has been suggested that uricotelism was an essential prerequisite for the evolution of the cleidoic (self-contained or closed) egg in reptiles and birds. Uric acid is obviously much better suited to long-term storage inside an egg than the more soluble and more toxic urea.

There are other nitrogenous wastes but they are less widespread in their occurrence. Marine teleosts excrete as much as one-third of their nitrogen as *trimethylamine oxide*, a soluble, non-toxic substance. Incidentally, this substance contributes to the characteristic 'high' smell of dead fish. Guanine, another nitrogenous waste, accounts for a large proportion of nitrogenous excretion in spiders.

EXCRETION IN PLANTS

Unlike animals, plants have no specialised excretory organs. Indeed, compared with animals, plants produce little excretory material. The way in which the carbon dioxide produced during respiration is eliminated was described in chapter 2. Plants can regulate the synthesis of proteins according to their needs, and so do not usually excrete nitrogenous wastes. Wastes from other processes are generally converted into a relatively insoluble, non-toxic form, which is deposited inside cells (e.g. in the innermost xylem vessels or heartwood of trees), or in the spaces between cells. They are then either stored for the rest of the plant's life, or removed when parts of the plant, such as leaves or bark, are discarded.

OSMOREGULATION

Water comprises on average about seventy per cent of protoplasm. It not only serves as a solvent but also participates directly in many metabolic processes. The concentration of water in protoplasm must be maintained at a relatively constant level – this is the task of osmoregulation. The internal solute concentration, especially that of the inorganic ions, must also be regulated. Ionic and osmotic regulation are interrelated, since the concentration of ions contributes to the osmotic concentration of the body fluids and this, in turn, affects the water concentration. In addition, the intake or removal of water will be accompanied by the intake or removal of ions in solution, which may need to be counteracted.

The nature of the problems posed by osmoregulation largely depends on the animal's environment, whether marine, brackish water, freshwater or terrestrial.

Living in the sea

Life is believed to have originated in the sea, and this is reflected in the body fluids of most marine invertebrates which have the same osmotic concentration as the surrounding seawater (they are *iso-osmotic* with their medium). Such animals face no difficulties due to osmotic movement of water, but they must still engage in ionic regulation as their solute composition generally differs from that of seawater.

Marine teleosts are not as fortunate, since their body fluids are less concentrated than the surrounding medium (they are *hypo-osmotic*); a fact that may be explained by the suggested freshwater origin of this class. They exhibit several adaptations which enable them to combat the osmotic withdrawal of water from their bodies (see Figure 63(a)). An impermeable covering of bony scales restricts water loss to areas such as the gut and the gills. The number of glomeruli (described later in this chapter) is greatly reduced. As a result, little filtration is carried out in the kidney, and urine production is scanty. Finally, they drink very large volumes of water to restore the body's water content. An unfortunate consequence of this last adaptation is that ions, far in excess of the body's requirements, are taken in with the water. These excess ions are excreted by the kidney and by special salt-excreting glands on the gills.

Marine elasmobranchs (cartilaginous fish) avoid osmotic problems in a rather unusual way. They retain large amounts of urea in the body fluid, thus raising the osmotic concentration to that of the surrounding seawater.

Living in brackish and freshwater

Animals in these environments share the problem of living in a medium that has a lower osmotic concentration than their body fluids (they are *hyper-osmotic* to their surroundings). They are consequently faced with continual osmotic flooding and leaching of their valuable salts. Most of these animals have similar adaptations which help them to overcome these problems. An impermeable body covering, such as fish scales and the arthropod cuticle, restricts water intake to permeable areas (the gills and the gut). Excretory organs, like the antennary gland of crustacea and the vertebrate kidney, eliminate excess water. These same organs usually reabsorb some of the valuable ions that would otherwise pass out with the surplus water. Additional mechanisms to replace 'leached' ions include active uptake in the gut and the gills (see Figure 63(b)).

Brackish water has a salinity lower than that of seawater and higher than that of freshwater. This definition includes river estuaries and salt-marshes together with certain land-locked seas such as the Baltic and the Caspian.

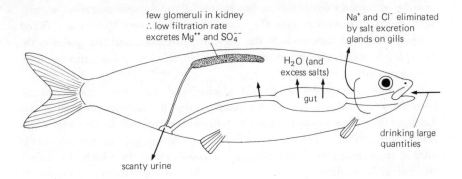

few glomeruli in kidney
∴ low filtration rate
excretes Mg^{++} and SO_4^{--}

Na⁺ and Cl⁻ eliminated
by salt excretion
glands on gills

H_2O (and
excess salts)

gut

scanty urine

drinking large
quantities

(a) A marine teleost lives in a hyperosmotic environment and must counteract osmotic desiccation.

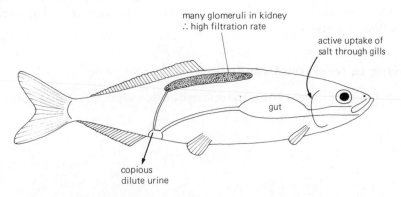

many glomeruli in kidney
∴ high filtration rate

active uptake of
salt through gills

gut

copious
dilute urine

(b) A freshwater teleost lives in a hypo-osmotic environment and must therefore counteract osmotic
flooding and the leaching of salts that accompanies the removal of excess water.

Figure 63   Diagrams summarising the ways that
(a) marine teleosts,
(b) freshwater teleosts,
overcome osmotic problems

Most brackish waters contain some marine species that can survive in
conditions of low salinity (e.g. the shore crab *Carcinus maenas*) as well as some
species that are restricted to brackish waters (e.g. the prawn *Palaemonetes varians*).
The truly brackish species have well-developed osmoregulatory powers and can
maintain a relatively constant internal osmotic concentration over a very wide
range of external salinities, from 0.5 to 100 per cent seawater. Many of the
marine species also regulate, but they tend to allow their body fluid concentration to fall, with that of the external medium, as far as is safely possible before
initiating regulatory mechanisms. They thereby reduce the amount of energy
that has to be expended in osmotic and ionic regulation. Even so, these animals
are generally less tolerant of low salinities than are brackish species. A few

'marine species do not regulate, but instead allow the concentration of their body fluids to fluctuate with the external salinity. Such species are called *osmoconformers* and they include the lugworm, *Arenicola*, and the spider crab, *Maia*. Understandably osmoconformers are less tolerant of low salinities than osmoregulators.

If animals are exposed to different salinities and the osmotic pressure of the body fluid is measured and then plotted against the osmotic pressure of the medium, the differing osmoregulatory abilities of the animals are revealed in the shapes of the curves so produced (see Figure 64). An animal like *Arenicola* that is unable to osmoregulate will produce a linear curve in which the blood concentration is directly proportional to that of the external medium. If extrapolated back, such a curve will pass through zero, although the animal will die before this point is reached. The more pronounced the deviation from a linear curve, the greater is the ability of the animal to osmoregulate.

Aquatic animals that can only live in a narrow range of salinities are described as *stenohaline*, while those that can survive in a wide range of salinities are described as *euryhaline*.

Living in terrestrial conditions

Terrestrial animals must take in water to replace that which they are continually

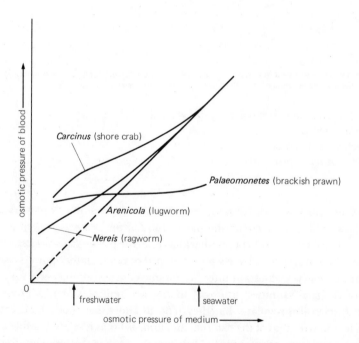

Figure 64   Graphs showing the relationship between the osmotic pressure of the blood and the osmotic pressure of the environment. (For explanation, see text.)

losing, in eliminating wastes, and by evaporation from the respiratory tract and body surface. In addition, water loss is reduced by impermeable body coverings (which restrict evaporative water loss), decreased glomerular filtration (in vertebrates), and reabsorption of water from the urine. The latter is particularly well developed in birds and mammals. These animals can produce urine that is more concentrated than their body fluids (*hypertonic* urine).

Most animals can also reabsorb water in other parts of the body, for example the rectal gland in insects and the large intestine in mammals. Finally, as already discussed, ureotelism and uricotelism contribute to water conservation in terrestrial animals.

Excretory organs

Most metazoans possess excretory organs that eliminate a watery fluid, usually called urine. These include the nephridia of annelids and flatworms, the antennary glands of crustacea, the Malpighian tubules of insects (see Figure 65), and the kidneys of molluscs and vertebrates. As mentioned earlier, these organs are not solely concerned with nitrogenous excretion, but also play a vital role in osmotic and ionic regulation. Indeed, most excretory organs are believed to have evolved primarily as a means of regulating ion and water levels; their role in nitrogen excretion seems to have been a relatively late development in the evolutionary process.

The mammalian kidney (see Figure 66)
This organ contains numerous excretory tubules or *nephrons* (see Figure 66(b)); each human kidney is estimated to contain around one million tubules. The kidneys receive more blood per unit body weight than any other organ. The high hydrostatic pressure of the blood in the *glomerulus* forces water, ions and small molecules such as glucose, amino acids and urea, through the wall of the capillary into the *Bowman's capsule*, a process known as *ultrafiltration*. The filtrate that passes into the tubule initially has a composition like that of plasma, but lacking the larger molecules. As the filtrate passes along the tubule many of the useful constituents are reabsorbed into the capillary network that surrounds the tubule. In man, the glomeruli yield about 180 litres of filtrate per day, of which about 178.5 litres are reabsorbed. It appears that glucose and amino acids are reabsorbed in the *first (proximal) convoluted tubule*, and ions are reabsorbed mainly in the *second (distal) convoluted tubule*; water is reabsorbed in both regions. This water movement is thought to depend in part upon osmosis; the proteins in the plasma create an osmotic gradient between the plasma and the filtrate. Active transport is believed to be involved in the reabsorption of glucose and many ions, and certainly, reabsorption of these substances can be reduced by the application of a respiratory-inhibitor such as cyanide. The presence of numerous mito-chondria in the epithelial cells of the tubule (Figure 66(c)) also lends support to this view, as they would be needed to provide energy for the transport process. Any remaining wastes in the plasma are apparently secreted into the second convoluted region of the tubule.

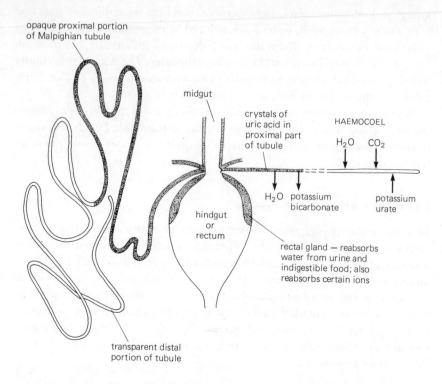

opaque proximal portion
of Malpighian tubule

midgut

crystals of
uric acid in
proximal part
of tubule

HAEMOCOEL

H_2O CO_2

H_2O potassium
bicarbonate

potassium
urate

hindgut
or
rectum

rectal gland — reabsorbs
water from urine and
indigestible food; also
reabsorbs certain ions

transparent distal
portion of tubule

Figure 65 Diagram summarising the function of the Malpighian tubules in *Rhodnius*, a blood sucking bug (the essential details of tubule function are believed to be the same in other insects).
Only one of the four Malpighian tubules is shown in full. They lie bathed in haemolymph, and open into the junction of the midgut and the rectum. Potassium urate, produced by the tissues, is actively taken up into the tubules where it reacts with water and carbon dioxide to form potassium bicarbonate and uric acid. The former passes back into the haemolymph, while the latter moves along towards the gut, apparently assisted by writhing movements of the tubules (these have spirally arranged muscle in their walls). Water is actively reabsorbed into the haemolymph, so that the proximal part of the tubule is filled with crystals of uric acid. These pass into the gut to be eliminated with the indigestible food material, after further water has been reabsorbed by the rectal gland.

The *loop of Henlé*, a structure found only in birds and mammals, enables these animals to reabsorb very large quantities of water from the filtrate, resulting in urine that is hypertonic to the blood. Birds can concentrate the urine to twice the plasma concentration, while some mammals can produce urine that is twenty-five times more concentrated than the plasma. Animals that live in dry habitats, such as deserts, tend to produce the most concentrated urine and have relatively long loops of Henlé.

Sodium is moved actively out of the ascending limb of the loop, and into the descending limb (see Figure 67). This means that, at any given level in

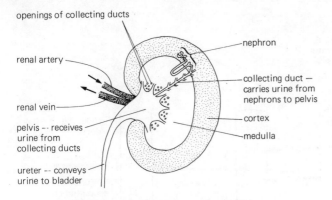

openings of collecting ducts

renal artery

renal vein

pelvis -- receives urine from collecting ducts

ureter -- conveys urine to bladder

nephron

collecting duct — carries urine from nephrons to pelvis

cortex

medulla

(a) **Diagrammatic vertical section through kidney —**
the collecting duct and nephron are not drawn to scale;
the kidney can contain several million nephrons.

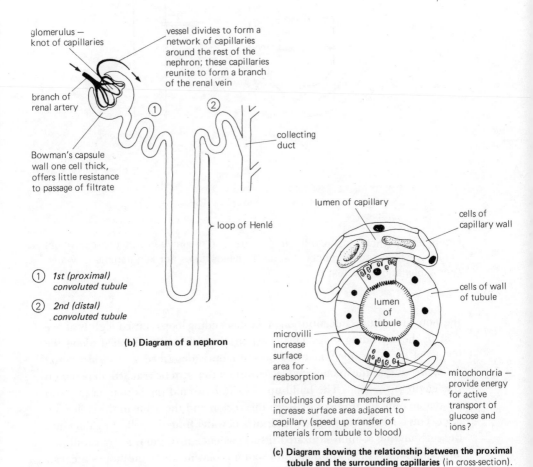

glomerulus — knot of capillaries

vessel divides to form a network of capillaries around the rest of the nephron; these capillaries reunite to form a branch of the renal vein

branch of renal artery

Bowman's capsule wall one cell thick, offers little resistance to passage of filtrate

collecting duct

loop of Henlé

① 1st (proximal) convoluted tubule

② 2nd (distal) convoluted tubule

(b) **Diagram of a nephron**

lumen of capillary

cells of capillary wall

cells of wall of tubule

lumen of tubule

microvilli increase surface area for reabsorption

mitochondria — provide energy for active transport of glucose and ions?

infoldings of plasma membrane -- increase surface area adjacent to capillary (speed up transfer of materials from tubule to blood)

(c) **Diagram showing the relationship between the proximal**
tubule and the surrounding capillaries (in cross-section).
Not all cells are shown in detail.

Figure 66   Structure of the mammalian kidney

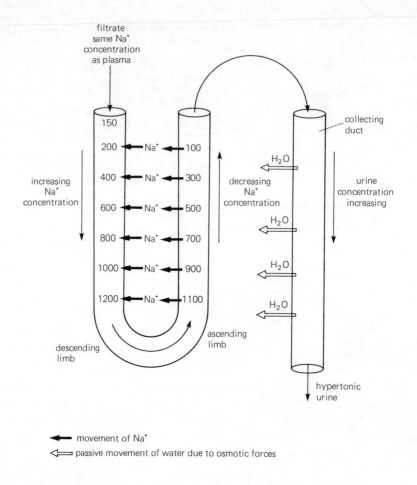

filtrate
same Na⁺
concentration
as plasma

collecting
duct

urine
concentration
increasing

decreasing
Na⁺
concentration

increasing
Na⁺
concentration

descending
limb

ascending
limb

hypertonic
urine

← movement of Na⁺
⇐ passive movement of water due to osmotic forces

Figure 67   Diagram to show the role of the loop of Henlé in water reabsorption. Figures refer to sodium concentration in milliosmoles per kilogramme of water. (For explanation, see text.)

the loop, the sodium concentration in the descending loop is raised slightly above that in the ascending loop. This concentrating effect is multiplied along the length of the loop (for which reason the loop is described as a *counter-current multiplier*) so that the maximum concentration that can be reached, depends on the length of the loop. The build-up of sodium around the bottom of the loop creates an osmotic gradient between this region and the urine in the collecting duct. This leads to the osmotic withdrawal of water from the collecting duct into the surrounding sodium-saturated tissues, whence it is removed by capillaries and lymphatic vessels. The higher the sodium concentration, the more water can be withdrawn from the urine – hence the correlation between the length of the loop and the concentration of the urine.

Hormonal control of water balance

Several different hormones help to control the body's water content. One of the most important is *vasopressin*, a hormone produced in the hypothalamus and released by the neurohypophysical region of the pituitary gland (see p. 193). Vasopressin increases the permeability of the renal tubules and collecting ducts, thus allowing increased reabsorption of water. Because it decreases urine flow vasopressin is also called anti-diuretic hormone (ADH); diuresis is the production of copious urine. Osmoregulators in the hypothalamus, that respond to changes in the osmotic concentration of the blood, regulate the secretion of vasopressin so that urine output can be altered to compensate for changes in the water concentration of the blood (see diagram below).

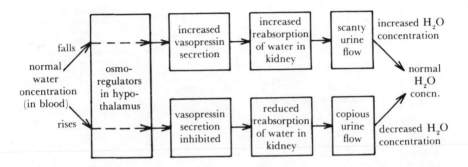

The level of sodium in the blood also affects water reabsorption. Reduced blood sodium causes the kidney to secrete a hormone, *renin*, which converts an inactive substance in the blood, known as *angiotensinogen*, into a hormone *angiotensin*. This hormone acts on the adrenal cortex, causing it to release the hormone *aldosterone*, which stimulates the reabsorption of sodium in the kidney. This creates an osmotic effect that favours water retention. Angiotensin is also called the 'thirst' hormone because it apparently stimulates the desire to drink.

OSMOREGULATION IN PLANTS

Transpiration creates special difficulties for plants living in habitats such as deserts where water is not readily available. Some desert plants avoid adverse conditions by completing their life cycle during the short rainy season, and passing the rest of the year as fruits or seeds that lie dormant in the soil. Some species take as little as ten days between germination and seed production. Other plants survive the dry months as underground perennating organs (bulbs, corms, tubers or fleshy roots).

Another group of plants have developed adaptations which enable them to resist drought conditions, rather than avoid them. Such plants are called *xerophytes*. Some xerophytic adaptations are listed overleaf and illustrated in Figure 68.

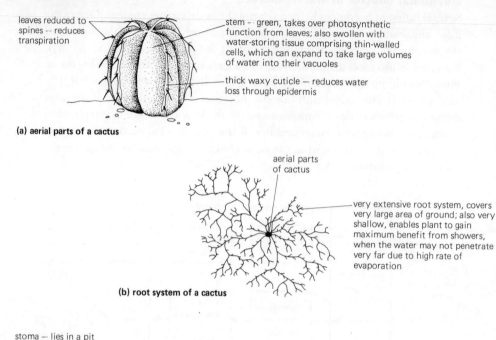

(a) aerial parts of a cactus

leaves reduced to spines -- reduces transpiration

stem – green, takes over photosynthetic function from leaves; also swollen with water-storing tissue comprising thin-walled cells, which can expand to take large volumes of water into their vacuoles

thick waxy cuticle — reduces water loss through epidermis

aerial parts of cactus

very extensive root system, covers very large area of ground; also very shallow, enables plant to gain maximum benefit from showers, when the water may not penetrate very far due to high rate of evaporation

(b) root system of a cactus

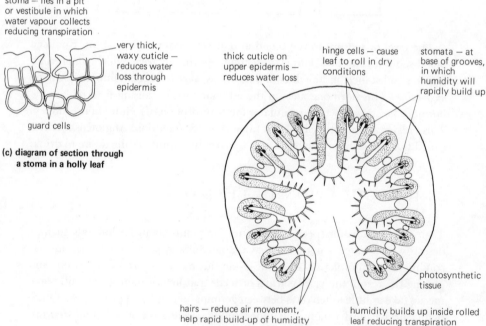

stoma — lies in a pit or vestibule in which water vapour collects reducing transpiration

very thick, waxy cuticle — reduces water loss through epidermis

guard cells

(c) diagram of section through a stoma in a holly leaf

thick cuticle on upper epidermis — reduces water loss

hinge cells — cause leaf to roll in dry conditions

stomata — at base of grooves, in which humidity will rapidly build up

photosynthetic tissue

hairs — reduce air movement, help rapid build-up of humidity

humidity builds up inside rolled leaf reducing transpiration

(d) diagram of transverse section of leaf of Marram grass (*Ammophila*)

Figure 68   Some xerophytic adaptations

1 The possession of a very extensive, shallow root system, and/or deep, 'water-seeking' roots (these may be up to fifteen metres long) to increase water uptake.

2 The presence of special water-storage tissues. Where these make up a large part of the plant, the plants are described as *succulents*.

3 The presence of one or more of the following *transpiration checks* (adaptations that reduce transpiration):– reduced leaf surface area, a thick cuticle, stomata sunk in pits or grooves, and leaves rolled with the stomata on the inside. It is uncertain whether all these adaptations do actually reduce transpiration; for when water is plentiful, many xerophytes transpire as fast as plants without such devices.

Similar adaptations are encountered in plants that inhabit salt marshes. These plants are subjected to *physiological drought* because, although water is present in the habitat, it is not readily available. The high salinity of the water surrounding the plants makes it difficult for them to take in water by osmosis. Plants adapted to life in saline conditions are called *halophytes*.

Plants in temperate regions may be subjected to physiological drought in the winter, if the water in the soil freezes. Many herbaceous plants avoid winter conditions as seeds or perennating organs, while deciduous trees and shrubs shed their leaves (which stops transpiration) and conifers reduce transpiration by adaptations that include reduced leaf surface area and the presence of a thick cuticle on the leaves.

QUESTIONS

1 By reference to named examples, distinguish between the following pairs of terms;
   (a) euryhaline and stenohaline,
   (b) osmoregulator and osmoconformer.

2 Suggest reasons why plants generally produce less excretory material than animals.

3 Explain the following observations as fully as possible:
   (a) succulent plants can be found in both deserts and salt marshes;
   (b) marine teleosts (bony fish) excrete large quantities of ions, especially Na^+, Cl^-, Mg^{++}, and SO_4^{--};
   (c) animals that live in dry habitats tend to have much longer loops of Henlé than animals that live in habitats where water is freely available;
   (d) eating a very salty meal leads to reduced urine output.

11 Coordination

When prodded or exposed to other unfavourable circumstances, most animals respond by moving away or exhibiting aggression. This ability to respond to changes in the environment, known as *irritability* or *sensitivity*, is characteristic of all living organisms. Irritability in plants is less easy to demonstrate, as changes in the environment generally evoke rather slow responses, most frequently expressed as changes in the direction of growth. Plant responses are discussed in detail in chapter 13.

The generally faster responses of animals result from the need to move about seeking food. Moving through the environment necessitates a system for the rapid coordination of movements, as well as a means of detecting the continual changes which the animal will be subjected to as a result of its movement.

Animals are able to respond to changes in their internal environment (inside their bodies) as well as changes in the external environment. Such responses form an integral part of homeostasis.

Any change in the environment which evokes a response on the part of an organism is called a *stimulus*. Light, gravity, temperature, pressure, and various chemical substances are the main types of stimulus to which organisms respond.

In order to respond to a stimulus an organism must possess:

receptors– to detect the stimulus, e.g. eyes, muscle stretch receptors,
effectors– to bring about the response, e.g. muscles, glands,
a coordinating system – to link together receptors and effectors.

In animals coordination is brought about by the *nervous system*, or by chemical messengers called *hormones*, or by nerves and hormones working together.

NERVOUS COORDINATION

As we shall discover in the course of this chapter, the nervous system does not simply provide a pathway for the passage of information from the receptors to the effectors. It also filters out non-essential information, draws together information from different receptors, determines and puts into effect the appropriate response, and, in more advanced nervous systems, stores information and retrieves this stored information when required to play a part in the 'decision-making' process.

The main parts of the vertebrate nervous system are as follows:

The *central nervous system* (CNS) – comprising the brain and spinal cord;
Peripheral nerves – cable-like structures that pass from the CNS to all parts of the body;
Receptors – (see chapter 12).

The organisation of the nervous system is examined later in this chapter. The nervous system is composed of *neuron(e)s*; cells specialised to convey information in the form of nerve impulses. A complex nervous system contains an immense number of neurons. The human cortex alone contains around 10^9 cells. There are many different kinds of neuron, each adapted for different functions (see Figure 69). Three important types are:

(i) *sensory* or *afferent neurons* – these convey impulses from receptors to the central nervous system;

(ii) *motor* or *efferent neurons* – these convey information from the CNS to effectors;

(iii) *association neurons* or *inter-neurons* – these form part of the CNS and link sensory and motor neurons.

All neurons share certain features. These are illustrated in the diagram of a vertebrate motor neuron (see **Figure 69(d)**). The nucleus is contained in an expanded portion of the cytoplasm called the cell body or *soma*. A number of thin cytoplasmic *fibres* extend out from the soma. Two types of fibre may be distinguished, *axons* and *dendrites*. Axons are usually long (in large animals they may be several metres long), and rarely branch, except at their termination. Dendrites are shorter (they rarely exceed one millimetre) and much-branched. Neurons of primitive invertebrates usually have several axons, and are called *multipolar* neurons, while those of higher invertebrates and vertebrates generally have only one axon, and are described as *monopolar*.

The soma is concerned with controlling and maintaining the cell and its activities, and, with the dendrites, serves as the main receiving area for the input of impulses from other neurons. The axons are the main pathways for the conduction of impulses away from the soma.

In most animals, the neurons are surrounded by non-nervous *glial cells* which may form sheath-like wrappings around axons. The most common type of axon covering in vertebrates is the *myelin sheath*. In this sheath the glial cells, known as *Schwann cells*, are wrapped around the axon so tightly that there is no cytoplasm between the layers of membrane (see **Figure 69(d)**). A single Schwann cell forms the wrapping for up to two millimetres of axon. The gap between adjacent Schwann cells, where the axon is exposed, is called the *node of Ranvier*. The function of the myelin sheath is not completely understood. As we shall see later, it increases the speed of nerve impulse conduction; it may also act as an insulating layer and help to maintain the axon.

Many hundreds, or even thousands, of axons together with their associated glial cells are surrounded by a common, connective tissue sheath to form the structure known as a *nerve*. Nerves themselves do not contain cell bodies; these are restricted to the CNS, to swellings of nerves called *ganglia*, and to receptors.

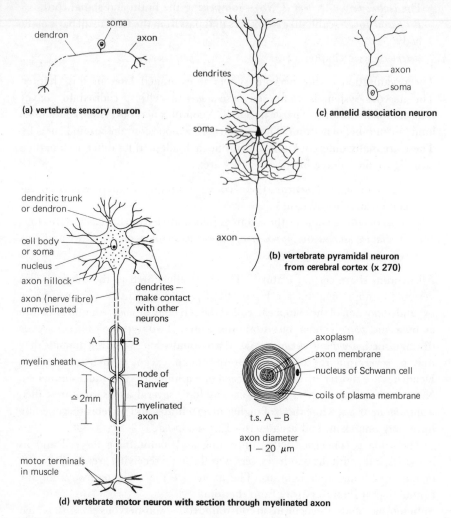

(a) vertebrate sensory neuron

soma
dendron
axon

dendrites

soma

(c) annelid association neuron

axon
soma

dendritic trunk
or dendron

cell body
or soma

nucleus

axon hillock

axon (nerve fibre)
unmyelinated

dendrites —
make contact
with other
neurons

A — B

myelin sheath

node of
Ranvier

≃ 2mm

myelinated
axon

motor terminals
in muscle

axon

(b) vertebrate pyramidal neuron
from cerebral cortex (x 270)

axoplasm

axon membrane

nucleus of Schwann cell

coils of plasma membrane

t.s. A — B

axon diameter
1 — 20 μm

(d) vertebrate motor neuron with section through myelinated axon

Figure 69 (a) – (d)   Diagrams of different neurons

Nerve impulse conduction

The conduction of a nerve impulse along a neuron is accompanied by chemical and electrical changes at the neuron membrane. When at rest, that is not conducting a nerve impulse, the neuron membrane is polarised; the outside is positively charged and the inside is negatively charged. This polarisation creates a potential difference or voltage drop across the membrane. This varies in magnitude between 30 and 100 millivolts (mV) according to the type of neuron, and to the species. Because this potential difference is characteristic of the nerve at rest it is known as the *resting potential*. In fact, membrane potentials are not restricted to neurons. Most cells including those of plants, maintain a membrane potential of about 10 mV.

The resting potential results from the unequal distribution of ions on the two sides of the membrane. Positively charged sodium ions are about ten times more concentrated outside the membrane than they are inside, due to the activity of a *sodium pump* which transports sodium out of the cell against the concentration gradient. This pump is thought to involve some sort of carrier molecule which transports the ion through the membrane. The operation of the pump requires the expenditure of energy and seems to be dependent on the availability of ATP. Sodium cannot diffuse back into the cell once it has been pumped out because the membrane is relatively impermeable to these ions. The presence of large, negatively charged organic molecules in the cytoplasm of the neuron is largely responsible for the negative charge on the inside of the membrane.

If the situation described above represented the complete picture, the membrane potential would be very much higher than it is. In fact, the membrane potential is reduced by the unequal distribution of potassium ions. These positively charged ions (cations) are more concentrated inside the membrane. It may be that they are moved into the cell by the operation of a potassium pump. There is some evidence for the existence of such a pump, possibly linked to the sodium pump. They may equally well be drawn into the cell by electrostatic attraction for the organic anions (anion = a negatively charged ion). The situation in an axon at rest is illustrated below.

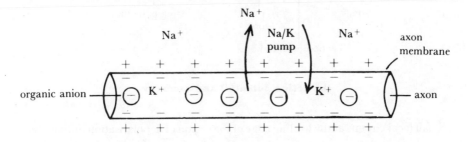

the resting potential

When a nerve impulse passes, it causes the resting potential to be momentarily abolished, *depolarised*, and in some cases reversed, so that the outside becomes negatively charged and the inside positively charged. The change in membrane potential that accompanies the nerve impulses is known as the *action potential*.

Depolarisation is caused by the membrane becoming permeable to sodium ions, thus allowing these ions to flood into the cell along their concentration gradient. The influx of cations first depolarises and then reverses the polarity across the membrane. The mechanism responsible for the change in membrane polarity is not known. The stopping of the sodium pump is thought to contribute to the influx of sodium.

For about five milliseconds after the onset of sodium inflow the membrane becomes relatively impermeable to potassium ions. After this period the membrane becomes permeable to potassium again and the ions start to flood out of the cell along their concentration gradient. This outflow of cations opposes the change in membrane potential brought about by sodium inflow, and so initiates the restoration of the resting potential. This *recovery period* is completed when the membrane once again becomes impermeable to sodium ions, and the sodium pump starts to operate, restoring the external sodium concentration to its resting level. The events that accompany the action potential and recovery are summarised below.

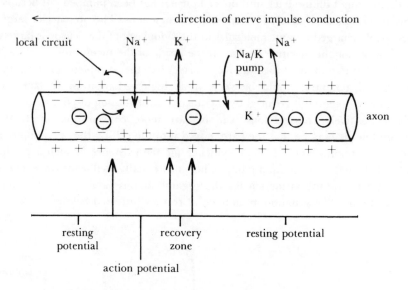

the action potential and recovery

Small local circuits at the leading edge of the region of depolarisation initiate the depolarisation of the next part of the axon membrane. In this way the action potential travels along the axon membrane. The nerve impulse is thus *self-propagating*, and can be visualised as a series of local action potentials arising in turn along the length of the axon, or as a wave of depolarisation passing along the axon.

Recording membrane potentials
Membrane potentials can be recorded by means of micro-electrodes connected to a cathode ray oscilloscope. This is essentially a television screen on which the signal from the electrodes is displayed as a continuous line of light. Any change in the membrane potential causes a horizontal deflection of the line. Because of the small size of the potentials, the signal is passed through an amplifier on its way to the oscilloscope.

When both recording electrodes are in the fluid that bathes the neuron under investigation, there is no potential difference between them, and the line on the screen represents zero potential. If one electrode is then pushed through the membrane, the line is immediately deflected downwards (see Figure 70(a)) to

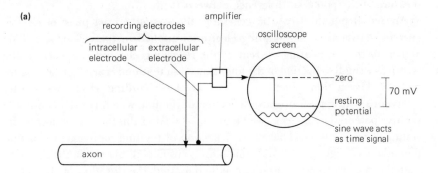

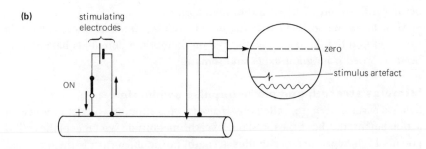

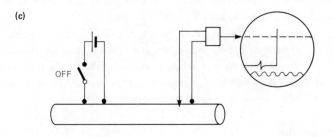

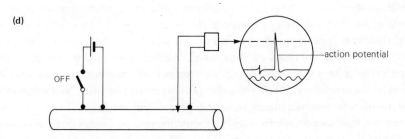

Figure 70 Recordings from a giant axon at rest and during stimulation (see text for explanation).

register an inside negative potential. The difference between the two lines is a measure of the potential difference between them.

An action potential can be generated by passing a brief pulse of electric current between two stimulating electrodes applied to the cell surface. The arrival of the stimulating current at the recording electrode appears on the screen as a small deflection of the line known as the stimulus artefact (see Figure 70(b)). The action potential arrives at the recording electrodes shortly afterwards, causing an upward deflection of the line which registers an inside positive potential at its peak (see Figure 70(c)). After this the line returns to the resting potential level. The whole deflection of the line represents the action potential (see Figure 70(d)). A time signal is usually displayed on the screen so that the speed of nerve impulse conduction, and the duration of the action potential can be calculated. The traces on the oscilloscope screen can be permanently recorded by means of photographs.

Most fibres are so small that the use of even the smallest micro-electrodes causes substantial damage. For this reason membrane potentials have mostly been recorded from giant axons and somata.

Stimulus strength and nerve impulse conduction

Below a certain strength, called the *threshold level*, a stimulus will not produce an action potential. Above the threshold level the magnitude (voltage) of the action potential is independent of stimulus strength, i.e. double or triple the threshold level of stimulus will elicit the same action potential as the threshold level. Because the stimulus either causes a full strength action potential or none at all, the action potential is described as an *all-or-nothing response*.

Information about stimulus strength is conveyed to the CNS by the frequency of the nerve impulses generated in response to the stimulus. Increased stimulus strength results in increased frequency of action potentials. This is illustrated in Figure 71 where the effects of increasing pressure on the frequency of action potentials generated in a human skin pressure receptor are shown.

The refractory period

After an action potential has been initiated, a second response cannot be elicited at the same site within a period of about one millisecond, no matter how strong the stimulus. This period is called the *absolute refractory period*. This is followed by a slightly longer, *relative refractory period*, during which a second action potential (often smaller than normal) can be evoked, but only if a stimulus stronger than the threshold level is applied. The refractory period represents the time that it takes for the membrane to recover and regain its resting potential. Refractoriness ensures that action potentials remain separate and do not overlap. It also imposes restrictions on the frequency at which action potentials can pass along an axon. The theoretical maximum in mammalian nerves is about 1000 impulses per second. This frequency has been recorded from auditory nerves, but, in most other nerves, frequencies are rarely higher than 200 per second.

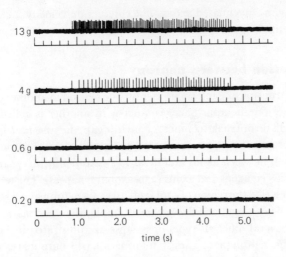

Figure 71 Impulses recorded from a pressure receptor on the human hand. A rod of one millimetre diameter was pressed onto the skin with the force indicated on each record. (From Hensel and Bowman, *Journal of Neurophysiology*, 23 (1960).)

The speed of nerve impulse conduction

Conduction velocity varies according to the type of neuron. The larger the axon diameter, the faster the conduction velocity. Many invertebrates possess giant axons, with diameters approaching one millimetre, to mediate their fast escape responses (see chapter 15), where rapid conduction is obviously of paramount importance. The difference in conduction velocity between normal fibres and giant fibres in earthworm, squid and cockroach are shown below.

	Conduction velocity	metres per second
	ordinary motor fibre	giant fibre
Earthworm	0.6	30
Squid	4	35
Cockroach	2	10

In vertebrates, the myelin sheath increases conduction velocity. Essentially what happens is that an action potential arriving at one node of Ranvier sets up an electric current between this node and an adjacent node which generates an action potential at the second node. This happens virtually instantaneously, so that the action potential appears to jump from one node to the next. Hence, the name of this type of conduction – *saltatory conduction*, from the Latin, 'saltare', to jump. Conduction velocities of around one hundred metres per second have been recorded from some myelinated axons. The conduction velocity, like the size of the action potential, is independent of stimulus strength.

Communication between neurons

Some means of transmitting information from one neuron to another is essential. The point where one neuron makes contact with another is called a *synapse*. Actually, the cells do not make contact – a narrow gap, the *synaptic cleft*, separates the two membranes. Synapses can occur between axons and somata (axo-somatal synapse), between axons and dendrites (axo-dendritic synapses), and, more rarely, between axons and axons (axo-axonal synapses). The term synapse is also used to describe the region of contact between a neuron and a sensory cell, and between a neuron and an effector, for example, the *nerve/muscle (neuromuscular) junction*. Several different types of synapse are illustrated in Figure 72.

The part of the neuron that passes on information (the output area of the cell) is called the *pre-synaptic element*, and the part that receives information (the input area) is called the *post-synaptic area*. Usually the pre-synaptic elements form swellings called *synaptic knobs* (see Figure 72(b)). Neurons with profusely branched dendritic processes, such as are found in the cerebral cortex of mammalian brains (see Figure 69(b)), make synaptic contact with many hundreds or thousands of other neurons.

Synaptic transmission

An action potential arriving at a synapse can generate an action potential in the post synaptic neuron in one of two ways.

(i) *Electrical transmission* The depolarisation that constitutes the nerve impulse can set up a current across the synapse. This current depolarises the post synaptic membrane and in so doing triggers an action potential in the post synaptic neuron. This occurs at special synapses, called *tight junctions* because the synaptic cleft is extremely narrow, usually less than ten nanometres across. Such junctions occur in coelenterate nerve nets, and in parts of the central nervous systems of more advanced animals, including vertebrates.

(ii) *Chemical transmission* The majority of synapses are thought to involve chemical *transmitter substances*. Such synapses have a much wider synaptic cleft than electrically transmitting synapses, usually between fifteen and sixty nanometres across. Their synaptic knobs contain numerous *synaptic vesicles* believed to contain the chemical transmitter substance (see Figure 72(b) and (c)). Little is known about the manufacture of these substances but it is thought that either they, or the materials from which they are made, are produced in the somata and then transported to the pre-synaptic terminals.

When an action potential arrives at a synaptic knob, it apparently causes the synaptic vesicles to move to the pre-synaptic membrane and there release the transmitter substance into the synaptic cleft. The transmitter then diffuses across the cleft and combines with special *receptor sites* on the post synaptic membrane. The receptor sites are envisaged as large molecules which combine with the

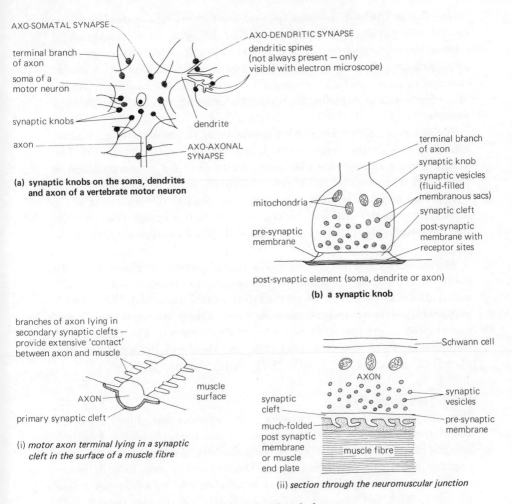

(a) synaptic knobs on the soma, dendrites and axon of a vertebrate motor neuron

(b) a synaptic knob

(i) *motor axon terminal lying in a synaptic cleft in the surface of a muscle fibre*

(ii) *section through the neuromuscular junction*

(c) neuromuscular junction of a frog

Figure 72 (a) – (c)   Diagrams of synapses

transmitter molecules by virtue of their complementary surfaces. The combination of transmitter and receptor is believed to alter the permeability of the post synaptic membrane to certain ions, possibly by enlarging channels in the membrane through which the ions pass. The subsequent movement of ions depolarises the membrane. This localised depolarisation is called the *excitatory post synaptic potential* (EPSP). If the EPSP reaches a certain level (its threshold level), it will initiate an action potential in the post synaptic neuron.

Because the receptor sites occur on only one side of the synaptic cleft, chemically transmitting synapses impose a *one-way system* on the passage of nerve impulses through the nervous system. Many different substances function as synaptic transmitters. The best known are acetylcholine and noradrenalin.

Acetylcholine (ACh) is released by vertebrate motor and parasympathetic neurons (see p. 178); such neurons are called *cholinergic neurons*. *Noradrenalin* is released by vertebrate sympathetic neurons (see p. 178). Such neurons are called *adrenergic neurons*. Noradrenalin and the hormone adrenalin have a very similar chemical structure, and it is therefore not surprising that adrenalin exerts many of its effects (such as increasing heart rate) by initiating impulses in sympathetic neurons.

The receptor sites do not remain permanently combined with transmitter substance; enzymes present in the synaptic cleft break down the transmitter. The action of these enzymes frees the receptors to receive a further emission of transmitter when another action potential arrives at the synaptic knob.

Repeated impulses arriving at a synapse can lead to the exhaustion of the supply of transmitter substance, in which case no further impulses can cross the synapse until the supply has been replenished. This phenomenon is called *synaptic fatigue*.

The neuromuscular junction is a special type of synapse (see Figure 72(c)). In many vertebrates, the membrane of the muscle fibre is thickened and much folded to form an *end-plate*, to which the axon terminal is attached. The folding is presumably a device to increase the surface area of the post synaptic membrane, and so speed up the action of transmitter substance upon it. The transmitter at neuromuscular junctions is acetylcholine, and the depolarisation of the end-plate is called the *end-plate potential* (EPP) rather than the EPSP.

Inhibitory synapses

Not all synapses are of the *excitatory* type just described. Many release a transmitter that combines with the receptor to alter the permeability of the post synaptic membrane in such a way that the inside of the membrane becomes more negative than usual (hyperpolarisation). This will make it more difficult for any excitatory synapses to depolarise that membrane and so initiate an action potential. Inhibitory synapses thus act as 'brakes' on the post synaptic cell, reducing the likelihood of that cell being activated by excitatory messages arriving along other channels.

The effect of drugs and poisons on synaptic transmission

Many drugs and poisons exert their effects by interfering with the mechanism of synaptic transmission. There are several different ways in which they can do this.

1 *By preventing the release of transmitter substance.* Botulinum toxin produced by the bacterium *Clostridium botulinum*, the causative agent of a mercifully rare form of food poisoning, produces paralysis by preventing the release of acetylcholine from the pre-synaptic terminals of motor neurons. This toxin is one of the most poisonous substances known to man. It has been calculated that 250 g would be sufficient to wipe out the entire world population.

2 *By preventing the transmitter from combining with the receptor.* Curare, the paralysing poison used by South American indians on their arrow tips,

has a chemical structure very like that of acetylcholine, and it competes with the transmitter for the receptor sites at neuromuscular junctions. As the combination of curare and receptor does not lead to the setting up of an end-plate potential, muscle paralysis results.

3 *By inactivating the enzyme that breaks down the transmitter.* A number of organophosphorus compounds, originally developed as nerve gases for use in wartime and now used as insecticides, inactivate the enzyme that breaks down acetylcholine (acetylcholinesterase). Such substances greatly prolong the end-plate potential and may initiate a series of action potentials in muscle fibres which give rise to uncontrollable muscle spasms.

Summation at synapses

The arrival of one action potential at a single synapse is rarely sufficient to generate an action potential in the post synaptic neuron. In general, the additive effect (*summation*) of several action potentials is required to release enough transmitter to trigger a nerve impulse; each action potential contributing to the depolarisation of the post synaptic membrane.

Temporal summation occurs when action potentials arrive at the same synapse in close enough succession to ensure that the depolarising effects of the preceding action potentials have not worn off. The EPSP can thus be built up to the level where it initiates an action potential. In such cases a nerve impulse will only be generated in the post synaptic neuron if the stimulus which initiated the nerve impulse is strong enough to produce a fairly high frequency of action potentials.

Spatial summation occurs when action potentials arriving at separate synapses on the same post synaptic neuron, between them, release enough transmitter to initiate an action potential.

Facilitation

A synapse is said to be facilitated when the arrival of one action potential, while not itself triggering an impulse, leaves a residual effect which makes it easier for subsequent action potentials to initiate an action potential in the post synaptic cell. The difference between this phenomenon and temporal summation is that the residual effect is not an electrical one. In other words, no measurable depolarisation of the post synaptic membrane persists between impulses at a facilitated synapse. Facilitation is thought to play an important part in memory and learning (see chapter 15).

The function of synapses

From this account of synaptic transmission we can deduce that synapses do not simply serve as a means of transmitting nerve impulses from one neuron to another. They can filter out weak stimuli. Some synapses will not generate an action potential in the post synaptic cell unless the action potential reaches a particular frequency (temporal summation).

Many synapses enable information from different sources to interact. For example, information from several different sources may be required to trigger a nerve impulse (spatial summation), and, in some cases, information from one source can, by activating inhibitory synapses, make it impossible, or more difficult, for information from other sources to reach its destination. This sorting out of nerve impulses which takes place at synapses is called *integration*.

NERVE PATHWAYS

Having examined the way nerve impulses are transmitted from one neuron to another, we will now consider the pathways through the nervous system taken by nerve impulses.

Most behaviour is brought about by the passage of impulses from a receptor to the CNS, and then from the CNS to an effector. The number of neurons in such a pathway varies enormously according to the number of receptors and effectors engaged in the response, and to the degree of difficulty involved in deciding the appropriate response. Where the so-called 'higher' or 'decision-making' centres of the brain are involved, the pathway tends to become very complex, and may involve many tens of thousands of neurons.

The simplest pathways are those involved in simple *reflex actions*. A reflex is defined as an unlearned, automatic response to a stimulus. Examples include the escape responses of many invertebrates, and in man, the knee jerk, the withdrawal of the hand or foot from a painful stimulus (the flexion reflex), and the control of heart and breathing rate.

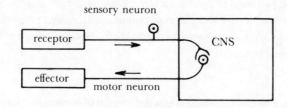

**plan of a reflex arc involving
two neurons**

The nerve pathway responsible for bringing about a reflex action is called a *reflex arc*. At its simplest, the reflex arc involves only two neurons – a sensory neuron and a motor neuron which make synaptic contact in the CNS. Nerve impulses triggered by the stimulus pass along the sensory neuron and then along the motor neuron to the effector that brings about the response. More common is the reflex arc consisting of three neurons, with an association neuron interposed between the sensory and motor neuron. This type of reflex is illustrated in Figure 73, where the events that bring about withdrawal of the hand from a painful stimulus are shown.

Actually it is doubtful whether any nerve pathway is quite as simple as those described above. Neurons in reflex arcs synapse with longitudinally-running neurons, some of which pass to the brain, and others which make synaptic

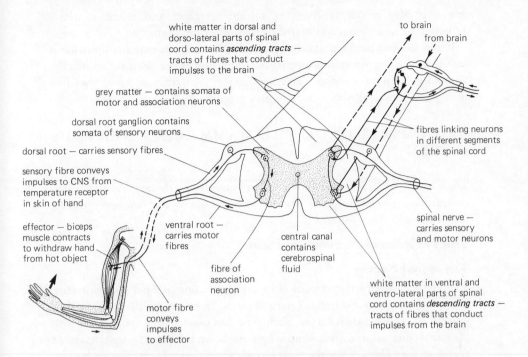

white matter in dorsal and dorso-lateral parts of spinal cord contains *ascending tracts* — tracts of fibres that conduct impulses to the brain

to brain

from brain

grey matter — contains somata of motor and association neurons

dorsal root ganglion contains somata of sensory neurons

dorsal root — carries sensory fibres

fibres linking neurons in different segments of the spinal cord

sensory fibre conveys impulses to CNS from temperature receptor in skin of hand

effector — biceps muscle contracts to withdraw hand from hot object

ventral root — carries motor fibres

central canal contains cerebrospinal fluid

spinal nerve — carries sensory and motor neurons

fibre of association neuron

white matter in ventral and ventro-lateral parts of spinal cord contains *descending tracts* — tracts of fibres that conduct impulses from the brain

motor fibre conveys impulses to effector

Figure 73   Diagram of a portion of the human spinal cord. The *right hand side* shows the way that neurons within a segment may be connected by longitudinal tracts of fibres with the brain and with neurons in other segments. The *left hand side* shows the neurons involved in the withdrawal reflex. When the temperature receptor in the skin of the hand is stimulated by a hot object, impulses pass via sensory and association neurons to a motor neuron. The motor neuron conducts impulses to the effector, the biceps muscle, which contracts withdrawing the hand from the painful stimulus.
Arrows indicate the direction of transmission of nerve impulses.

contact with neurons in other parts of the cord. If this were not so, the activities of the organism could not be coordinated. In the example shown in Figure 73, impulses pass to the cerebral cortex resulting in an awareness of the sensation in the finger (by which time the hand is already being withdrawn by virtue of the impulses conducted around the reflex arc). It is also possible to repress this reflex – by an exertion of will it is possible to touch and hold something very hot. This indicates that the motor neuron involved can receive impulses from the brain which override the reflex impulses. In addition, the biceps muscle can, of course, be operated voluntarily by impulses passing from the brain via neurons that synapse with the motor neuron that activates the muscle.

The fibres that connect the different areas of the cord with one another, and with the brain, run in ascending and descending tracts located in the white matter of the nerve cord (**Figure 73**).

More complex reflexes, such as the one controlling breathing rate, require more complex circuitry, involving several receptors and effectors, whose activities are generally coordinated by centres in the brain.

Reflex actions perform a very important function, in that they provide a means of carrying out vital protective and homeostatic reactions automatically, without involving the higher, 'decision-making' centres; in so doing, they free these centres to deal with more complex problems.

ORGANISATION OF THE MAMMALIAN NERVOUS SYSTEM

There are two principal divisions of the nervous system – the *central nervous system*, comprising the *brain* and *spinal cord*, and the *peripheral nervous system*, comprising the *cranial* and *spinal nerves*.

The Peripheral Nervous System

The Spinal Nerves

In man there are thirty one pairs of spinal nerves, one pair per body segment. They carry fibres to and from all parts of the body, except for the head which is innervated by the cranial nerves. Each nerve has two separate connections with the spinal cord, a dorsal and a ventral root. As shown in Figure 73, the dorsal root carries sensory fibres, while the ventral root carries motor fibres. The roots unite to form the spinal nerve which is a *mixed nerve*, carrying both sensory and motor fibres.

On emerging from the vertebral column, each spinal nerve divides into a number of branches or *rami*. There is generally a major dorsal ramus, which innervates the skin and muscles of the back, and a ventral ramus that innervates the skin and muscles of the ventral part of the body. In many spinal nerves, there is also a visceral ramus which innervates the internal organs (the viscera).

The Cranial Nerves

There are twelve pairs of cranial nerves in man. They arise from the ventral surface of the brain, and pass to various receptors and effectors in the head, except for the vagus, the wandering nerve, which gives off branches to the heart and gut. Some cranial nerves are mixed, while others are either sensory or motor. Information about this, and the structures served by the different cranial nerves is shown in Table 5.

The Visceral and Somatic divisions of the Peripheral Nervous System

The peripheral nervous system is divided into two functionally distinct parts, the *somatic system* and the *visceral system*. The former is chiefly concerned with detecting and responding to external stimuli, while the latter is concerned with detecting and responding to internal stimuli. Thus, the neurons involved in the flexion reflex are part of the somatic system, while those involved in the reflex control of heart rate are part of the visceral system. The structures innervated by the two systems are set out opposite.

Table 5 The cranial nerves of man. The responses, or perceptions, in which the nerves are involved are indicated in brackets

	Cranial nerve	Type of nerve, and organs innervated
I	Olfactory	sensory from olfactory organs (smell)
II	Optic	sensory from eyes (vision)
III	Oculomotor	motor to four of six eye muscles (eye movements)
IV	Trochlear	motor to eye muscle (eye movements)
V	Trigeminal	motor to jaw muscles (jaw movements) sensory from face (muscle stretch and skin receptors)
VI	Abducens	motor to eye muscle (eye movements)
VII	Facial	motor to salivary glands (salivation), and to face muscles (change of expression) sensory from tongue and palate
VIII	Acoustic	sensory from internal ear (hearing and balance)
IX	Glossopharyngeal	sensory from tongue (taste) motor to pharynx muscles (swallowing)
X	Vagus	sensory from external ear motor to heart, stomach and intestines (decreased heart rate, peristaltic movements of gut)
XI	Accessory	motor to head and neck muscles (head movements)
XII	Hypoglossal	motor to tongue and neck muscles

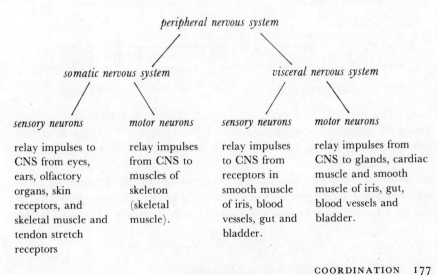

peripheral nervous system

somatic nervous system

visceral nervous system

sensory neurons

relay impulses to CNS from eyes, ears, olfactory organs, skin receptors, and skeletal muscle and tendon stretch receptors

motor neurons

relay impulses from CNS to muscles of skeleton (skeletal muscle).

sensory neurons

relay impulses to CNS from receptors in smooth muscle of iris, blood vessels, gut and bladder.

motor neurons

relay impulses from CNS to glands, cardiac muscle and smooth muscle of iris, gut, blood vessels and bladder.

Some of the visceral system's receptors are located in the brain, for example, the chemoreceptors involved in breathing control.

Effectors innervated by the visceral system are not generally under conscious control, unlike the effectors of the somatic system. Some visceral reflexes are mediated by the spinal cord alone, but the majority are controlled by centres in the medulla and hypothalamus (regions of the brain).

The entire visceral system is sometimes called the *autonomic system*, although many authors reserve this term for the efferent (motor) parts of the system alone. In the description that follows, 'autonomic' is used in the second, more restricted, sense.

The autonomic nervous system

Autonomic means 'self-governing': this refers to the negative feedback control mechanisms (p. 142) with which this system is largely concerned. The autonomic nervous system is involved in such vital reflexes as the control of heart rate and blood pressure, the peristaltic movements of the gut, and the secretion of sweat and saliva.

The autonomic system has two sub-divisions, the *sympathetic* system and the *parasympathetic* system. In both systems, impulses pass from the CNS to effectors via two motor neurons. The systems differ in the transmitter system they release from their synaptic terminals; sympathetic neurons are adrenergic while parasympathetic neurons are cholinergic. They also differ in the position of the ganglia where the two motor neurons synapse. The parasympathetic ganglia are situated on, or very near, the effectors so that the *post-ganglionic* fibres are very short, whereas the sympathetic ganglia lie close to spinal cord so that the post-ganglionic fibres are relatively long (see Figure 74). The sympathetic ganglia are linked to form two sympathetic chains that lie on either side of the spinal cord.

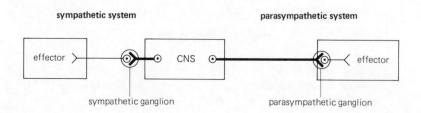

Figure 74   Diagram showing the position of the autonomic ganglia. Bold lines represent pre-ganglionic fibres; light lines, post-ganglionic fibres

Autonomic fibres pass to the effectors in the cranial or spinal nerves. Figure 75 shows the structures served by the autonomic system. As you can see, most viscera are innervated by sympathetic and parasympathetic neurons. The two

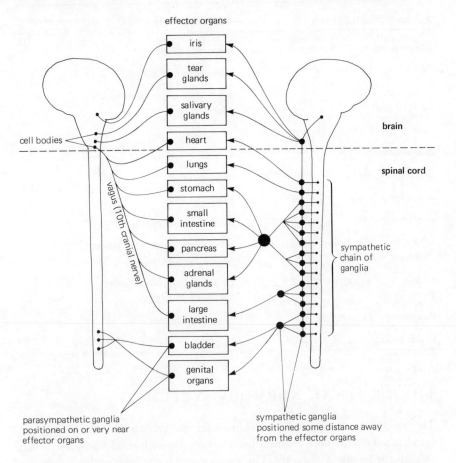

Figure 75   Diagrammatic representation of the human autonomic nervous system (one side only is shown, both systems are paired). Autonomic neurons that arise in the brain are carried to the effector organs in cranial nerves, while those that arise in the spinal cord are carried in spinal nerves.

have antagonistic or opposite effects, so that, while one nerve stimulates a particular organ, the other inhibits it. In general, the sympathetic system tends to prepare the body for strenuous activity while the parasympathetic reverses these effects. The main responses initiated by the two systems are set out in Table 6.

It is interesting to note that while most autonomic responses are involuntary, the relaxation of the anal and bladder sphincter muscles can be brought under conscious control, indicating that connections do exist between the higher, 'conscious' centres of the brain and at least some parts of the autonomic system.

COORDINATION   179

Table 6 Summary of the responses evoked by the mammalian autonomic system

Sympathetic	Parasympathetic
dilates pupil	constricts pupil
	stimulates tear gland
suppresses secretion of salivary gland	stimulates secretion of salivary gland
contracts hair erector muscles	
dilates bronchioles	constricts bronchioles
accelerates heart	slows heart
constricts arteries	dilates arteries
slows peristalsis	accelerates peristalsis
contraction of anal and bladder sphincter muscles	relaxation of anal and bladder sphincter muscles
relaxation of blood vessels (vasodilation)	contraction of blood vessels (vasoconstriction)
increases sweat secretion	
causes secretion of adrenalin	

THE CENTRAL NERVOUS SYSTEM

The central nervous system develops from an infolding of the embryonic ectoderm. This infolding forms a hollow, dorsally-positioned *neural tube* which extends the length of the body. The anterior end of the tube swells to form the brain, while the rest develops into the spinal cord. The hollow centre of the neural tube persists as the cavities or *ventricles* of the brain, and the *central canal* of the spinal cord. The ventricles and central canal are filled with *cerebro-spinal fluid*, which distributes nutrients and oxygen to the nervous tissue.

The entire CNS is covered by a system of membranes, the *meninges*. There is a tough outer membrane, the *dura mater*, and a more delicate inner membrane, the *pia mater*. Between the two is a space packed with a network of fibrous tissue, called the *arachnoid layer*. This layer is filled with cerebro-spinal fluid, and serves a cushioning, protective function, as well as nourishing the underlying nervous tissue.

The central nervous system is a coordinating centre. It receives impulses from all the body's receptors via sensory or afferent neurons, and sends impulses to all the effectors via motor or efferent neurons.

The spinal cord

The spinal cord stretches from the base of the brain to the end of the backbone. It is enclosed and protected by the vertebrae. The nerve cord is composed of white and grey matter (see Figure 73). The grey matter contains cell bodies and non-myelinated fibres. The white matter owes its lighter colour to the fatty white sheaths of myelinated fibres. Both white and grey matter include large numbers of non-nervous glial cells.

The spinal cord has two main functions: it connects the spinal nerves to the brain, and it is a coordinating centre, mediating reflexes such as the knee jerk.

The brain

Anatomy of the vertebrate brain

As the brain develops from the anterior end of the neural tube it becomes divided into three regions, forebrain, midbrain, and hindbrain. At a slightly later stage, the forebrain expands, and becomes sub-divided into endbrain and tweenbrain. The brain tissue encloses four ventricles filled with cerebro-spinal fluid. This fluid derives the nutrients and oxygen, which it distributes to the tissues of the brain and spinal cord, from two areas of vascular membrane (membranes containing a dense network of capillaries), located in the roof of the midbrain and hindbrain, and known as the *anterior choroid plexus* and the *posterior choroid plexus* respectively. Ciliated cells lining the vesicles, maintain the circulation of the fluid.

As the embryonic brain continues its development, further differentiation of regions occurs. Paired outgrowths from the endbrain, the *olfactory lobes*, receive impulses from the olfactory organs. The roof of the endbrain expands to form two *cerebral hemispheres*. The *thalamus* and *hypothalamus* develop in the floor of the tweenbrain, while the *pineal gland* arises from the roof of this region. The roof of the hindbrain expands to form the *cerebellum*, and the floor and posterior region develop into the *medulla oblongata*. The pairing of many structures imposes a bilateral symmetry on the brain.

All vertebrate brains possess the features described above and illustrated in Figure 76(a). However, the regions are not always easy to distinguish. During the evolution of the vertebrate brain different regions have come to assume special significance in different vertebrate classes, and are accordingly expanded, while the importance of others has diminished, and they are reduced in size. In the mammalian brain (Figure 76(b)), the cerebrum is enormously expanded by the development of a region called the *neopallium* (a region that first appears in the reptiles). The outer surface of the neopallium consists of a thin layer of grey matter known as the *cerebral cortex*. The latter is the dominant brain area in mammals, directing and coordinating all voluntary, and some involuntary, activities. In man, the cerebral cortex is so large that it covers many of the other brain regions.

Functions of the brain

In order to gain a more than superficial idea of how the brain works, we must do more than simply consider its anatomy, and then ascribe functions to each region. The 'wiring' of the brain should also be examined, to see how the brain

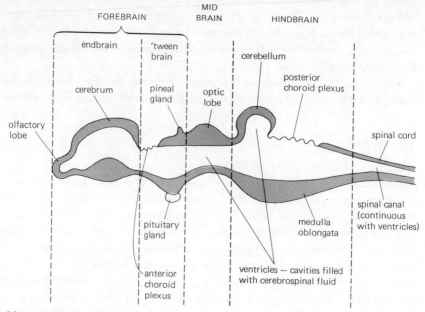

(a) l.s. generalised vertebrate brain

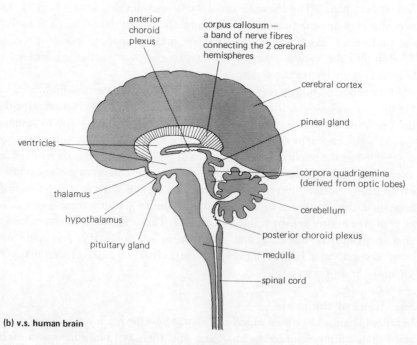

(b) v.s. human brain

Figure 76   Vertical sections through vertebrate brains.

regions are connected with one another, and with other parts of the nervous system.

The brain, like the spinal cord, is composed of white and grey matter. The area of grey matter, known as *centres* or *nuclei*, comprise groups of cell bodies making contact with incoming or outgoing, fibres, and with one another. These centres range in size from tiny clusters of cells, visible only with the microscope, to the whole of the cerebral cortex, which contains some 10^9 cells.

The white matter consists of bundles or tracts of fibres that link the centres with one another, and with the body's effectors and receptors. A number of tracts, called *commissures*, connect the two sides of the brain. The *corpus callosum* is one such tract, that connects the two cerebral hemispheres. Figure 77 shows the main centres and tracts in the mammalian brain. This figure should be studied in conjunction with the description of brain regions and their functions that follows.

Investigating brain function

A variety of techniques are used to investigate the functions of the different brain regions. Removal of parts of the brain, and the creation of lesions (cuts), have provided a lot of useful information. Such methods are not normally applied in investigations of the human brain, but similar information has been obtained by observing the effects of accidental brain damage, and disease of brain regions.

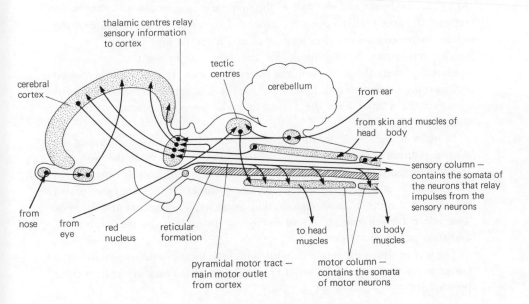

Figure 77 Simplified 'wiring' diagram of the mammalian brain. Shaded areas represent centres. To avoid confusion the connections of the cerebellum and the reticular formation are not shown. The cerebellum receives fibres from the tectic centres, the ear, and the skin and muscle receptors. Fibres pass from the cerebellum to the cerebral cortex (via the red nucleus) and to the motor column. The reticular formation receives an input from sensors in all parts of the body. Fibres pass from the reticular formation to the cerebral cortex.

Stimulating electrodes applied to different areas of the brain can be used to evoke observable responses, or to create sensations. Such experiments have been carried out on human volunteers during brain operations. This type of operation can be carried out under local anaesthetic, so that the patients can report back on any sensations they experience. Recording electrodes can also be inserted into the brain to find out which areas of the brain show a change in their electrical activity when a particular stimulus is applied, or when a particular activity is carried out.

Brain regions and their functions in a mammal

The hindbrain

Medulla oblongata

This region connects the spinal cord with the rest of the brain and as might be expected, contains tracts of fibres passing to the brain from the nerve cord, and vice versa. It also contains the cell bodies of the last five cranial nerves, and a number of important reflex centres. The latter control the regulation of heart beat, blood pressure (p. 125), ventilation rate (p. 33) swallowing, salivation, vomiting, sneezing and coughing.

Cerebellum

As in the cerebrum and the roof of the midbrain, and unlike all other brain regions, the grey matter lies on the surface of the cerebellum. The underlying white matter consists of fibres leading to and from the grey matter.

The cerebellum is responsible for the reflex adjustment of posture. It continually alters the tensions in the skeletal muscles. It also coordinates and refines voluntary movements initiated by the cerebral cortex. If the cerebellum is removed the animal loses the ability to make smooth, accurate, voluntary movements.

In order to move a limb, the brain must have information concerning the current position of the limb, the state of tension of the muscles in the limb, and the general position of the body and its relation to the outside world. This information is relayed to the cerebellum along fibres that pass from the tension receptors in the muscles and tendons, skin receptors, the inner ear and the eyes. This information is assembled and sorted out (integrated) by the cerebellum, and then passed to the cortex.

The way in which the cerebellum influences the motor impulses sent from the cortex to the skeletal muscles is not known for certain. There are at least three possibilities.

(i) It may receive a sensory input from the muscles that have been activated by the cortex, and then send out its own independent, modulating impulses to refine the movement.

(ii) Motor signals originating in the cortex may go to the cerebellum, at the same time as other motor signals are sent to the muscles, so that the cerebellum sends impulses which can add to, and modulate those from the cortex.

(iii) The cerebellum integrates information from muscles, ears and eyes, as described above, and relays the integrated information to the cortex, so that the motor impulses from that region can be sent out in a pre-modulated form.

Midbrain

As might be expected of a region that connects the dominant forebrain with the rest of the nervous system, the midbrain contains all the fibre tracts that connect these regions. However, it is more than a through-route; it also contains several, important centres. Four swellings in the roof of this region, the *corpora quadrigemina*, are all that remains of the *tectum*, the dominant coordinating centre in fishes and amphibians. The anterior pair of swellings receive fibres from the eyes and head, and mediate visual reflexes, for example the turning of the head and eyes to focus on an object that suddenly appears in the field of vision. The posterior pair of swellings receive auditory fibres, and mediate auditory reflexes such as the pricking-up of the ear pinnae, and movements of the head in response to an unexpected sound.

Another centre, the *red nucleus* (see Figure 77), located in the floor of the midbrain, is connected by fibre tracts with the cerebral cortex, the thalamus, and the cerebellum. Its functions are imperfectly understood but it appears to be an integral part of the mechanism that controls the coordination of movements. If it is destroyed, a condition known as decerebrate rigidity results. In this condition, all the extensor muscles (p. 221) of the limbs are held out rigidly from the body.

Tweenbrain

Thalamus

This is a large and important centre in mammals. It is sometimes called the gateway to the cortex, because almost the entire sensory input to the cortex arrives by way of the thalamus (Figure 78). Incoming fibres from all the somatic receptors, except the olfactory organs, make synaptic contact in the thalamus with the neurons that pass impulses on to the cortex. The thalamus also appears to play an important role in the perception of pain.

Hypothalamus

Although small, this is a very important region with many complex regulatory functions. It controls the visceral nervous system, and thus plays a part in the regulation of heart rate, ventilation rate, blood pressure and gut movements. In connection with this role, the hypothalamus receives fibres from the olfactory and taste organs, as well as many of the visceral receptors. It also sends fibres to the centres in the medulla and spinal cord which mediate most of the visceral reflexes. The degree of influence that the hypothalamus exerts over these other centres is not clear.

The hypothalamus also contains centres for the regulation of body temperature, fat and carbohydrate metabolism, appetite, water balance and sleep (several of these processes are examined in earlier chapters).

There is some evidence that the hypothalamus plays a part in controlling

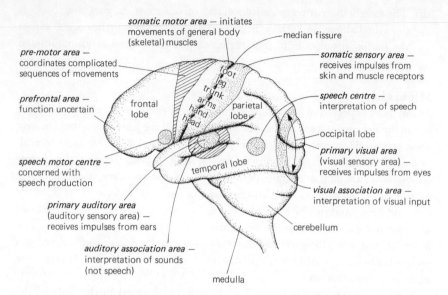

Figure 78   The human cortex, showing localisation of function

certain emotions. Electrical stimulation of certain areas in this region can elicit rage in a previously docile animal.

Finally, the hypothalamus also controls the functioning of many of the body's endocrine organs by regulating the output of certain hormones from the pituitary gland. The relationship between the hypothalamus and the pituitary is examined in detail later in this chapter.

Endbrain

The cerebrum

The appearance of the cerebrum has already been briefly described. The outer layer of the cerebrum, the cerebral cortex, is the centre that controls all voluntary, and some involuntary, activities in mammals. It receives information from all the somatic receptors, and can transmit information to all the voluntary (skeletal) muscles. The fibres that carry this information cross over, mainly in the hindbrain, so that the left cerebral hemisphere coordinates the activities of the right hand side of the body, while the right hemisphere controls the left hand side. The precise role of the cerebrum varies from species to species. A dog with its cortex removed will lose its sense of smell, and its ability to see, but will still move in a coordinated way, eat, drink, and even bark and growl. However, it also loses all interest in its surroundings, and becomes impossible to train. In other words, it loses the characteristics which we associate with intelligence. The effects of cortex removal are even more profound in man, reducing him to a vegetable-like state, incapable of making any voluntary movements.

As already indicated the cortex is a thin layer of grey matter, up to one hundred cells thick. This layer contains some 10^9 cell bodies (in man), each of which makes synaptic contact with many hundreds, or thousands, of others throughout the cortex; and with incoming and outgoing fibres (these fibres constitute the white matter of the cerebrum). The sheer complexity of this arrangement defies the imagination, and we are still, not surprisingly, a long way from understanding how the cortex carries out its varied functions. However, it is clear that the ability to correlate information from different receptors, to store and then retrieve information, and to initiate a response appropriate to a particular sensory input, is dependent on the complexity of interconnections within the cortex. Such processes obviously require that neurons in different parts of the cortex are in communication.

Experimental work of the type described earlier, particularly electrical stimulation of the brain, has enabled us to build up a picture of the functions of different areas of the cortex (see Figure 78). The following main functional areas can be distinguished:

sensory areas – these receive impulses from the receptors

motor areas – these transmit impulses to the effectors

association areas – these sort out and interpret impulses from the different receptors, determine the appropriate response and, if necessary, relay impulses to the motor areas. They are also thought to be involved in storing information and learning.

Sensory areas

As shown in Figure 78, different receptors are connected to different parts of the sensory cortex. Input from the eyes, passes to the visual sensory area in the region of the cortex known as the occipital lobe. Input from the cochlea in the ear, passes to the primary auditory area. Impulses from the skin and muscle receptors are received and interpreted in the sensory area, located just behind the median fissure (the fissure of Orlando), while the input from the taste organs passes to the lower end of this region.

Association areas

Most of the association areas are located next to the sensory area whose input they interpret (see Figure 78). The *visual association area* is responsible for making sense of the visual input. Damage to this region results in the visual field appearing as a meaningless kaleidoscope of coloured patches. Interpretation of sounds is carried out in the *auditory association area*, but in man further analysis is carried out in the *speech centre* – damage to this region impairs the ability to understand spoken words. Yet another area, the *speech motor centre* is concerned with speech production, and damage to this centre results in an inability to produce intelligible speech.

The region of the temporal lobe cortex below the auditory centres is thought to be the seat of memory, in which sensory impressions can be recalled to consciousness. Electrical stimulation of this area can elicit vivid recall of scenes long past. Centres embedded in the white matter beneath the temporal cortex form part of the *limbic system* which, with the hypothalamus, regulates feeding, aggression and sexual behaviour.

Motor areas

Electrical stimulation of circumscribed parts of the motor area, elicits motor responses from groups of muscles, or, if the stimulus is sufficiently localised, from individual muscles. The localisation of functions in the somatic motor area (the area that controls the general body muscles) bears a generally inverse relationship to the body. Thus, the uppermost portion stimulates the lower parts of the body and vice versa (Figure 78). This same relationship exists in the adjacent somatic sensory area. The hands and face in man carry out the most complicated movements, and are accordingly controlled by a large number of neurons, occupying a relatively large proportion of the motor cortex. The *premotor area* is concerned with synthesising muscle movements into complex acts, and thus stimulates the production of coordinated sequences of movements, rather than isolated muscle responses.

Motor impulses pass from the motor cortex to motor neurons in the medulla and spinal cord via fibres in the two large *pyramidal tracts* (Figure 77), and the *reticular formation*. The latter is a network of neurons and fibres that passes through the midbrain and medulla. It also receives sensory impulses, and has recently come in for a great deal of attention from biologists because it appears to be of importance in controlling consciousness. While you are asleep, sensory input to the cortex continues, but you will only become conscious of this input if sensory impulses are relayed to the cortex from the reticular formation. These impulses activate the sensory cortex, and you wake up. Because of its 'cortex-activating' function the reticular formation is sometimes called the *reticular activating system*, usually abbreviated to RAS. Lesions in various parts of the RAS result in permanent sleep or coma.

Apparently, the RAS has the ability to be selective in its sensitivity to stimuli. Thus a mother might wake instantly when her baby whimpers, while her husband sleeps on oblivious to the sound. Similarly, someone used to sleeping near a busy road, will be undisturbed by traffic noise, but wake immediately in response to an unexpected creak of a door, or the smell of smoke. It has also been suggested that the RAS continues to direct our attention to selected stimuli when we are awake, thus enabling us to concentrate on a particular stimulus (object, sound, etc.).

The prefrontal area

The anterior part of the cortex, known as the prefrontal area, is one of several cortical *silent areas*, so-called because stimulation of these areas evokes no sensations or motor responses. Removal of the prefrontal area produces subtle changes in attitude and behaviour, that vary from one individual to another, but generally involve impairment of the ability to learn. In man, removal usually leads to impairment of intellectual ability, a lessening of drive and creativity, and an inability to concentrate and make long-term plans. Obviously such changes tend to have a profound effect on the personality. For this reason surgical operations involving the removal of the prefrontal area (prefrontal lobotomy), or its severence from the rest of the brain, have now been largely discontinued. Such operations used to be carried out to relieve extreme anxiety.

Evolution of nervous systems

In this chapter, only the most highly evolved nervous system has been considered; that of mammals. To gain a wider view of nervous organisation, we will now briefly consider more primitive nervous systems. This will enable us to identify and attempt to explain the main changes in nervous organisation that have occurred during the course of evolution.

The most primitive nervous organisation is found in coelenterates, e.g. *Hydra*, where the neurons are linked together by their axons forming a *nerve net* which makes contact with receptor cells and muscle fibres. Nerve nets allow impulses to spread out in all directions from the point of stimulus. Nerve impulse conduction in such a system is rather slow, and while adequate for a small, usually sessile organism like *Hydra* would not suffice for larger, more active animals.

In more advanced nervous systems, two trends can be distinguished. One is the assembling of neurons into tracts – usually a single longitudinal tract. The other is the grouping of nerve cell bodies into ganglia. The former trend facilitates fast conduction of impulses from one part of the body to another. This effect is largely achieved by the increased length of axons in such tracts, as compared with those in nerve nets. Longer axons mean fewer synapses and therefore less delay as impulses cross synapses. The appearance of one-way synapses in the tracts also helps speed up nerve impulse transmission (synapses in *Hydra* allow transmission of impulses in both directions). The development of ganglia makes possible the gathering of information from different receptors and the coordination of responses by different effectors.

The larger and more active coelenterates, such as sea anemones and jellyfish, possess a nerve net, parts of which are organised into tracts called *through-conduction* tracts. Conduction is much more rapid in these tracts, ranging from 0.7 to 2.0 metres per second, as compared to 0.5 centimetres per second in the rest of the nerve net. These tracts mediate responses where rapid conduction is important, such as the defensive shortening of the column and withdrawal of tentacles in sea anemones.

The appearance of a single longitudinal tract, or nerve cord, as seen in annelids, many arthropods, and vertebrates is associated with the development of bilateral symmetry, ensuring as it does rapid communication between the two ends of the body. In bilaterally symmetrical animals, the anterior end of the body becomes very important, because it is the first part to make contact with the 'new' environment into which the animal is moving. This has resulted in a tendency for receptors to be concentrated at the anterior end, which in turn has led to an enlargement of the nervous system at this end, to deal with the increased sensory input, and to relay impulses to the effectors. The development of a definite head region is called *cephalisation*. The aggregations of neurons in the heads of animals, such as the earthworm and the locust, are known as *cerebral ganglia* and can be thought of as forerunners of the brain. The cerebral ganglia in these animals do little in the way of integration and coordination, being chiefly concerned with relaying impulses from the head receptors, via the nerve cord, to effectors in the body. The fact that a decapitated earthworm can still move quite normally demonstrates that the cerebral ganglia are not involved in coordinating movements. In lowly animals like the earthworm, movements are coordinated by the segmental ganglia.

In more advanced animals the anterior part of the nervous system takes over more and more directive functions, starting with the control of movement and eventually exerting control over the whole of the animal's behaviour, as in mammals.

HORMONAL COORDINATION IN MAMMALS

Hormones are chemical coordinators or messengers. They are mainly produced in well-defined *endocrine organs*; also called ductless glands, because their hormonal secretions are not removed in special ducts, but instead, pass into the blood vessels that pass through the organs. Hormones are carried in the bloodstream to parts of the body, known as *target cells* or *target organs*, where they evoke a specific response. Because hormones are carried in the blood, they are usually slower in producing a response than the nervous system; although their effects tend to be longer-lasting.

Figure 79(a) shows the location of the main endocrine organs in man. In spite of their physical separation from one another, endocrine organs and their secretions do not work in isolation. They interact with one another, and with the nervous system, to form an integrated coordinating system. The pituitary gland plays a key role in linking the endocrine and nervous systems. It is through the

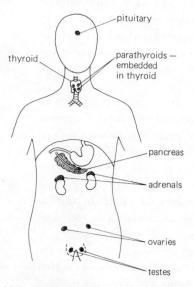

(a) the position of the main endocrine organs

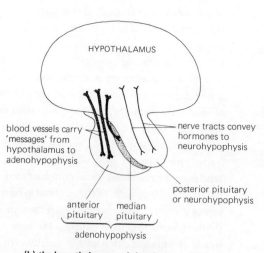

(b) the hypothalamus and the pituitary gland

Figure 79 (a) and (b)   Human endocrine organs

medium of this gland that the hypothalamus directs the activities of many of the other endocrine glands. The functions of the pituitary hormones, and those produced by all the other important endocrine organs, are summarised in Table 7.

Table 7 Some important vertebrate hormones

Endocrine organs	Hormones	Major functions
Hypothalamus	Release and release-inhibiting hormones	Control release of hormones from adenohypophysis
Hypothalamus via neurohypophysis	Oxytocin	Stimulates release of milk and uterine contraction
	Anti-diuretic hormone (ADH)	Stimulates reabsorption of water in kidney (see chapter 10)
Adenohypophysis	Adrenocorticotropic hormone (ACTH)	Stimulates adrenal cortex
	Follicle-stimulating hormone (FSH)	Stimulates development of ovarian follicles and seminiferous tubules
	Luteinising hormone (LH)	Stimulates ovulation and conversion of empty follicle into a corpus luteum; also stimulates progesterone and testosterone production
	Melanocyte-stimulating hormone (MSH)	stimulates dispersion of pigment (melanin) in skin of amphibians; stimulates melanin production in man
	Prolactin	Maintains lactation after pregnancy; maintains secretion of progesterone during pregnancy
	Thyroid-stimulating hormone (TSH)	Stimulates thyroid gland
	Growth hormone	Promotes growth
Thyroid	Thyroxine and tri-iodothyronine	Increase metabolic rate by stimulating cellular respiration; play an important role in growth, tissue development and differentiation
	Calcitonin	Inhibits excessive rise in blood calcium level by suppressing removal of calcium from bone
Parathyroid	Parathormone	Acts in opposition to calcitonin – brings about removal of calcium from bone and increases reabsorption of calcium in kidney, thus raising blood calcium level

Table 7 (contd)

Endocrine organs	Hormones	Major functions
Adrenal cortex	Glucocorticoids, e.g. cortisone	Regulate carbohydrate metabolism
	Mineralosteroids, e.g. aldosterone	Regulate salt and water balance (see chapter 10)
Adrenal medulla	Adrenalin and noradrenalin	Prepare animals to meet emergency conditions, e.g. fight, flight or shock, by increasing heart rate, and blood supply to skeletal muscles, lungs and liver, and raising the blood sugar level
Pancreas	Glucagon	Increases blood sugar level by converting glycogen to glucose
	Insulin	Decreases blood sugar level by stimulating the formation of glycogen
Stomach	Gastrin	Maintains flow of gastric juice
Duodenum	Secretin	Stimulates secretion of intestinal juice
	Pancreozymin	Stimulates secretion of pancreatic juice
	Cholecystokinin	Stimulates release of bile from gall bladder
Ovary	Oestrogens	Initiate and maintain female secondary sexual characteristics; initiates thickening of uterus lining; inhibits FSH
	Progesterone	Maintains thickening of uterus lining; inhibits FSH and LH
Testis	Testosterone	Initiates and maintains male secondary sexual characteristics

The pituitary/hypothalamus partnership

The pituitary is a small knob-like gland that lies in a depression in the floor of the cranium. It is formed by the union of a glandular outpushing of the embryonic buccal cavity, and an outgrowth of the hypothalamus. The part of the pituitary derived from the gut is known as the *adenohypophysis*; while that derived from nervous tissue is called the *neurohypophysis*. These terms have now largely superceded the old terms anterior and posterior lobes (see Figure 79(b)).

The adenohypophysis

This region produces seven hormones. One promotes growth, one influences pigmentation, while the others, called *tropic* or *trophic hormones*, active or stimulate other endocrine organs. It is through the medium of the tropic hormones that the pituitary exerts its influence over other parts of the endocrine system.

The production of adenohypophysial hormones is regulated by the hypothalamus. Neurons in the latter secrete hormones into the blood vessels that pass to the adenohypophysis. These neurohormones either release, or inhibit the release of, the adenohypophysial hormones; and are known as *releasing hormones* or *release-inhibiting hormones* accordingly. Some of the adenohypophysial hormones, namely growth hormone, prolactin, and melanocyte-stimulating hormone, are under dual control: their output is determined by the relative amounts of releasing and release-inhibiting hormone present. In the case of the other hormones, only releasing hormones have been identified.

The neurohypophysis

It was formerly believed that the hormones ADH (anti-diuretic hormone) and oxytocin were actually produced in the neurohypophysis. It is now known that these hormones are produced by neurons in the hypothalamus, and pass to the neurohypophysis in the nerve tracts that connect the two regions. The neurohypophysis thus serves as a storage and releasing organ. The release of the hormones is triggered by the passage of impulses along the nerve tracts that pass from the hypothalamus.

Endocrine organs not under pituitary control

Not all endocrine organs are under pituitary control. Some are self-regulating, for example, the secretion of insulin and glucagon appears to be regulated directly by the blood sugar level, a rise stimulating insulin production (which tends to lower blood sugar), and a fall stimulating glucagon release (which tends to raise blood sugar level).

Other organs such as the adrenal cortex are under direct nervous control: release of their secretions is triggered by the arrival of nerve impulses.

Interaction between hormones

We are only just beginning to appreciate the complexity of interactions in the endocrine system. Many hormones trigger the production or release of others, e.g. the trophic and hypothalamic releasing hormones. Others have the reverse effect, and inhibit the production or action of another hormone, e.g. the hypothalamic release-inhibiting hormones.

Certain hormones, such as insulin and glucagon, control a response by exerting opposing (antagonistic) effects. Parathormone and calcitonin also work in this way. By contrast, some hormones work together, having mutually enhancing or *synergistic* effects. For example, progesterone supplements oestrogen in inducing mammary gland development.

The mechanism of hormonal action

Considerable progress has been made recently in elucidating the mechanism of hormone action. Hormones are thought to exert their effects by altering the activities of their target cells in one, or more, of the following ways:

(i) Some (androgens, growth hormone, oestrogens, progesterone and thyroid hormone) appear to stimulate the synthesis of specific proteins by affecting the RNA or the ribosomes.

(ii) Some (ADH, glucagon, LH, MSH and TSH) act by stimulating the membrane-bound enzyme, *adenosine monophosphate* (cyclic AMP), in the target cells. This enzyme then acts as a 'second messenger', and activates the metabolic process that produces the response.

(iii) A few, e.g. insulin, appear to act by regulating the permeability of the membrane to specific substances.

These proposed mechanisms do not explain why hormones affect some cells and not others. It is generally believed that the hormone must combine with a specific receptor in, or on the surface of, the target cell, before it can exert its effects on that cell's activities.

The roles of hormones in reproduction are discussed in chapter 8 of *Heredity, development and evolution*. Steroid hormones are discussed in chapter 3 of *The cell concept*.

QUESTIONS

1   What is a nerve impulse? Explain how a nerve impulse (a) travels along the axon membrane, (b) crosses a synapse.

2   Distinguish between the following pairs of terms:
    a) temporal summation and facilitation,
    b) inhibitory and excitatory synapses.
    Explain the significance of these phenomena in the functioning of the nervous system.

3   What is a reflex arc? Draw a diagram of the structures involved.

4   The nerve impulse is described as an all-or-nothing response. What does this mean? How is information about stimulus strength conveyed to the central nervous system?

5   Distinguish between the somatic and visceral divisions of the peripheral nervous system.

6   Discuss localisation of function in the human cerebral cortex. Explain briefly how our knowledge of this subject has been acquired.

7   Explain why the cerebellum of birds is a very large, complex organ. Why should the human cerebellum be so much more complex than that of most other mammals?

8   How does hormonal coordination differ from nervous coordination? In what ways are the two interdependent?

12 Receptors

A sensitivity to the changes that take place inside and outside the body is obviously essential for survival. In view of this it is hardly surprising that most animals possess a remarkably varied array of receptors, ranging from single sensory cells to organs comprising many cell types. While many receptors can respond to several different types of stimulus, most are specialised so that they are particularly sensitive to just one type. Receptors are usually classified according to the nature of the stimulus to which they respond. The main categories of receptor, together with the mammalian receptors in each category are set out in the table below.

Type of receptor	stimulus	mammalian receptors
chemoreceptors	chemical substances	taste organs, olfactory organs
photoreceptors	light	eyes
thermoreceptors	temperature	thermoreceptors in skin and hypothalamus
mechanoreceptors	mechanical distortion	touch and pressure receptors in skin; muscle and tendon stretch (tension) receptors; auditory (hearing) and equilibrium receptors in inner ear

All receptors perform essentially the same function, that is, they convert or transduce the environmental energy of the stimulus into the electrical energy of nerve impulses. Thus, whatever the nature of the information received by receptors, it is all encoded into a common form, action potentials, and then relayed to the central nervous system where the impulses are interpreted. When a stimulus is received by a receptor, the stimulus brings about a change in the permeability of the sensory cell membrane and in so doing depolarises the membrane and sets up a *generator potential*. Exactly how the stimulus achieves this will vary according to the nature of the receptor, and in most cases has not been fully explained.

The generator potential resembles an excitatory post-synaptic potential in that it is not self-propagating; but, if it reaches or exceeds a certain level (the *firing threshold*), it can trigger one or more action potentials. The greater the intensity of stimulus, the higher the frequency of action potentials generated. However, during prolonged stimulation, the frequency of action potentials decreases with time, so that eventually there is little or no response, a phenomenon known as *adaptation*. An example of this is that you stop responding to an unusual smell in a room after a few minutes exposure to the smell.

PHOTORECEPTION

Sensitivity to light is common to most organisms. Animals almost invariably possess photoreceptors of some kind, and many can respond to light without special receptors; for example certain protozoans, amphibians and fish have a light-sensitive body surface.

The simplest type of photoreceptor is the light-sensitive cell found in the epidermis of earthworms. It is, however, unusual to find photoreceptive cells occurring singly; in most animals they are gathered together into groups, often with non-nervous accessory structures such as a lens, to form eyes. The simplest eyes can only distinguish between different intensities of light. In the most complex photoreceptors, many thousands, or even millions, of photoreceptor cells are grouped together, enabling the animal to build up a composite picture, or image, from the individual points of light and shade. In some cases the photoreceptors are sensitive to light of different wavelengths, perceived as different colours. Image-forming eyes have evolved independently in arthropods, cephalopod molluscs (octopus and squid) and vertebrates.

The mammalian eye

The structure of the mammalian eye is shown in Figure 80. Light rays from objects pass through the pupil and are brought to focus on the light-sensitive cells of the retina by the combined converging power of the cornea, the aqueous humour and the crystalline lens. The curvature of the latter can be altered by the contraction and relaxation of the ciliary muscles. This alters the tension on the ligaments that hold the lens in position. The adjustment of lens curvature to focus on close objects is called *accommodation*. Figure 81 illustrates the difference between the unaccommodated and the accommodated eye.

Objects in the visual field are brought into sharp focus by projecting the light rays from those objects onto a special region of the retina, the *fovea*. This region is able to perceive objects in greater detail because it contains a very large number of photosensitive cells in very close proximity. The human fovea contains some 150 000 cells per mm^2, and many vertebrates possess more. Seurat, a French impressionist painter, pioneered a technique that involved applying tiny dots of paint very close together. One can imagine that if every other dot of paint were to be removed from such a painting, the detail and clarity of the picture would be greatly reduced. The same principle applies to image formation in the eye. The more numerous and more closely packed the visual elements that receive

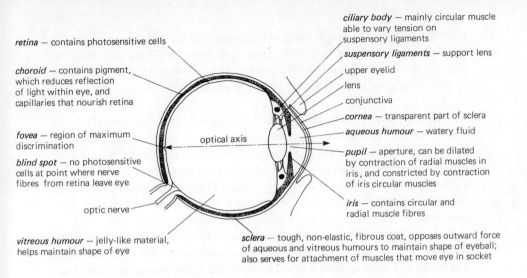

retina — contains photosensitive cells

choroid — contains pigment, which reduces reflection of light within eye, and capillaries that nourish retina

fovea — region of maximum discrimination

blind spot — no photosensitive cells at point where nerve fibres from retina leave eye

optic nerve

vitreous humour — jelly-like material, helps maintain shape of eye

ciliary body — mainly circular muscle able to vary tension on suspensory ligaments

suspensory ligaments — support lens

upper eyelid

lens

conjunctiva

cornea — transparent part of sclera

aqueous humour — watery fluid

pupil — aperture, can be dilated by contraction of radial muscles in iris, and constricted by contraction of iris circular muscles

iris — contains circular and radial muscle fibres

optical axis

sclera — tough, non-elastic, fibrous coat, opposes outward force of aqueous and vitreous humours to maintain shape of eyeball; also serves for attachment of muscles that move eye in socket

Figure 80   Diagrammatic vertical section through a mammalian eye

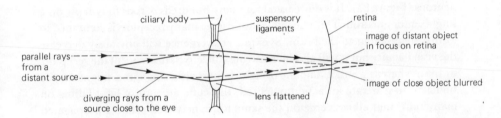

ciliary body — suspensory ligaments — retina

image of distant object in focus on retina

parallel rays from a distant source

diverging rays from a source close to the eye

lens flattened

image of close object blurred

(a) the unaccommodated eye

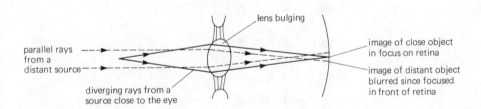

lens bulging

parallel rays from a distant source

diverging rays from a source close to the eye

image of close object in focus on retina

image of distant object blurred since focused in front of retina

(b) the accommodated eye

Figure 81   Accommodation. (a) When the eye is focused on distant objects (in practice, objects more than ten feet away), close objects appear blurred, and the eye is said to be *unaccommodated*. In this condition the lens is flattened by the relaxation of the circular muscle in the ciliary body which imposes tension on the ligaments that support the lens. (b) To focus on close objects (*accommodate*), the converging power of the lens is increased by the contraction of the circular muscles in the ciliary body, this reduces tension on the suspensory ligaments and allows the lens to bulge due to its natural elasticity.

information, the more detailed will be the image. Put another way, two points in the visual field will only be perceived as separate entities if the rays from the points activate two separate visual elements. Thus, the closer together the visual elements, the greater the resolving power or *visual acuity* (sharpness of vision) of the eye.

The Retina develops as an outgrowth of the brain. It comprises several types of sensory neuron and two types of photosensitive cell, *rods* and *cones*, so-called because of their usual shapes in a mammal (see Figure 82). Both photosensitive cells have an inner and an outer segment and a pre-synaptic terminal. The outer segment contains a stack of membranous discs. These membranes incorporate a photosensitive pigment which is broken down when exposed to light, an event that leads to the setting up of a generator potential.

Rods are generally restricted to regions of the retina outside the fovea. They respond to much lower light intensities than cones and so are used mainly for night vision. They also have a much lower visual acuity than cones. There are two reasons for this; they are not as closely packed as cones, and there is a far greater degree of convergence at the point where they synapse with sensory neurons (Figure 82). It is quite usual for many hundreds of rods to synapse on a single sensory neuron. Thus the information from many receptors is combined to form a single input to the brain. Synaptic convergence will obviously decrease the visual acuity but it will also increase the collective sensitivity of the receptors so that, whereas a small amount of light falling on a single rod might not be sufficient to generate an action potential, the same amount of light falling on many rods, that all converge on the same fibre, may well excite a propagated response.

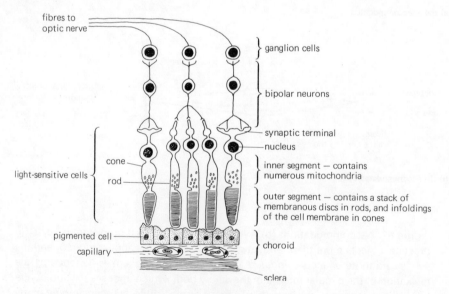

Figure 82 Diagram of a portion of the mammalian retina. Synaptic connections in the retina are greatly simplified in this diagram.

Cones are found throughout the retina but they are most abundant in the fovea. They are much less sensitive to light than rods and so are suited for daytime vision. They have a much higher visual acuity than rods because they are more closely packed, and there is less synaptic convergence. The balance of rods and cones is determined by the animal's pattern of activity. Most vertebrates have a mixed retina containing both rods and cones but a mainly diurnal animal (one that is active during the day) will have a preponderance of cones. Completely nocturnal animals like the bush baby have a retina composed entirely of rods. Another adaptation commonly encountered in nocturnal animals is a *tapetum*, a reflective layer behind the retina. This reflects light back into the eye, thereby increasing the light that falls on the retinal cells and so improves the chances of the cells responding. The presence of the tapetum explains why the eyes of many animals appear to glow at night.

The photochemical pigment

All the photosensitive or photochemical pigments extracted to date consist of a protein conjugated with a carotenoid pigment derived from vitamin A, known as retinene. The best known pigments are the *rhodopsins* or visual purples in which the protein is opsin. Rhodopsin is found in rods. When light falls on rhodopsin the pigment is broken down into retinene and opsin, and bleached. It is not yet understood how this bleaching process affects the permeability of the membrane.

The identification of the cone pigment has proved more difficult. It is suggested that *iodopsin*, a combination of retinene and cone opsin, is present in many cones but the search continues for the variants of these pigments, or other pigments, that must be present to account for the differing sensitivity to different wavelengths on which colour vision depends.

Colour vision

It has been shown that in certain fish and mammalian retinas the cones are of three types, having a sensitivity to wavelengths in the red, green and blue parts of the spectrum respectively. When these three colours are mixed in different proportions, they can produce any other colour. This *trichromatic mechanism* appears to form the basis for colour vision, but recent experimental findings suggest that the complete explanation may be more complicated.

It is perhaps worth mentioning at this point that all living organisms respond to light within a fairly narrow range of wavelengths, between 300 and 900 nanometres (this includes the wavelengths used by plants in photosynthesis). The reason for this is not difficult to appreciate. Longer wavelengths do not carry sufficient energy per quantum to have any significant photochemical effect, while shorter wavelengths carry too much energy per quantum and can damage organic molecules.

It is no accident that so many advanced animals have come to place such reliance on photoreception. For practical purposes light rays may be said to travel in straight lines. Because of this, vision is a much more directional sense than many others, and can provide very precise information about the location of objects and events. It also confers the ability to acquire much more detailed information, over much greater distances than most other senses.

THE MAMMALIAN EAR

The structure of the mammalian ear is shown in Figure 83. The outer and middle ear serve to relay sound waves to the auditory receptors in the inner ear. The latter comprises a system of fluid-filled (*perilymph*) canals and cavities in the bone of the skull. Inside these cavities there is a membrane-enclosed system, the *membranous labyrinth*. This is filled with fluid (*endolymph*) and contains two types of mechanoreceptors – auditory receptors and equilibrium receptors. The former are located in the coiled region of the labyrinth known as the *cochlea*. The equilibrium receptors are to be found in the two sac-like structures, the *sacculus* and the *utriculus*, and in the swellings or *ampullae* at the bases of the three *semicircular canals*.

Hearing

Sound waves are directed by the pinna into the external ear causing the tympanic membrane (eardrum) to vibrate, which in turn causes the three bony ossicles in the middle ear to vibrate. In transmitting vibrations from the relatively large area of the eardrum (50 to 90 mm^2 in man) to the relatively small

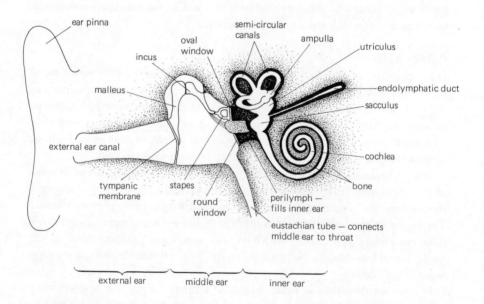

Figure 83 Schematic representation of a generalised mammalian ear. The incus, malleus and stapes are the three ear ossicles, and the muscles that hold these bones in position are shown, but not labelled.

area of the oval window in contact with the stapes (3.2 mm^2), the ossicles reduce the amplitude and concentrate the force of the vibrations, so that the pressure on the oval window is twenty two times greater than the pressure on the eardrum. Without this mechanism, only a small proportion of the vibrations would be transmitted to the fluid in the inner ear (the perilymph). The latter transmits the vibrations to the auditory cells in the cochlea.

The route just described is not the only way sound waves reach the inner ear. Sounds can also be heard through the skull by bone conduction. When we speak or sing, we in fact hear both air and bone conducted sounds, which explains why it is sometimes difficult to recognise your own voice from a recording, as this will only pick up air conducted sounds. The cochlea is subdivided longitudinally into three canals by the basilar and Reissner's membranes (Figure 84). The former bears the groups of auditory cells and their attached hairs that comprise the *organs of Corti*. The two outer canals, the *vestibular canal* and the *tympanic canal*, are filled with perilymph, and communicate with the middle ear via the oval

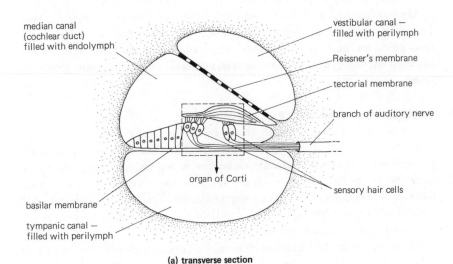

median canal
(cochlear duct)
filled with endolymph

vestibular canal —
filled with perilymph

Reissner's membrane

tectorial membrane

branch of auditory nerve

organ of Corti

sensory hair cells

basilar membrane

tympanic canal —
filled with perilymph

(a) transverse section

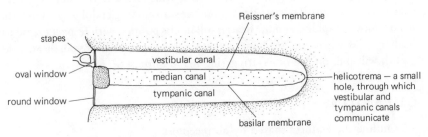

Reissner's membrane

stapes

oval window

round window

vestibular canal

median canal

tympanic canal

helicotrema — a small hole, through which vestibular and tympanic canals communicate

basilar membrane

(b) simplified diagram of uncoiled cochlea in longitudinal section

Figure 84   Diagrammatic sections throughout the mammalian cochlea

window and round window respectively. The middle canal is filled with endolymph. Vibrations of the oval window are transmitted via the fluid in the vestibular canal to the Reissner's membrane and then via the endolymph to the basilar membrane, and finally on to the round window via the fluid in the tympanic canal. Movements of the basilar membrane relative to the tectorial membrane cause the hairs to pull on and distort the auditory cells thus setting up a generator potential.

The ear of mammals is able to distinguish the pitch (frequency of vibrations) and loudness (amplitude of vibrations) of sounds. Loud sounds have a greater amplitude than quieter sounds and so will produce greater distortion of the auditory cells. The ability to distinguish pitch appears to be partly dependent on the structure of the basilar membrane. This membrane becomes broader and thicker along its length, from base to apex; this means that high frequency vibrations will not travel as far as low frequency vibrations. In addition, it seems that the auditory cells differ in their ability to respond to different frequencies. Cells near the base respond to high and low frequency vibrations, while those near the apex only respond to low frequency vibrations.

The human ear is sensitive to auditory stimuli in the range 40 hertz to 20 000 hertz (cycles per second). Some mammals can hear much higher frequencies, for example, dogs can hear up to 40 000 hertz, while bats can hear up to 100 000 hertz. Incidentally, most human conversation takes place in the 300–3000 hertz range.

Equilibrium receptors (Figure 85)

The semi-circular canals occupy three separate planes at right angles to one another. At one end of each there is an ampulla containing sensory hair cells grouped into *cristae*. The hairs are embedded in a gelatinous mass, the *cupula*. Acceleration or decceleration of the head in the plane of a canal causes movement of endolymph which moves the cupula. This causes the hairs to pull on and deform the hair cells on one side of the crista which triggers action potentials in the associated nerve fibres.

The receptors in the sacculus and utriculus consist of clusters of sensory hair cells grouped on plates called *maculae*. Each chamber usually contains two or more maculae. The hairs of the cells are embedded in a gelatinous *otolith* which contains high density particles. The otolith will normally rest lightly on the sensory cells because it is more dense than the surrounding endolymph, but if the head is moved rapidly, or if the head is still but its position with respect to gravity is altered (as when you are lying on your side or standing on your head), the otolith will pull on the hairs, triggering nerve impulses.

QUESTIONS

1 Outline the features shared by all receptors.
2 Describe how nerve impulses are generated in the retina.
3 What does 'visual acuity' mean? Explain why rods have a lower visual acuity than cones.

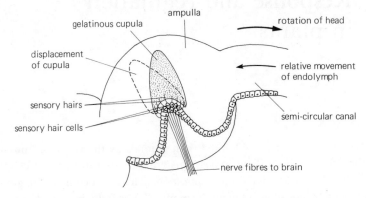

(a) section through ampulla organ (crista) showing how rotation of the head results in displacement of the cupula

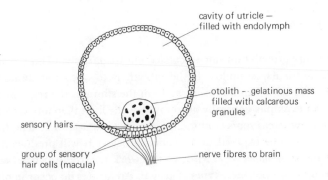

(b) section through utricle showing otolith organ (macula)

Figure 85   Mammalian equilibrium receptors

4   Explain the following observations:
(a) At night it is sometimes possible to see a very faint star in the margin of your field of vision, but if you try to look at it directly it disappears.
(b) With increasing age the human lens loses its elasticity, and correcting lenses generally become necessary for reading.
(c) Very loud sounds can cause permanent hearing loss.

5   Explain how the mammalian ear can distinguish between sounds of different pitch.

13 Response and regulation in plants

Plants are obviously far more limited than animals by the range of stimuli to which they can respond. Plant movements are discussed in the next chapter. Here we shall be considering those responses which are concerned with growth and controlled by the action of plant hormones. These influence a wide range of growth and development, including growth curvature in response to light and gravity, root initiation, onset of flowering and the development of buds, seeds and spores.

TROPISMS

Tropisms are growth movements carried out by part of a plant towards or away from a particular stimulus. If the growth is towards the stimulus then the response is positive and if it is away from the stimulus the response is negative. Stems, for example, generally bend towards the light therefore they are *positively phototropic*, whereas roots tend to be *negatively phototropic*. The length of time the plant needs to be exposed to the stimulus before it will produce a response is called the *presentation time*. Most of the work on tropisms has been done on flowering plants but these types of growth curvatures do occur in other groups, for example the fruiting bodies of many fungi orientate themselves with respect to gravity, showing *geotropism*. In addition to light and gravity, plants may respond to touch – *thigmotropism* (as in climbing plants), or water – *hydrotropism*, (as shown by most roots), or chemicals – *chemotropism*, (as when a pollen tube grows down the style).

Phototropism

In the 1880s Charles Darwin and his son Francis discovered that if the tip is removed from a growing shoot, it will no longer bend towards the light, even though the region that normally bends is below the tip. They also found that an opaque cover placed over the tip would prevent it bending towards the light. These results suggested that it was the tip of the shoot that detected the light but the response was made below the tip, therefore some communication must exist between the two regions.

These, and some of the later phototropic experiments, are shown in Figure 86. The later experiments were carried out using coleoptiles of grasses, particularly *Avena* (oat). A *coleoptile* is a tubular leaf-like structure, closed at the top, which

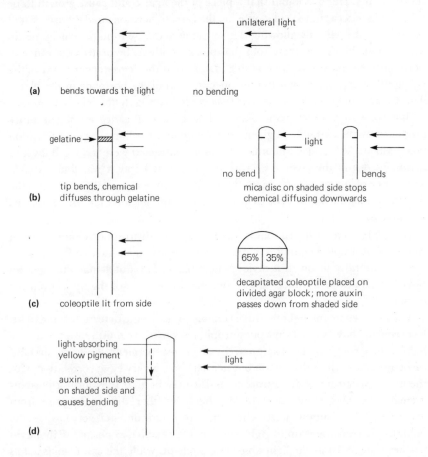

Figure 86 Phototropism
(a) – (c) Some early experiments
(d) The auxin explanation of phototropism

surrounds and protects the first leaf of the plant during its passage through the soil.

In 1913 the Danish plant physiologist Boysen-Jensen showed that the communication from the tip to the region that bent was a chemical one. He compared the results of a barrier of gelatine, through which a chemical could diffuse, and a piece of impervious mica. His results showed that the chemical would diffuse through the gelatine, but that if the mica disc was inserted on the shaded side of the coleoptile, bending did not occur. With the obstruction on the lit side bending occurred normally. He concluded that the chemical coordinator diffused from the tip down the shaded side of the coleoptile where it stimulated growth and caused a bend towards the light.

The growth stimulator or hormone was first extracted by the Dutch botanist F. W. Went in 1928. He removed coleoptile tips and placed them on agar jelly for several hours. He then found that a piece of the agar could cause growth to be resumed in a decapitated coleoptile i.e. the growth hormone had diffused out of the tip into the jelly. By allowing the hormone to diffuse from the coleoptile tip into an agar block and then from that block to others, he prepared a range of hormone concentrations and was able to show that the degree of curvature of the coleoptile was proportional to the concentration of the hormone in the block. This became the basis for a *bio-assay technique* to investigate the relative amounts of hormone in various plant tissues. The greater the degree of curvature produced by the extract in a given time the greater the hormone concentration it contained. At first the amounts of hormone extracted were too small for it to be analysed and the term *auxin* was applied to it. Later it was found that a wide range of auxins occur in plant tissues. Probably the most important and the first to be identified was *indoleacetic acid* (IAA), the formula for which is given in Table 8.

Went later demonstrated that it was the unequal distribution of auxin which caused phototropic bending. He placed a coleoptile tip which had previously been unilaterally lit on to a divided agar block. He found that the agar received nearly twice as much auxin from the shaded side of the tip as from the lit side.

The first step in any light sensitive response must be the detection of the light. Experiments have shown that phototropic responses are most sensitive to blue light which suggests its absorption by a yellow pigment. Both flavins and carotenoids absorb in this region but neither show a very close correlation with the action spectrum of phototropism and it may be that they form a protein-pigment complex which absorbs the light. Further difficulties arise from examples such as mutant maize, where the carotenoid content is very low, yet the phototropic response is up to eighty per cent as reactive as normal. Riboflavin has been suggested as the light-absorbing pigment, while the carotenoids act as screens controlling the amount of light received.

The unequal distribution of auxin between the lit and shaded side may occur because the riboflavin causes photo-oxidation of the enzymes which synthesise the auxin on the lit side, therefore more reaches the shaded side.

Geotropism

The response of roots and shoots to gravity can be shown by means of a *klinostat* (see Figure 87). This is a vertical, cork-covered wheel to which seeds may be pinned and caused to rotate at various speeds. At very slow speed the developing roots and shoots will grow in random directions as gravity is continually exerting its effects from different positions. If the wheel is stopped, the roots will grow downwards and the shoots upwards, since gravity is now exerting a constant effect. A decapitated root, however, will not respond to gravity.

Tests have shown that auxin tends to accumulate on the lower side of the root and the shoot but the effect it produces in each is different. In the shoot the auxin causes increased growth and the shoot produces an upward curvature. Roots, however, are much more sensitive to auxin and the amount which collects on the

Rotating cork-covered wheel
of Klinostat. Shoots and roots
grow in random directions
while wheel rotates slowly.

Wheel stopped. Roots begin to
grow down; shoots upwards,
in response to gravity.

Figure 87　Use of klinostat to demonstrate geotropism

lower side of the root actually inhibits growth, while that on the upper side may promote it, so that the root bends downwards towards gravity.

The perception of gravity by the plant has led to a search for mobile structures which could fall under gravity to the lower sides of the cells. The root cap and endodermis of many plants have been found to contain mobile starch grains which could act as statoliths in this way and the time they take to fall across the cell coincides well with the presentation time required for a response to gravity. They also disappear along with geotropic sensitivity if the plant is kept at low temperatures and reappear again together with geotropic sensitivity on return to normal temperatures. They are not of universal occurrence in geotropically sensitive organs, however. If they are involved, they may alter the permeability to auxin of the cell membrane on the lower side of each cell where they come to rest.

THE RANGE OF PLANT HORMONES

In recent years a wide range of other types of plant hormone have been discovered and the main groups together with their effects are shown in Table 8. It is only possible here to examine a few examples of the various interactions of the plant hormones, and much research remains to be done on these topics.

Senescence and abscission

Signs of senescence include reduced protein synthesis, loss of chlorophyll and breakdown of cell membranes. It may involve the whole plant as in annuals, having one flowering period and then dying (*monocarpic*) or just part of the plant may die, like the leaves of a deciduous tree, the rest surviving to flower again later (*polycarpic*).

Table 8 A range of plant hormones

Plant hormone	Effects	
auxins e.g. IAA promotes cell elongation	Phototropism, geotropism apical dominance root initiation parthenocarpy abscission respiration callus formation extends bud dormancy	Synthetic auxins can be used to promote root growth in cuttings, kill broadleaved weeds, prevent premature fruit fall etc.
abscisic acid (dormin)	Accelerates abscission and senescence in a variety of species. Inhibits germination in some species.	Effects can be counteracted by auxins, gibberellins and cytokinins.
gibberellins gibberellin A$_3$ promote cell elongation	Promote stem elongation, cell division, parthenocarpy, cambial activity. Induce new RNA and protein synthesis. Overcome genetic dwarfism. Cause bolting and flowering. Mobilise food stores in seeds.	Can act independently or together with auxin depending on species or position in plant.
cytokinins promote cell division	Stimulate cell division and enlargement, root initiation and growth, shoot initiation and growth. Break dormancy.	Appear to work with auxin to promote mitosis.

Table 8 (contd)

Plant hormone		
ethylene	Accelerates fruit ripening. Inhibits bud growth.	Low concentration of auxins induce ethylene formation.
May alter membrane permeability.		Blocks lateral movement of auxins and prevents geotropic responses.

Senescence seems to ensure that only the productive parts of the plant remain attached. In whole plant senescence for example, food is sent to the developing fruits at the expense of the dying vegetative parts. Removing the flowers can promote a longer life for the plant and is the reason why removing dead flowers before they fruit usually prolongs a plant's flowering period. Young parts of the plant produce auxin and remain attached. If auxin production declines an abscission layer forms and that part falls off. Cytokinins and gibberellins tend to delay senescence whereas abscisic acid and ethylene promote it.

Young leaves developing on a plant often speed up the abscission of the older ones, especially if they are shaded and not photosynthesising efficiently. Similarly, unfertilised flowers soon fall whereas developing seeds cause auxin release and hold the fruit on the plant. Auxin sprays are now used by some apple growers to prevent premature fruit drop.

Bud and seed dormancy

Bud dormancy in deciduous woody species is initiated by shorter days and caused by levels of hormones which prevent the buds developing. Some require a period of low temperature to break dormancy, for example, apple and lilac need a few days at 0–10°C and even chilling one bud on a twig will allow it to develop while the others remain dormant. The inhibitor appears to be abscisic acid which gradually breaks down under cold conditions. This helps prevent frost damage to buds opening too early. Gibberellins can break dormancy in most buds and a rise in gibberellin content has been demonstrated in many woody species in spring.

In seed dormancy the inhibitor is often abscisic acid again and the dormancy can be broken by gibberellins, or by exposure to cold – *stratification*. The gibberellins would normally diffuse out from the embryo and cause the production of hydrolysing enzymes which mobilise the seed's food reserves making them available for germination.

THE MODE OF ACTION OF PLANT HORMONES

Most of the investigations on the action of plant hormones have concerned auxins, either natural or synthetic. The evidence suggests that the auxin combines with protein, acting as the prosthetic group of an enzyme involved in growth. It seems that the auxin must combine with the protein at two separate sites and only molecules which can do this have auxin properties. Substances which can make only one point contact appear to act as inhibitors. This may explain why auxins themselves may be inhibitors at high concentrations e.g. one thousand parts per million instead of one part per million. At low concentration the auxin can easily make its two point contact but at high concentration there would be competition for the points of attachment. IAA oxidase would remove some of the excess auxin but growth would be retarded. This is the basis for synthetic weedkillers like 2, 4D (dichlorophenoxy ethanoic acid), which at low concentration cause excessive distortion of growth and eventually kill, whereas at high concentration they just slow down growth. Being more effective on dicotyledons than on grass they can be used as selective weedkillers.

EFFECTS OF LIGHT ON PLANT GROWTH

A plant grown in the dark becomes *etiolated*, being tall and yellow with no chlorophyll, with very long internodes and leaves which do not open. It is now known that light and in particular certain wavelengths, can have a profound effect on the growth of various parts of the plant.

Some seeds for example, only germinate if exposed to light, even very briefly and tests show that for many, red light in the range 580–660 nm is the most effective, whereas far red light at 700–730 nm inhibits germination. Even if only flashes of light are used, the seeds always respond to the last flash and, if it was far red, germination does not occur. Since red light is involved, a blue pigment was postulated to absorb it, and finally extracted in 1960, and called *phytochrome*. It exists in two inter-convertible forms called P665 and P725, the numbers referring to the wavelength at which each shows maximum absorption. Since sunlight contains more red than far red wavelengths, P665 is converted to P725 during the day and at night gradually turns back to P665. The P725 activates various enzymes, some of which stimulate growth and some which inhibit it. In Grand Rapids lettuce seeds red light results in germination in the presence of P725, whereas far red light removes the P725 by converting it back to P665 and prevents germination. Some other results of phytochrome interconversions are shown below:

red light	*far red light*
inhibits stem elongation	stimulates stem growth
inhibits lateral root growth	stimulates lateral root growth
stimulates leaf expansion	inhibits leaf expansion

The phytochrome appears to exert its effect via plant hormones which then stimulate cell expansion or cell division in various parts of the plant.

Photoperiodism

Phytochrome is also involved in the response of plants to varying lengths of day and night, called *photoperiodism*. One of these responses which has been investigated in some detail is flowering. Plants can be divided into three groups:

1   *Long day plants* only flower when the day length exceeds a minimum of about ten hours e.g. spinach, lettuce, petunias, barley.
2   *Short day plants* only flower when the day length is less than a minimum length e.g. chrysanthemums, poinsettias, cocklebur (fourteen and a half hours maximum for cocklebur).
3   *Day neutral plants* which do not react to day length e.g. tomato, dandelion. There are of course many gradations in between these groups & collectively they explain the cycle of flowering by different species throughout the year.

Experiments have shown that in short day plants $P725$ inhibits flowering, therefore they are really long night plants, requiring a long enough period of darkness for the $P725$ to be converted back to $P665$.

In long day plants however, the accumulation of $P725$ stimulates flowering so short nights are required to keep most of the phytochrome in its $P725$ form.

The reception of the light is by phytochrome in the leaves. The correct form of phytochrome is then believed to trigger production of a hormone called *florigen* which passes through the phloem to the flower meristems and causes flowers to develop.

TEMPERATURE AND PLANT GROWTH

We have seen how temperature can affect the rate of many physiological processes including photosynthesis and respiration, as well as the breaking of seed and bud dormancy. In general the tropical and subtropical species require higher temperatures for germination and flowering than those needed by temperate species. In fact, many temperate species need a period of cold treatment known as *vernalisation* before they will flower. Two species which have been particularly investigated are the biennial type of henbane (*Hyoscyamus niger*) and the winter strain of Petkus rye. In these plants a minimum length of winter cold is required to release the floral hormone which stimulates flowering.

QUESTIONS

1   Explain why
    a) decapitated coleoptiles do not respond to unilateral light
    b) selective weedkillers must be applied at low concentration
    c) petunias flower in the summer but chrysanthemums flower in the autumn.
2   Distinguish between:
    (a) vernalisation and stratification
    (b) auxins and gibberellins
    (c) phytochrome and florigen

14   Movement

Movement can occur at the cellular level as cytoplasmic streaming or as the passage of food vacuoles around a cell (*cyclosis*). Movements of organs could include contractions of the heart or a limb, whereas movement of a whole body is called locomotion. Locomotion is much more common in animals than in plants where only the simplest move their whole bodies e.g. by flagella in some algae. This is presumably the result of differences in nutrition, requiring most animals to seek their food, whereas most plants photosynthesise and do so more effectively stationary. Motility also provides access to new habitats for animals or to a mate for sexual reproduction. At the cellular level movement by gametes, usually just the male, is essential for fertilisation. Plants have evolved more passive methods of spreading by spores and seeds, which avoid overcrowding, but, except in the higher plants, a swimming male gamete is still involved in fertilisation.

Movement in animals can be classified as amoeboid, ciliary, flagellar and muscular. Amoeboid, ciliary and flagellar movements are typical of the simpler animals or parts of more complex ones, such as the lining layer of a gut or respiratory surface. Muscular movements are found in all groups of multicellular animals and, coupled with the development of limbs, have led to a wide range of locomotion from walking and jumping to swimming and flying.

AMOEBOID MOVEMENT

Amoeboid movement involves the production of temporary projections of cytoplasm called *pseudopodia*. It is found in amoeboid Protozoa and in wandering cells of some multicellular animals such as vertebrate white blood cells. The exact means of pseudopodial formation is uncertain, but it seems to include variations in viscosity at different points in the cytoplasm. In its viscous state the cytoplasm is *plasmagel* and in its liquified state *plasmasol*. Where a pseudopodium is forming, the cytoplasm appears to solate inside a hyaline gel layer. The sol flows forwards and then gelates on either side. Meanwhile at the opposite end of the cell the gel solates and flows forwards, (see Figure 88). Different theories have postulated that the forward flow is produced by squeezing-action of the gel at the back of the cell, or by a pull at the front from the gelating molecules. A third suggestion is that the protein molecules of the gel and sol could slide past each other in filamentous form, moved by chemical ratchets similar to those of muscle filaments, see p. 218. Indeed actin, a contractile protein found in many metazoan muscles, has been isolated from certain amoebae.

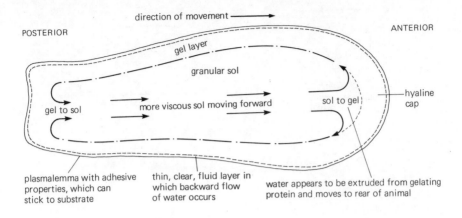

direction of movement ———→

POSTERIOR   ANTERIOR

gel layer

granular sol

gel to sol   more viscous sol moving forward   sol to gel

hyaline cap

plasmalemma with adhesive properties, which can stick to substrate

thin, clear, fluid layer in which backward flow of water occurs

water appears to be extruded from gelating protein and moves to rear of animal

Figure 88   Interconversions of cytoplasm from gel to sol during amoeboid movement.

CILIA AND FLAGELLA

The distinction between cilia and flagella is made on their length and the numbers present. *Cilia* are about ten to twenty micrometres long and usually occur in large numbers; *flagella* are longer, up to two millimetres and normally occur singly or in pairs. Both may be used to propel small organisms through the water or across wet surfaces, but they also occur inside the bodies of animals, where they may draw in feeding currents, circulate fluids or keep passageways clear of debris or secretions.

Despite their variations in size and uses, cilia and flagella have a remarkably similar internal structure. Each consists of a circular or oval *sheath* containing an *axial filament* composed of fibrils. The fixed end is attached to a *basal granule* probably derived from the centrosome of the cell. The internal fibrils are arranged with two in the centre and nine pairs of peripheral ones. One of each of the peripheral pairs has two projecting arms of a protein called *dynein* in which ATPase activity has been demonstrated. Radiating strands appear to connect the central and peripheral filaments and thickenings are sometimes seen on them, said by some investigators to be smaller subfilaments.

Movements of cilia can be either a straight backward and forward beat or a straight downstroke and a limp, bent recovery stroke (see Figure 89). Cilia may also form a compound structure or *undulating membrane* in which they all beat according to an inbuilt or *metachronal rhythm*. This can be seen in ciliates such as *Paramecium*. Flagella may exhibit an undulating movement from base to tip or a beat like cilia. A flagellum which pushes an organism forwards is called a *pulsellum* as in vertebrate sperm, whereas many flagellates have flagella in front which impart a spin to the body of the organism and pull it through the water. This is a *tractellum*.

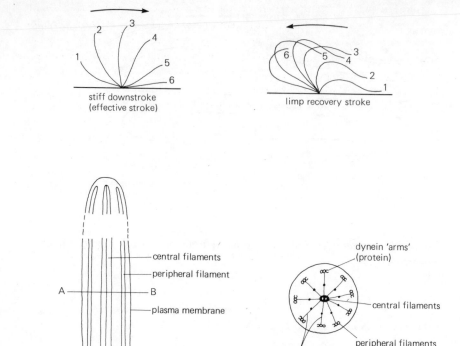

stiff downstroke
(effective stroke)

limp recovery stroke

central filaments

peripheral filament

A —— B

plasma membrane

basal granule

l.s.

dynein 'arms'
(protein)

central filaments

peripheral filaments

radiating strands
with apparent
central thickening

t.s. A—B

l.s. and t.s. cilium showing ultrastructure visible with electron microscope

Figure 89   Structure and action of a cilium

The mechanism by which cilia and flagella beat is not clear, but it is believed that the outer filaments are contractile and a protein similar to that of muscle fibres has been isolated from them. It may be that the five filaments on one side bend to make the effective stroke and then the four on the other side contract for the recovery stroke. The central filament may transmit the stimulus for contraction along its length. The control and coordination, particularly of groups of cilia, seems to involve the basal granules as separate pacemakers. In some ciliates, like *Paramecium*, strands or *neuronemes*, appear to connect the basal granules and may transmit the metachronal rhythm, whereas in metazoa, experiments have shown that the beat is under nervous control.

MUSCULAR MOVEMENTS

The simplest forms of contractile fibrils in cells are the *myonemes* found in some Protozoa, such as *Euglena*, which produce a wriggling or *euglenoid movement* when they contract.

At the tissue level, the coelenterates exhibit musculo-epithelial cells with *muscle tails* containing contractile fibrils controlled by a nerve net. More complex invertebrates, such as annelids, some molluscs and most arthropods, begin to show two different types of muscle for different functions, a striped skeletal muscle and a non-striped or smooth type for steady prolonged contraction of the viscera, in gut movements for example.

Vertebrate muscle is divided into three types according to its histology, and position in the body. *Skeletal, striated or voluntary* muscle is associated with the skeleton, shows microscopic striations and is under the control of the voluntary nervous system. It can be used for rapid contractions, but tires quickly. *Smooth, non-striated or involuntary* muscle is found in blood vessels and various organs of the body including the gut. It is under the control of the autonomic or involuntary nervous system and both contracts and tires slowly. The third type is *cardiac muscle*, found only in the walls of the heart (see chapter 7). Its fibres are striated and joined by cross-connections. It contracts to a rhythmic inbuilt beat and does not fatigue. Muscle with the inbuilt ability to contract is called *myogenic*, unlike other kinds which are *neurogenic* and only contract after nervous stimulation.

Properties of muscle

Most investigations of muscle contraction have dealt with vertebrate striated muscle and consequently its properties are better understood than those of the other types. Skeletal muscle normally contracts in response to a nerve impulse arriving at a motor end plate and causing release of *acetylcholine*. We can imitate this process by applying electrical stimuli to the muscle, either directly, or via a nerve fibre. A piece of fresh muscle, bathed in an isotonic solution and well-oxygenated, will respond to stimuli for several hours after removal from an experimental animal. The calf muscle (gastrocnemius) of a frog is often used, the electrical stimulus being provided by a stimulator, and the results recorded on the revolving drum of a kymograph (see Figure 90).

In order to produce a response, the stimulus must be above a certain level, called the *threshold*. A single stimulus will produce a *twitch*. The short period between the application of the stimulus and the contraction is the *latent period*, usually about 0.05 seconds. If a second stimulus is applied before the first contraction has completely relaxed the two twitches become continuous. This is *summation* and the summated response is larger and longer than that of a single twitch. Repeated stimuli close together result in a smooth sustained contraction called *tetany*. Muscular movements in the intact animal are tetanic and therefore smooth rather than twitches. Tetany can only continue until the muscle becomes fatigued due to exhaustion of acetylcholine and build up of lactic acid. (See p. 220.)

Muscles work by contracting and the work they do is measured as the force exerted multiplied by the distance over which this force is exerted. Usually the muscle is exerting its force on various lever systems of the skeleton. It expends some energy in mechanical work and the rest as heat, which helps to maintain a suitable body temperature. Many skeletal movements involve both *isotonic* and *isometric* contractions. Isotonic ones occur when the muscle is able to contract and shorten, whereas in isometric contractions the muscle attempts to shorten and tension increases in it, but no work is done because the load is too great. This can be seen when muscles work against each other providing greater control of movements as, for example, in the maintenance of human posture, where the muscles of the neck, back and thighs exert a steady pull to hold the body upright.

The electrical properties of muscle are investigated by inserting micro-electrodes into individual muscle fibres. These show very similar properties to those of neurons having a resting potential of 50–100 millivolts (inside negative), which is then reversed to an action potential of 30–40 millivolts, with the inside positive relative to the outside of the fibre. These potential differences are caused by the movement of ions, beginning when acetylcholine is released at the motor end plate and alters the selective permeability of the fibre membrane. Muscle fibres also show an 'all or nothing response' like a nerve fibre, only responding to

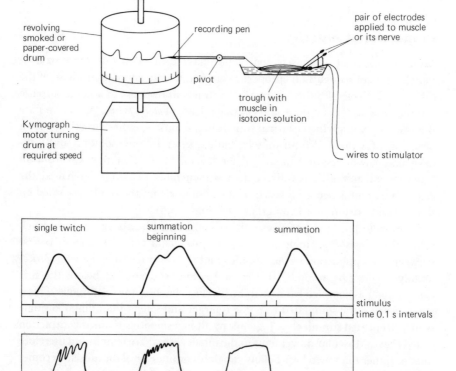

Figure 90 A kymograph and typical tracings using frog gastrocnemius muscle

stimuli above a certain threshold level. After the response there is an *absolute refractory period* during which no contraction is possible, followed by a *relative refractory period* when only a very strong stimulus evokes a response. During these periods the ions are returning to their original positions, reinstating the resting potential.

Structure of skeletal muscle

A vertebrate skeletal muscle is attached via tendons to the *periosteum* – the fibrous layer of tissue covering the bones. The muscle consists of hundreds of muscle fibres varying from less than a millimetre to over forty millimetres in length. Each fibre is covered by an elastic sheath called the *sarcolemma*, inside which is cytoplasm, *the sarcoplasm*, in which numerous nuclei lie close to the surface. Embedded in the sarcoplasm are fine *myofibrils* only one to two micrometres in diameter. Under the light microscope these myofibrils are seen as a pattern of striations, especially if the fibre is suitably stained (see Figure 91).

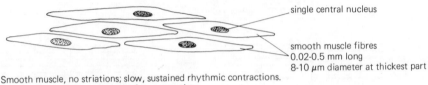

Smooth muscle, no striations; slow, sustained rhythmic contractions.
Impulses from CNS not essential for contraction.

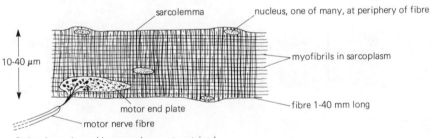

Striated muscle, rapid contractions, not sustained.
Neurogenic, contracts in response to motor impulses from CNS.

Figure 91   The appearance and activity of smooth muscle and striated muscle

With an electron microscope it is possible to see the detail of these striations as alternating dark and light bands on each fibril and referred to as *A* and *I bands* respectively. Maceration techniques have shown that the fibrils are composed of units called *sarcomeres*, which stretch from one *Z membrane* to the next; these membranes being in the centre of each light I band as shown in Figure 92. A lighter *H band* and *M membrane* are usually also visible in the A band.

Greater magnification reveals that each myofibril is composed of even finer filaments of two kinds; thick, eleven to fourteen nanometres in diameter, and thin, four nanometres in diameter. The darkest bands are caused by the

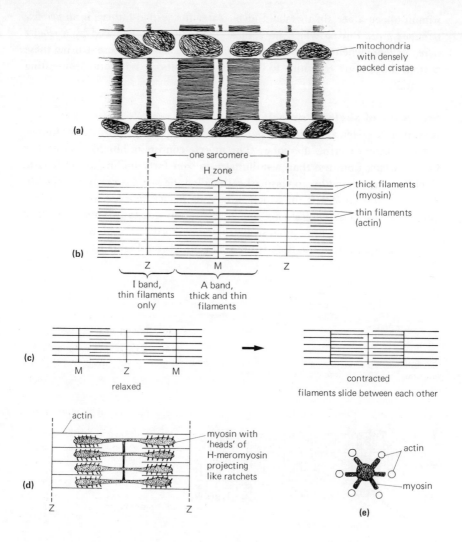

Figure 92 Arrangement of myofibrils in striated muscle
(a) fibre as seen in longitudinal section with electron microscope
(b) diagram of filament arrangement in (a)
(c) sliding of filaments resulting in contraction
(d) arrangement of the ratchet mechanism for sliding
(e) myosin filament surrounded by six actin filaments

overlapping thick and thin filaments, the lighter H bands are thick filaments only and the light bands are thin filaments alone, joined to those of the next sarcomere at the Z membrane. (See Figure 92(b).) Differential extraction techniques have shown the thick filaments are composed of a protein called *myosin* and the thin ones of a protein called *actin*. The myosin molecules have a distinct 'head' made up of H meromyosin (H for heavy because the molecular weight is higher) and a 'tail' of L (lighter) meromyosin. The H meromyosin is a globular protein with an enzyme, adenosine triphosphatase, capable of splitting off the terminal phosphate group of ATP and thereby providing energy for contraction. The 'heads' stick out on each side of the filament about forty five nanometres apart surrounded by actin filaments. Where the actin filaments are absent in the H zone there are no projections. Actin consists of globular protein molecules with an ATP molecule attached to each and arranged as a double helix. In cross section it can be seen that each myosin filament is surrounded by six actin filaments shared by neighbouring myosin filaments (see Figure 92(e)).

In between the myofibrils is an extensive endoplasmic or *sarcoplasmic reticulum* consisting of longitudinal channels connecting to transverse tubules in the A and I bands. A separate transverse *T-system* of canals at the A-I junction connect the sarcoplasmic reticulum to the surface of the fibre. The function of these tubules is to regulate the level of calcium ions in the sarcoplasm as a necessary pre-requisite for the splitting of ATP.

The mechanism of contraction

A relaxed muscle fibre has a resting potential due to the selective permeability of its sarcolemma. When a nerve impulse reaches the fibre, depolarisation occurs and an action potential is set up. This triggers the release of calcium ions into the sarcoplasm from the outer channels of the sarcoplasmic reticulum. It may be that the stimulus for their release is spread by electrical signals passing through the transverse tubules. The increased level of calcium ions activates the ATPase on the H-meromyosin, causing the ATP on the actin molecules to be split and the energy provided allows the formation of cross bridges between the actin and myosin filaments. Electron micrographs suggest that during contraction the filaments slide past each other, probably pulled along by the attachment, release and reattachment of the cross bridges six or seven times, giving a contraction in length of up to thirty per cent. If the contraction is very strong the filaments may actually meet and even buckle. When the action potential has passed a particular point, the calcium ions are somehow actively pumped back into the outer channels of the sarcoplasmic reticulum, the selective permeability of the membrane returns and the resting potential is restored. This period of readjustment is represented by the absolute refractory period during which further contraction is impossible.

The contractile process obviously requires the continual replacement of the ATP used up in the operation of the chemical ratchet system between the filaments. Skeletal muscle is very well supplied with mitochondria and the initial regeneration is by oxidative phosphorylation (see Chapter 2), but the ATP attached to the actin molecules appears to be regenerated very quickly, using a substance called *creatine phosphate* in vertebrate muscle or *arginine phosphate* in most invertebrate muscle. The creatine phosphate acts as a source of terminal high energy phosphate groups for the conversion of ADP back to ATP. The creatine phosphate is then remade from creatine and ATP from the mitochondria. This intermediate system appears to allow a constant level of ATP to exist in the muscle fibrils.

During rapid contractions a muscle may not be able to receive enough oxygen via the respiratory system and circulation to maintain oxidative metabolism. It can continue to work however, for a time at low oxygen levels by converting pyruvic acid to lactic acid instead of oxidising it to carbon dioxide and water. This is anaerobic respiration and, as explained in chapter 2, it is far less efficient than aerobic respiration. The lactic acid produced is toxic and must be constantly removed by the blood. While anaerobic respiration continues an *oxygen debt* is built up and must be repaid when the activity slows down. About four fifths of the lactic acid can then be resynthesised to glycogen in the liver, the remaining one fifth being oxidised to carbon dioxide and water, providing the energy required for glycogen formation.

We can see the effects of an oxygen debt in athletics, since a rapid burst of activity is followed by panting, during which the oxygen debt is repaid. Excessive use of a muscle may also result in cramp due to the build up of lactic acid in it.

MUSCULO-SKELETAL SYSTEMS

There are three basic types of skeleton in animals (see Figure 93). Soft-bodied ones have no hard tissues but use their tissue fluids under pressure as a firm structure against which muscles can pull. This is called a *hydrostatic skeleton* and is well-illustrated in the earthworm. Here the coelomic fluid is surrounded by circular and longitudinal muscle which can contract against it. The division of the coelom into compartments by septa helps to ensure that puncturing and loss of fluid does not result in loss of movement as it does in *Arenicola*, the lugworm, where there are no septa.

A skeleton of hard tissue can be arranged either on the outside or the inside of the body. On the outside it is an *exoskeleton* typical of arthropods, with the muscles enclosed inside. The joints are like hinges worked by *flexor* and *extensor* muscles. A flexor bends the joint when it contracts; an extensor straightens it. (See Figure 93(c).)

A skeleton on the inside is an *endoskeleton* and here the muscles are attached on the outside, as in vertebrates. The joints may be hinged like the elbow or knee, or they may allow rotation as with the ball and socket joints of the human shoulder and hip. In our wrist and ankle are sliding joints where small bones move past each other, and we have a pivot joint where the atlas vertebra, supporting the head, swivels on the axis below it, allowing the head to turn. We also have joints of limited movement between our vertebrae and joints with no movement between the bones of our skull where they meet and fuse. Most other four-limbed (tetrapod) vertebrates have similar arrangements of their joints, though the degree of rotation at shoulder and hip is more limited, particularly in running and jumping animals where the legs must be kept under the body.

The attachment of muscles to a bone is by *tendons* made of collagen which are continuous with the periosteum. At one end a skeletal muscle is fixed to an immovable bone. This is called the *point of origin*, while the other end, the *point of insertion*, is normally fixed to a movable bone. Skeletal muscles work in opposition to each other, frequently in pairs and are therefore called *antagonistic* muscles. For

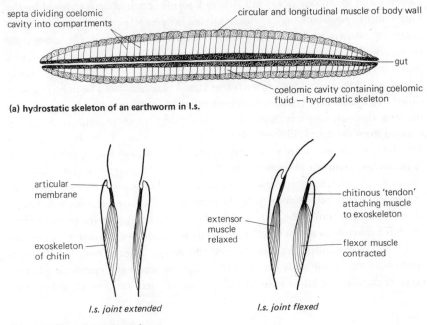

septa dividing coelomic
cavity into compartments

circular and longitudinal muscle of body wall

gut

coelomic cavity containing coelomic
fluid — hydrostatic skeleton

(a) hydrostatic skeleton of an earthworm in l.s.

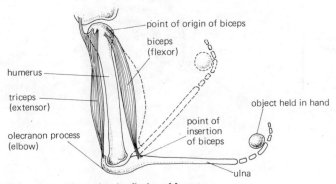

articular
membrane

exoskeleton
of chitin

extensor
muscle
relaxed

chitinous 'tendon'
attaching muscle
to exoskeleton

flexor muscle
contracted

l.s. joint extended

l.s. joint flexed

(b) exoskeleton of an arthropod

point of origin of biceps

biceps
(flexor)

humerus

triceps
(extensor)

olecranon process
(elbow)

point of
insertion
of biceps

object held in hand

ulna

(c) endoskeleton of a vertebrate showing flexion of forearm

Figure 93   A comparison of the three types of skeleton

example the biceps flexes the elbow joint whereas the triceps extends it (see
Figure 93(c)). Ligaments of elastic fibres also help to control movement of joints
by allowing flexibility but keeping the bones in their correct relative positions.

Bone and cartilage

The basic material of the endoskeleton is bone, which is a connective tissue with a
matrix of mineral salts. About 85 % by weight of mammalian bone is calcium
phosphate, ten per cent calcium carbonate, about four per cent magnesium

chloride and about one per cent calcium fluoride. Each bone is covered by the tough fibrous *periosteum* under which is dense *compact bone* composed of *Haversian systems* as shown in Figure 94. Each system has a central *Haversian canal* containing blood vessels, lymph channels, nerves and bone cells or *osteocytes*, in a packing tissue called *areolar tissue*. Around the canal are successive circular lamellae of bone dotted with more osteocytes. These bone cells lie in little spaces called *lacunae* and they connect with each other by fine protoplasmic connections running through tiny *canaliculi*. The connections mean that no bone cell is isolated from the supply of food and oxygen inside the blood vessels. At intervals the Haversian systems are connected transversely by *Volkmann's canals*.

Below the compact bone is a zone of *cancellated* or *spongy bone* made up of a network of bone struts or *trabeculae*. This is arranged so as to take the compression and tension required, while keeping the bone as light as possible. (Bone makes up about fifteen per cent of the body weight of most mammals). In the centre of long bones is a marrow cavity in which blood cells are made (see chapter 7). The shaft of a long bone is called the *diaphysis* and the 'knobs' at each end, the *epiphyses*. Growth occurs at the ends between the diaphysis and each epiphysis where a layer of cartilage is present until full size is reached and the bone becomes

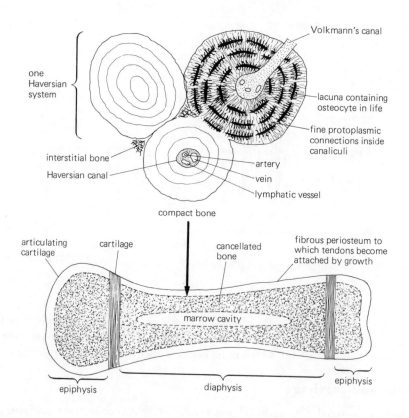

Figure 94 The structure of compact bone and its location in a typical mammalian long bone

continuous. The epiphyses have a layer of cartilage over their articulating surfaces which reduces friction and prevents the wearing away of the ends of the bones. Friction is further reduced by the lubricating *synovial fluid* produced inside the capsule of the joint.

Cartilage has a matrix of *chondrin*, mainly composed of a mucopolysaccharide, more elastic than bone. Most of the embryonic mammalian skeleton exists first as cartilage which is gradually replaced by bone. Of the vertebrate groups, only the elasmobranch fishes have a totally cartilaginous skeleton. Figure 95 shows the three types of cartilage found in mammals. Cartilage at the ends of bones is *hyaline*, without fibres, but elsewhere in the body, fibres may be present. *Fibro-cartilage* contains white fibres of collagen, which give extra firmness, and is found in the intervertebral discs, which cushion the vertebrae while allowing slight

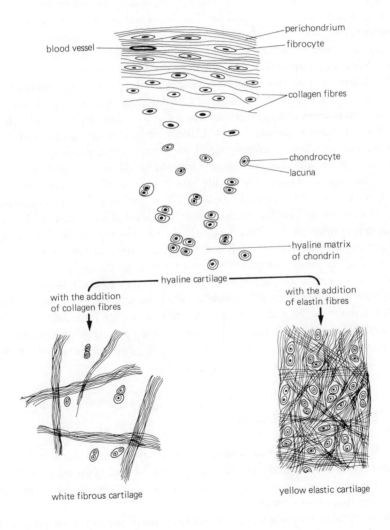

Figure 95   The three types of cartilage

movement. More flexible is *elastic cartilage* with yellow elastic fibres as found in the epiglottis, the pinna of the ear and the Eustachian tube, since here fast recovery of shape after bending is important.

MOVEMENT IN WATER

Being much denser than air, water gives greater support to an animal, but also offers greater resistance, so that aquatic animals tend to be obviously stream-lined, as shown in fish. Propulsion in most fish comes mainly from the tail where segmental blocks of muscle called *myotomes* contract alternately on either side of the flexible vertebral column. Each sideways push of the tail against the water results in the tail being pushed forwards and to the opposite side. The sideways force the water exerts is *lateral drag* and is counteracted by the pressure of the water against the head and dorsal fin. The result is that the fish tends to move forwards rather than from side to side. (See Figure 96(a).) Similar movements are seen in many swimming invertebrates like annelids, while whales make similar movements up and down with their horizontal tail flukes.

The degree of buoyancy a fish has depends on the presence or absence of a *swim bladder*. (See Figure 96(b) and (c).) Cartilaginous fish, like dogfish, do not have a swim bladder and are heavier than water so if they stop swimming they sink. Bony fish have gas-filled swim bladders. Some communicate with the pharynx and are filled by gulping air at the surface like a goldfish; others are closed and gas, usually mainly oxygen, is secreted into them from the blood. The greater the amount of gas in the bladder, the less the relative density of the fish and therefore it will float higher in the water. By withdrawing gas or blowing out air bubbles from the bladder the fish can sink. The air bladder may be derived from a similar structure in existing tropical lung fish. The tail and fins of the bony fish need not provide lift so the tail is usually symmetrical or *homocercal* and the fins are small and can be flattened against the sides of the body.

As well as needing lift, a fish must be able to steer its body using its fins. Horizontal deflection from side to side is called *yawing* and is corrected by the head, the shape of the body and the vertical fins. *Rolling* from side to side is stabilised by the vertical and paired fins, while *pitching* up and down is prevented by the paired fins and, in cartilaginous fish, by the flattened underside of the body. (See Figure 96.)

MOVEMENT ON LAND

Animals on land must receive support from the ground and have evolved a complex system of limbs and levers for pressing against it and pushing themselves along. Figure 97 shows a comparison between the primitive tetrapod reptilian stance and that of a mammal.

The vertebral column of a tetrapod is often compared to a cantilever bridge, as seen in Figure 98, the chain of vertebrae being under compression like the

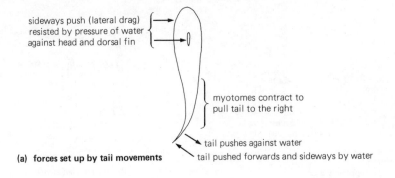

sideways push (lateral drag)
resisted by pressure of water
against head and dorsal fin

myotomes contract to
pull tail to the right

tail pushes against water
tail pushed forwards and sideways by water

(a) forces set up by tail movements

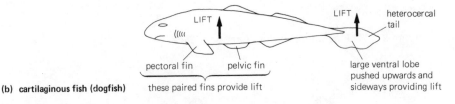

LIFT

LIFT   heterocercal
        tail

pectoral fin   pelvic fin

large ventral lobe
pushed upwards and
sideways providing lift

(b) cartilaginous fish (dogfish)   these paired fins provide lift

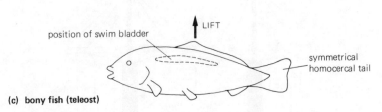

LIFT

position of swim bladder

symmetrical
homocercal tail

(c) bony fish (teleost)

Figure 96   Locomotion in fish
(a) The forces acting on the body of the fish
(b) and (c) a comparison of the generation of lift in a cartilagenous fish and a
bony fish

horizontal compression member of the bridge, while the limbs provide upthrust like the piers of the bridge. The head and tail are 'hung' under tension from ligaments running from the neural spines of the vertebrae to the transverse processes of other nearby vertebrae. Most of the weight is taken by the back legs and pelvic girdle, while the weight of the head is supported by attachments to the pectoral girdle, which allow the head to be kept steady irrespective of other movements.

Walking in tetrapods usually involves a diagonal movement of the limbs lifting one at a time: front right, left hind, front left, right hind etc., keeping the centre of gravity within the tripod made by the three limbs on the ground. Fast-moving mammals like horses or the big cats may increase speed until both front and both hind legs are coming off the ground almost simultaneously. Many animals can sit back on their hind legs, like squirrels or monkeys, giving a better look-out for predators and freeing the fore limbs for feeding or grooming. Man's permanent

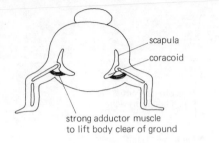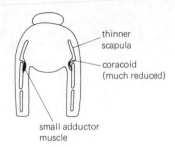

(a) reptilian stance —
'elbow' and 'knee' project outwards.
Movement slow and ponderous.

(b) mammalian stance —
legs brought under body.
Much faster movement.

Figure 97   The evolution of the tetrapod stance

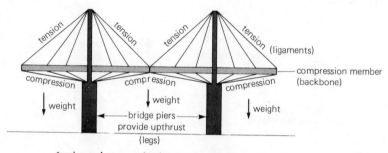

tension and compression in a cantilever bridge

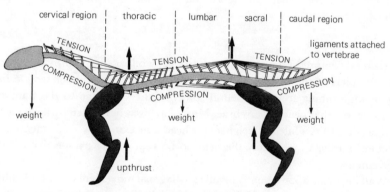

tension and compression in the tetrapod backbone

Figure 98   A comparison between the tetrapod vertebral column and a cantilever bridge

bipedal gait has allowed the hand to develop into a more delicate manipulative structure.

The propulsive force for a tetrapod comes from the feet pressing downwards and backwards against the ground. The flatter the foot on the ground (plantigrade) the greater the upward force relative to the forward one. With the heel raised (digitigrade) the main force is forwards resulting in faster movement, as when a man runs.

MOVEMENT IN AIR

True flapping flight has only been achieved by birds, bats and insects, though a few other vertebrates can glide short distances, like the flying squirrel. Each group has developed wings, which act as aerofoils receiving upthrust from the air.

In birds if a wing is aligned so that the forward edge is tilted upwards, the air moving over the longer upper surface speeds up and loses pressure, generating the greater proportion of the lift (see **Figure 99**). Below the wing the air is only slightly deflected and slows down, increasing its pressure and giving additional lift. The air also exerts a drag force on the wing tending to push it backwards.

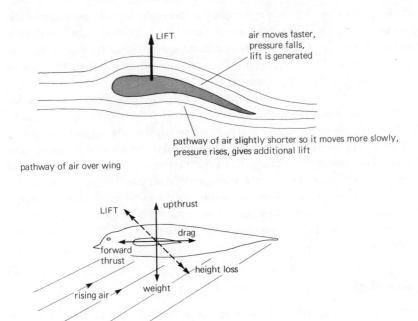

Figure 99   Comparison of the forces acting upon a bird's wing in still and rising air

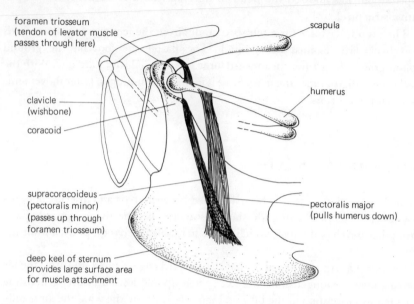

foramen triosseum
(tendon of levator muscle
passes through here)

scapula

humerus

clavicle
(wishbone)

coracoid

supracoracoideus
(pectoralis minor)
(passes up through
foramen triosseum)

pectoralis major
(pulls humerus down)

deep keel of sternum
provides large surface area
for muscle attachment

Figure 100   The chief flight muscles of a bird

The lifting power of the wing is therefore achieved by varying the angle of the wings to the main axis (angle of attack) until lift is at maximum and drag is minimal. A bird can glide horizontally in moving air if the air is rising at the same speed that the bird is losing height. Birds frequently use rising air from warm thermals to allow them to gain height.

Active flapping flight is complicated but basically produces lift in a similar way to gliding. The downstroke is first vertical, giving strong lift, then forward. The front edge is tilted up and more lift is gained, then the upstroke is up and backwards, providing forward thrust. The tail and wings are used in steering and braking. The downstroke is produced by contracting the *depressor muscle* attached to the underside of the humerus at one end and the deep keel of the sternum at the other. The upstroke is performed by contracting the *levator muscle*. This is inserted on the upper surface of the humerus and passes down through a hole, the *foramen triosseum*, surrounded by the scapula, coracoid and clavicle, to the sternum (see Figure 100).

Insect flight

Insect flight may be relatively slow like a butterfly where each wing beat is produced in response to a single nerve impulse, but many smaller insects have very fast wing beats; 100–1000 beats per second, much too fast for triggering by individual nerve impulses. These wing muscles are therefore said to be *asynchronous*. They are arranged as vertical and horizontal blocks attached to the inside of the thorax (see Figure 101). When they contract the thorax distorts, and

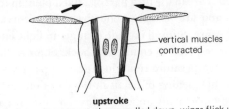

upstroke
vertical muscles contract, thorax pulled down, wings flick up

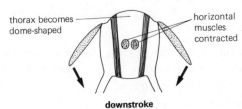

downstroke
horizontal muscles contract, thorax becomes dome-shaped, wings flick down

Figure 101   Indirect flight muscles of an insect

each distortion of the thorax sends the wings up or down while the muscles keep the thorax oscillating. Up to forty wing beats have been counted for a single nerve impulse. These muscles are called *indirect flight muscles* because they are not actually attached to the wings. There are also *direct flight muscles* at the base of each wing, which can adjust the angle of the wings or fold them after flight.

MOVEMENT IN PLANTS

Plant movements can be divided into those which are mechanical and those which involve the sensitivity of the plant to a particular stimulus. Mechanical movements are often *hygroscopic*, caused by tissues drying in the air as in the release of spores from bryophyte capsules, or from fern sporangia, or in the dehiscence of anthers.

Movements resulting from sensitivity can be tropic, tactic or nastic.

Tropic movements (tropisms) are directional growth movements under the control of plant hormones, and are explained further in chapter 13.

Tactic movements (taxes) are made by a whole organism or entity, such as a gamete, towards or away from variations in light intensity and direction (phototaxis), chemical concentration (chemotaxis), oxygen concentration (aerotaxis), osmotic conditions (osmotaxis) or direction of flow of water (rheotaxis). Chemotaxis, for example, has been demonstrated in the swimming male gametes or antherozoids of many plants. The female sex organ or archegonium releases a chemical, such as sucrose in mosses, and the antherozoids swim towards it along the concentration gradient of the substance.

Nastic movements (nastes) are made by a part of a fixed plant in response to a non-directional stimulus and are brought about by growth curvatures or sudden changes in turgor pressure. Stimuli include changes in light intensity, temperature and humidity or response to contact or shock. Some of the movements in response to light and temperature result in a diurnal pattern sometimes called *sleep movements*, as in the opening of petals in the day time and their closure at night. Some of these movements appear to involve differential growth of the upper or lower side of the base of the petal.

QUESTIONS

1   Describe the structure and action of cilia. How may they be coordinated?
2   Give an illustrated account of the structure of skeletal muscle. What changes are believed to occur when it contracts?
3   Compare and contrast
    a)   the swimming of a cartilaginous fish and a bony fish
    b)   the flight of a bird and of an insect.

15   Animal behaviour

The behaviour of animals is a topic of immense scope and complexity, since it encompasses all the physiological and biochemical mechanisms of the body. When we see an animal performing any action we are watching only the outward manifestation of all this internal activity.

The scientific study of behaviour is *ethology* and stretches from the simplest responses of microscopic organisms to the complex behaviour of primates such as chimpanzees and ourselves. Human behaviour, being so much more complicated than that of other animal groups is usually studied as a separate science called *psychology*.

Ethology is a relatively new science, but owes much to the careful observations of Victorian naturalists such as J. H. Fabre in France and Charles Darwin in England. Their work in this field was mainly descriptive and often recounted in terms which credited the animals with human emotions and sometimes even human intelligence. This is called *anthropomorphism*.

Modern studies involve not only observation in nature but also experiments, either in the field or the laboratory, to test the observers' hypotheses. Observation of behaviour in an animal's natural habitat is often difficult. It is also hard to achieve the right conditions in the artificial surroundings of a laboratory. There is also the problem of repeating the same experiment many times with different individuals, under exactly the same conditions, to arrive at scientifically valid conclusions. Even the terminology used is inexact because of differences of opinions, and the difficulty of arriving at precise definitions. Nevertheless, there is now a wealth of observational and experimental information available, although it is only possible to give a few examples here.

The techniques for studying animal behaviour rely very much on observation, either directly or through various kinds of recording devices. These include slow-motion cinematography and multiple-flash photography for very fast movements, and time-lapse photography for very slow movements. Sometimes activity recorders are helpful to record repeated movements, such as a bird alighting on a perch, so that the researcher does not have to count them.

Some forms of animal behaviour seem to be characteristic of a particular species, whereas others are shown only by individuals. These are referred to as *species-characteristic behaviour* and *individual-characteristic behaviour* respectively.

It is also usual to make a distinction between inbuilt or *innate behaviour* and behaviour which has been *learned* by an animal during its lifetime. This is a somewhat artificial distinction since each depends on the other. It is also confusing that the term instinct is sometimes used in animal behaviour studies to refer to innate behaviour, but has much wider implications outside the science, in everyday speech. For instance we may say that we instinctively dislike someone. This does not mean that we were born with a built-in dislike of someone that we had never met, but that the person reminds us of someone else we had previously learned to dislike. In complex behaviour, learning plays a very large part and quickly obscures any innate behaviour pattern present.

Animal behaviour may be placed in different categories as shown below and examples of each are given in the rest of the chapter.

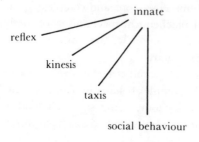 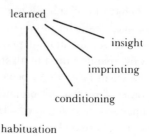

INNATE BEHAVIOUR

Reflex action (See also chapter 6 of *The cell concept*)

We have already discussed the production of reflex actions in chapter 11, and here we are concerned with their place in the behaviour of an animal. A reflex is an automatic short-lived response to a specific stimulus. It requires no thought and is usually outside the conscious control of the animal.

Reflexes make up a large part of the behaviour of the simpler animals, good examples being provided by the *escape reactions* of many invertebrates such as earthworms, crayfish and squid. These produce very fast movement away from harmful stimuli, using a typical reflex arc composed of receptors, fast nerve conduction and appropriate muscle contraction. The details of this action will be described for the earthworm because it is easily demonstrated in the laboratory.

Worms rarely leave their burrows, but on warm humid nights they partially emerge and lie on the surface. This is necessary for the complicated method of sperm exchange which initiates their reproduction, and requires contact with another worm. Some worms also collect leaves from the surface, either as future food, or to plug the entrance to their burrow. Any disturbance such as touch, or even vibration, results in the worm darting back down into its burrow very quickly.

The mechanism involves the stimulation of receptors at the head end, which cause impulses to be passed back down the body along the median giant axon of the nerve cord. The nerve cord of an earthworm has three large fibres in its dorsal part and nerve cells in the ventral part as shown in Figure 102. The three giant fibres conduct impulses quickly, the median one from head to tail and the lateral ones from tail to head.

The impulse passing back along the median fibre causes the longitudinal muscles of the body wall to contract rapidly and the *chaetae* (bristles) to be protracted, so that they grip the walls of the burrow. The chaetae are also hooked and may be rotated by a set of retractor muscles as seen in Figure 102. When the head of the worm is stimulated the chaetae point forward and hook into the sides of the burrow making it harder for a predator, such as a bird, to pull it out. If the stimulus is to the tail end, the reflex movement will be forward using the lateral giant fibres, and the chaetae will rotate to point backwards.

Kinesis and taxis

Kinesis and taxis are *orientation responses*. They are sometimes difficult to distinguish from reflexes but are not short-lived and involve the movement of an organism with regard to the direction of the stimulus. For example, they may lead the animal towards food or away from unpleasant stimuli.

A typical kinesis is shown by the effect of humidity variations on woodlice. They are crustaceans, using gills for gas exchange and having a relatively thin cuticle, so that they are not particularly well-adapted for a terrestrial way of life. Woodlice tend to congregate in groups under stones or vegetation where their rate of water loss is reduced. That this is the result of kinesis and not conscious thought can be shown using a piece of apparatus called a *choice chamber*, as shown

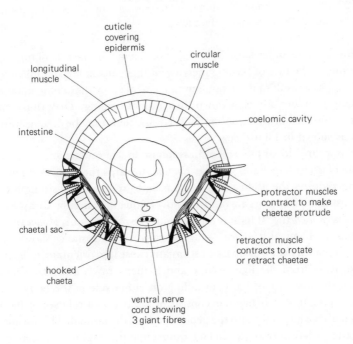

Figure 102   Transverse section of an earthworm showing the chaetae and their musculature

in Figure 103. This apparatus is often used in behavioural experiments and consists of two chambers with an interconnecting passage. The conditions in either of the chambers may be varied with respect to features such as light and dark, temperature and humidity, one feature being varied at a time, and the resulting movements of the animals inside studied.

If the choice chamber is set up as shown in Figure 103 it is possible to see that the woodlice move fast where the humidity is low and tend to slow down as the humidity increases. This means that they tend to eventually remain in the humid half if left for a prolonged period. A kinesis of this kind which results from changes in speed of movement is an *orthokinesis*.

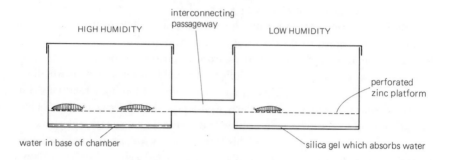

Figure 103   A choice chamber being used to compare the rates of movement of woodlice under different levels of humidity

Klinokinesis on the other hand is the result of changes in the rate of turning. In most organisms the rate of turning increases if they encounter an unfavourable stimulus and as a result of these random movements they may come upon more favourable conditions and slow down their rate of turning. They thus, tend to stay in the more favourable environment. Klinokinesis may be demonstrated in planaria as shown in Figure 104.

A *taxis* is a directional movement in response to a stimulus; for example the swimming of green flagellates, such as *Euglena*, towards the light. A directional movement requires the ability of the organism to measure the strength of the stimulus using its sense organs and to move either towards or away from it (*positive or negative taxis*). If light is the stimulus the movement is *phototaxis* and if the stimulus is chemical it is *chemotaxis*. A mealworm for instance shows *negative phototaxis*. If placed near a lamp its sense organs cause it to orientate itself with its head end away from the light source and it then crawls away continuously comparing the intensity of the light falling on either side of the body.

Instinctive or innate behaviour consists of a variety of reflexes of the kind mentioned above and built into the genetic code of the animal. This means that there is little variety of response, in fact, quite often the response is a stereotyped series of movements known as a *fixed action pattern*. These, once initiated, may continue to completion regardless of any new circumstances arising. Konrad Lorenz and Niko Tinbergen, two famous ethologists, have demonstrated typical

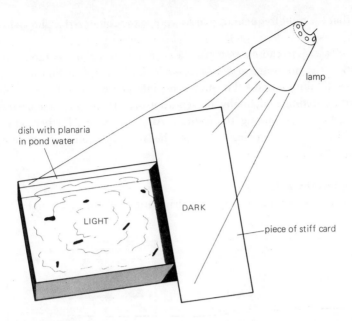

Figure 104 Klinokinesis in planaria. The planaria eventually accumulate in the shadow under the card. In nature they may be found under vegetation or stones in ponds and streams

fixed action patterns in ground-nesting birds, such as geese. Their nests tend to be shallow so that the eggs are easily knocked out. The sitting bird responds to the sight of an egg outside the nest by hooking its beak over the egg and rolling it towards the nest. Should the egg be lost on its way to the nest the bird will continue to roll the non-existent egg all the way to the nest to complete the behaviour pattern. If it then sees the egg still outside the nest the whole behaviour pattern will be repeated.

This does not mean that inherited behaviour patterns may not be improved by repetition during the animal's life. Both bird flight and song appear to be innate behaviour patterns which improve with practice and imitation.

Stimulus, motivation and response

Although innate behaviour is relatively simple and stereotyped it obviously needs a trigger to set it in motion. The triggering stimulus is called a *releaser* and is probably recognised by a mechanism in the brain called the *innate releasing mechanism (IRM)* or *stimulus filtering mechanism*. A releaser may be an act, or a structure of a particular colour or shape. Tinbergen and his colleagues investigated the relative importance of colour and shape of the herring gull's beak in producing a response in the chick. The chick feeds on fish which its parents regurgitate when the chick pecks at their beaks. The chick normally pecks at a red spot near the tip of the parent's yellow beak. The investigators found that the most frequent responses were to the colour red as shown in Figure 105.

If a releaser is to cause a response the animal must be in a suitable state i.e. it must have the necessary *motivation* or *drive*. For example a lion motivated by hunger will hunt for and kill its prey. The sight and smell of the prey will act as releasers for feeding and, finally, the sensation of a distended stomach will act as a *terminating stimulus*, ending the feeding. After this stage, further sight of the prey will not release feeding behaviour because the motivation of hunger no longer exists.

Displacement activity
Occasionally two strong and opposing drives may occur in an animal at the same

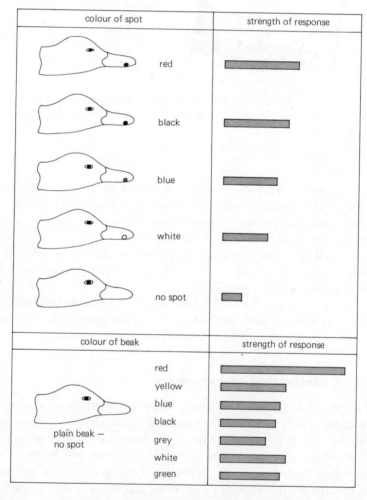

Figure 105 Relative importance of colour of beak and colour of beak spot in eliciting begging response from herring gull chick. (From N. Tinbergen *Social Behaviour in Animals* (Methuen and Co. Ltd.) *Behaviour* Vol 3, 1–38 (E. J. Brill).

time. For instance two domesticated cats meeting at the boundary of their territories may howl threateningly at each other. At the edge of their territory neither cat feels very 'secure' and if the aggressive drive and the urge to retreat are not resolved either or both may resort to irrelevant washing and grooming. This kind of behaviour which is quite separate from the stressful situation is called *displacement activity*.

Similar examples occur in birds defending territory and even some aspects of human behaviour illustrate it. For instance head scratching when we are trying to weigh up a situation and decide what to do. We recognise these signs in other people too, so even displacement activity helps us to 'read' the reactions of those around us.

Vacuum or overflow activity
If motivation for a particular kind of behaviour builds up and the appropriate releaser is not available, the behaviour may still be produced in its absence. For instance the very strong maternal instinct of some pregnant mammals may result in them 'adopting' the young of another of their species until their own young are born.

Social behaviour
Releasers are also important in ensuring the correct sequence of events in complicated social behaviour such as courtship. Each action of one partner is a signal releasing the next activity in the other partner. Failure to produce the correct response may result in conflict or displacement activity by the other partner. Figure 106 shows the stages in the courtship and egg laying of the three-spined stickleback.

In spring the males become solitary and select territories which they defend against members of either sex. The male becomes more brightly coloured with a very distinctive red belly. He begins to build a tunnel-like nest of algal threads. Meanwhile the females are developing a characteristic swollen appearance because of the eggs developing in their ovaries. If such a female approaches the male's nest he will perform an odd zigzag dance to which the female responds by displaying her swollen shape. The male swims to the nest and the female follows responding to his red colouring. At the nest the male indicates the entrance with his snout and the female swims in. The male prods the base of her tail with a trembling movement, which stimulates her to release her eggs. She then swims out of the nest and the male chases her away. He enters the nest and fertilises the eggs. He may guide several females to the nest and accumulate a number of egg clutches before his sex drive decreases. He begins to guard the nest and fan water over the eggs with his pectoral fins. This increases the supply of oxygen around the eggs and near to the time of hatching may take up to three-quarters of the male's time. He continues to guard the young when they have hatched, but gradually loses his red colour as they become increasingly independent. Finally the male returns to a shoal of adult males and the young remain in a small group by themselves.

The three-spined stickleback is an example of an animal with no permanent

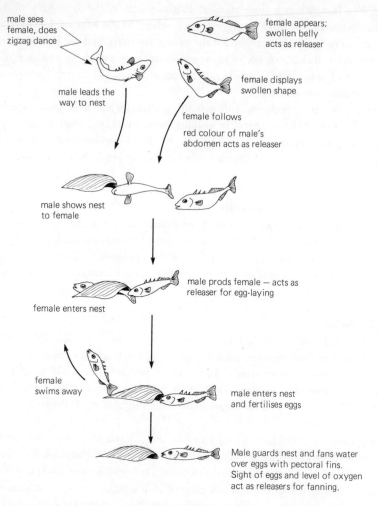

male sees female, does zigzag dance

female appears; swollen belly acts as releaser

male leads the way to nest

female displays swollen shape

female follows

red colour of male's abdomen acts as releaser

male shows nest to female

female enters nest

male prods female — acts as releaser for egg-laying

female swims away

male enters nest and fertilises eggs

Male guards nest and fans water over eggs with pectoral fins. Sight of eggs and level of oxygen act as releasers for fanning.

Figure 106 Sequence of courtship in three-spined stickleback

social structure but there are many examples of animals which maintain social groups and illustrate co-operative behaviour of varying kinds. Honey bees for example, communicate by touch, smell and hearing. More than thirty years ago Karl von Frisch showed that bees indicate the position of a source of pollen or nectar by performing a particular kind of 'dance' when they return to the hive. The other bees jostle around the dancing bee and detect the speed and direction of its movements, the frequency of its buzzing and any flower scent that lingers on it. The *round dance* is performed if the food is less than one hundred metres from the hive and the *waggle dance* if the distance is greater. The greater the distance the slower the dance, and the angle between the middle section of the waggle dance and the vertical indicates the direction of the food relative to the hive and the sun.

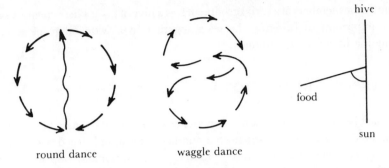

round dance   waggle dance

The bee hive demonstrates a rigid caste system and stereotyped behaviour patterns, but there are social groups, particularly amongst the mammals e.g. baboons, where there is a hierarchy and division of labour. The relationships between the animals are less rigid however, and there is the possibility of behaviour being modified by experience and passed on to other members of the group.

Hormones and behaviour

In chapter 11 we have seen how certain hormones are associated with some human emotions, such as fear and anger in the case of adrenalin from the adrenal cortex. The effect of other hormones in many animals has been shown experimentally by either removing a particular endocrine organ or giving additional injections of a certain hormone. For example the mammalian testes secrete the hormone testosterone, which is responsible for maintaining the male sex drive. A castrated animal fails to show sexual behaviour but this may be restored by administering testosterone injections.

The singing, courtship, nest-building cycle of many song birds is a product of the increasing levels of testosterone secreted by the enlarging testes in the spring. In this case the sequence of events probably begins with the eyes detecting increasing day length. This information is passed to the pituitary which in turn influences the rate of development of the reproductive organs.

Although hormones may be easily demonstrated to be involved in many aspects of behaviour it is not yet clear how they act. We do know, however, that the rate of growth of nerve connections in the developing brain may be affected by hormones, and so may nerve cells and synapses, so that conducting pathways might either be opened up or closed. Evidence also suggests that the sensitivity of receptors and the efficiency of effectors may be varied by some hormones.

Pheromones

Pheromones are odorous substances produced by one animal and which influence the behaviour of another. An obvious example is the way in which dogs 'mark' lamp posts or trees with their urine leaving a smell message to other dogs. Pheromones in the urine will identify the dog and give its sex and social position in the local dog hierarchy. Foxes and wolves also mark their territory in this way. Pheromones may also be used to leave a trail to follow as in the case of ants, or to identify the members of a social group, such as a hive of bees. These chemicals are very important in bringing the sexes together in a wide range of animals including insects and mammals.

LEARNED BEHAVIOUR

Learned behaviour is the result of experience modifying the innate behaviour of an animal. It is usual to distinguish a number of forms of learned behaviour of varying complexity and termed habituation, conditioning, imprinting and insight.

Habituation

Habituation is a very simple form of learned behaviour, in which the animal merely becomes 'used to' a certain stimulus and ceases to react to it. For example a human being may react sharply to a sudden loud noise, but as the noise is repeated and the person is more prepared for it, the sound may be identified and then more or less ignored. The value of this kind of behaviour is that it allows the animal to concern itself with important stimuli at the expense of repeated stimuli to which no response is necessary.

We have already looked at the reflex escape reaction of earthworms (see p. 232), but if a worm is repeatedly made to produce this response it will soon cease to do so. Experiments have shown that the failure to respond is caused by synaptic blocks between the afferent neurons from the touch receptors and the median giant fibre, and also between the median giant fibre and the efferent neurons to the longitudinal muscles as shown below:

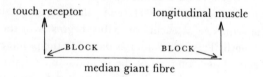

Associative learning

In this kind of learning the animal comes to associate a particular response with either a reward or a punishment, using these terms in their broadest sense. Reward for example could mean finding food, and punishment the absence of food or perhaps attack by another animal. In order to show associative learning the animal must be able to remember its past experience and modify its behaviour in the light of that experience, but there need be no conscious thought involved.

Conditioned reflex

Ivan Pavlov the Russian physiologist first demonstrated this type of associative learning when he was investigating the secretion of digestive juices in dogs. He noted that the sight and smell of food resulted in an increased flow of saliva from the dogs. Later he taught the dogs to associate the presence of food with another separate stimulus, such as the ringing of a bell. After the food and the bell had become associated together in the minds of the dogs he found that merely ringing the bell would cause them to salivate, whether food was presented to them or not.

Conditioning is important in establishing suitable patterns of social behaviour, as we see for instance in children, where the reward may be as tenuous as words of praise, and the punishment, to be told that they have been naughty.

Trial and error (operant conditioning)

The simplest form of *trial and error learning* may be illustrated by a maze in which an animal must choose between making left and right turns in order to arrive eventually at a point where a food reward is waiting. Even relatively simple animals such as flatworms and earthworms may learn to perform such a task. In many cases the animal will learn more quickly if 'punished' by unpleasant stimuli for taking the wrong turning.

Although this kind of simple learning is demonstrable in a wide range of animals, it is found, as one would expect that animals with more complex brains learn more quickly and retain the memory longer. In all cases the memory is kept longer if *reinforced* at intervals by repeating the task.

Exploratory (latent) learning

Even without the presence of reward or punishment most animals explore their surroundings and store this information in their memories. Later, it may prove useful, for instance by aiding flight from, or hiding from, a predator. Experiments have shown that a rat which has been allowed to explore a maze beforehand, will learn to find food in it, or escape from it, much faster in subsequent trials than one which has not had this advantage.

Insight

Insight implies the 'thinking out' of a problem and sudden understanding without having to resort to trial and error. Even in man it is doubtful how much of our response to a new set of circumstances is actually due to insight and how much to combinations of memories of past experiences, trial and error etc. In other animals it becomes still more difficult to surmise.

Experiments with chimpanzees have shown that they are capable of using tools to get at food which is just out of reach and that they appear to arrive suddenly at the solution, which suggests insight. Some insight behaviour however, requires the use of abstract generalisations which can later be used in new situations. Chimpanzees have been shown to be capable of understanding and using abstract ideas, such as possession and the use of signs and symbols, but most mammals show only the rudiments of this behaviour.

The speed with which an animal recognises and solves a new problem gives some measure of its *intelligence*, but it is difficult to compare intelligence in different species by means of a test suitable for them all.

Social learning – imprinting

The first moving object that a chick sees when it hatches is rapidly and permanently fixed in its mind as its parent and the chick will follow it. Konrad Lorenz induced goslings and ducklings to imprint on him. Goslings only require a moving object of suitable size; whereas the ducklings also need the foster-parent to make quacking noises.

Young hoofed animals which must move off soon after birth and follow their mother, may also become imprinted on a human mother-substitute.

Imprinting presumably keeps the young close to the parents and aids their survival in nature, but imprinting on a foster-parent of another species often results in failure by the young animal to recognise members of its own species later in life.

Learning from others

Observational learning has been demonstrated in several mammal species including rats and kittens, where a trained animal performs a task such as running through a maze, while visible to other untrained animals of that species. These animals learn the task much faster than others that have not seen the task performed. In kittens for example, it was found that they learned four times as fast if they could watch their own mother.

This kind of learning is likely to be important in social groups such as a flock of birds or a troop of monkeys. Japanese zoologists studying Macaque monkeys have found instances of *cultural development* such as the washing of food. One female monkey began to wash the sweet potatoes provided by the observers and within three years the habit had spread to eleven other individuals in the troop.

THEORIES OF LEARNING AND MEMORY

In order to learn from experience an animal must be able to remember, but so far it has not been possible to explain what memory is or where it is located in any brain. One theory is the result of work by J. Z. Young and others on octopus brains, and suggests the existence of *memory units* or *mnemons*. (See Figure 107.) Part of each is a *classifying cell* which is excited by a particular stimulus, such as a shape. Leading from the cell are two pathways, one leading to attack, the other to retreat. When a stimulus is received the attack pathway is activated. If the result of the attack was rewarding e.g. food obtained, then the retreat pathway is closed; but if the attack resulted in unpleasant stimuli then the attack pathway is closed. The closure is done by nearby short axon cells which produce an inhibitory substance blocking the synapse.

Thus each memory unit responds to a specific piece of information and the

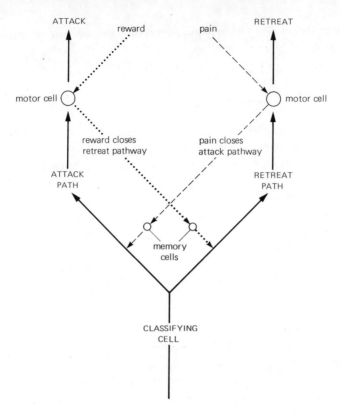

Figure 107   Hypothetical single memory unit or mnemon

result is recorded in the form of an open or closed pathway. The inhibitory cells are therefore acting as memory cells by producing a store of information about the results of the animals actions.

Another theory about memory storage involves the use of macromolecules such as RNA and protein. There is evidence for separate stores for long and short term memory. *Short term memory* is labile (easily lost) and probably stored in the *hippocampus*, just below the cerebral cortex. *Long term memory* is probably stored in the cortex itself. The time taken to transfer the short term memory to long term storage has been variously estimated as from a few minutes to several hours.

Forgetting from the short term memory is speeded up by shock such as concussion or electrocortical shock treatment, but the long term memory is not affected, even by treatment in animals which stops all electrical activity in the brain. This suggests that laying down a long term memory involves a stable change, perhaps in the structure of a synapse or in the internal organisation of the cell. These changes could include memory fixation in a stable macromolecule and evidence does suggest that when information is stored changes occur in the rates of synthesis of RNA and protein. It may be that actual molecules are being produced to store the memory, or perhaps more likely, that the biochemical changes are altering the probability of a particular nerve cell firing, either by altering the structure of the synapse or varying the amount of transmitter substance released.

QUESTIONS

1 Explain with examples the meaning of the terms:
releaser, displacement activity, fixed action pattern.
2 Discuss the differences between innate and learned behaviour.

16 Disease and its implications

THE ROLES AND NATURE OF DISEASES*

Homeostasis and interactions with the environment

A broad view of disease concerns the relationships of cells and whole larger organisms to their environment and helps us to place in perspective specialised studies of given disorders. Organisms react to changes in their environment by making internal adjustments which usually maintain the conditions essential for physiological processes. We call the adjustments homeostasis. An example of homeostasis in a cell in the leaf of a plant is the removal during the night of starch made during the day to other parts of the plant, so that by next morning the cell is ready to accumulate the next deposit of starch. An example in an animal cell is the removal by chemical changes of substances accumulated by prolonged contractions of a muscle fibre (a multinuclear cell). The contractions grow weak as fatigue sets in, and after a period of rest the substances have been dispersed and the fibre can return to full activity. Homeostasis in whole bodies is the result of collective actions by individual cells.

Many homeostatic processes concern the cell and its environment, for every cell has a site or niche in which it lives and to which it reacts. The niche may be in air or water in which free-living single cells occur, or it may be within an organ of a large body of an organism. Examples of niches are displayed in Figure 108. The homeostatic processes may affect the conditions in the niche, e.g. the hair-like rhizoids of lichens penetrate cracks in rocks and produce carbonic acid which decomposes the carbonates in the rocks. Some cells alter the conditions in such a way that later on other types of cells can live there. The soil bacterium *Nitrosomonas* forms nitrites which another bacterium, *Nitrobacter*, can use and make nitrates, which in turn are a chief form of nitrogen compound entering the root hair cells of flowering plants.

---

* The study of diseases involves many aspects of biology. Therefore the readers of this section will be greatly helped if they already have some knowledge of the pests and parasites discussed in the following parts of *The diversity of life*: chapters 2 on Bacteria, 3 on Protozoa, 5 on Fungi, 7 on Platyhelminthes, 8 on Nematoda and 9 on Arthropoda. The relationships of cells to their environment are concerned in disease and so chapters 6 and 7 of *The cell concept* on water and salt relationships and homeostasis should also be read. Normal physiological processes may change in disease and thus the preceding chapters of the present book provide an important foundation on which an understanding of abnormal conditions in plants and animals may be built. Aspects of ecology and disease occur in *Man and the ecosystem*.

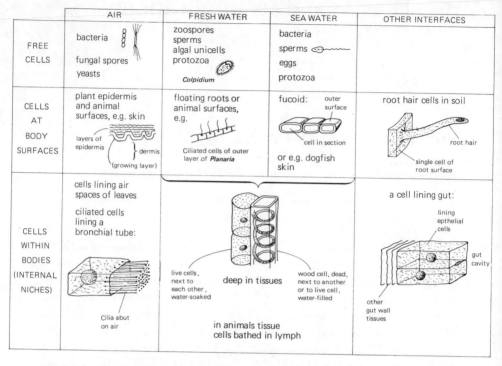

Figure 108   Diagrammatic representation (not to scale) of examples of cell niches

Symbiosis and the balance of nature

Because cells affect each other they do not lead isolated lives. When de Bary first used the term symbiosis in 1879, he intended it to denote all known ways in which organisms co-exist. Later the term was confined to cases where only two organisms lived in close contact, each benefitting the other in some way. In recent years, however, it has become clear that there is a delicate balance between cells and organisms and the environment, so that we tend to return to de Bary's original wide view. A root of a plant growing in soil, for instance, has several types of relationships with the soil forming the niche. The region close to the root is the *rhizosphere*, inhabited by many protozoa, bacteria and fungi, all of which form substances affecting each other and the root. The root too exudes substances which affect the micro-organisms nearby. It is not hard, therefore, to realise how in such complex conditions a change from mutual benefit could occur and lead to invasion of the root by one or more of the potentially (or facultative) parasitic fungi. Thus the organisms in nature achieve a balance with each other and their environment, thriving within the physical limits imposed by factors like intensity of light or availability of water.

It is appropriate to note that until recent space exploration there was no way of finding directly if organisms existed in the universe outside our earth. A start has been made by the landing of apparatus on Mars. The material on the planet's surface was placed in solutions in which earthly micro-organisms live and evolve carbon dioxide, but none of this gas was formed, not did any micro-organisms grow in other suitable fluids. Knowledge of the rest of the universe suggests that evolution of life could have occurred on other planets similar to our earth. At present however the study of organisms is confined to our earth.

Hazards and disease

The balance of nature is not static and even if the numbers and types of organisms seem at first sight to be unchanged this may hide the real alterations caused by deaths from age and the activities of predators, as well as the births of new animals and reproduction of plants. The decay of dead bodies in soil or water sets free substances which are used as food by future plants and animals. Death also removes weak or ill-adapted organisms. Short of death the ecological and homeostatic changes may bring into action the in-built means of protection against hazards and disease. For instance, blood clots in wounds and prevents further bleeding, and a protective layer of callus forms in damaged parts of plants. Recovery from disease can prolong the life of well-adapted individuals so protecting species from extinction. In terms of homeostatic change, to succumb to a disease represents runaway feedback – a failure to adjust to too great an adverse change in the conditions of a niche. Recovery is corrective feedback – a response which restores the organism's condition for normal life.

Disease is a condition an organism reaches or passes through in response to some internal or external agent. Thus disease involves both the organism and its environment and is not a 'thing' or state which can exist by itself apart from them. Although some hazards and diseases have resulted from human activities, such as cancers following the dispersal of radio-active materials, all the known types of disease exist in nature as part of the ecological system. (See Table 9 on page 248.)

If we were merely objective scientists we would observe that there is a wide range of diseases and responses resulting from all causes, not only in humans but also in animals and plants. We would study the roles and effects of disease and not attribute to them benefits or harm. We are however responsible citizens and so we admit to the existence of suffering and the loss of produce we need to keep healthy and in fact we apply human values to these events. The practical consequence has been the increasing efficiency, as science has developed, of three main forms of applied biology:

plant pathology (the study of plant diseases)
veterinary medicine (the study of animal diseases)
human medicine.

In the few pages available in this book it is only possible to mention the main principles involved in such a huge range of phenomena.

Table 9   The principal causes of disease:

external causes	non-living agents	changes in conditions of niches causing physiological imbalance, e.g. shortage of food, harmful substances or radiations, natural accidents like landslides
	living agents	pests and parasites including micro-organisms as *pathogens* (live cells causing disease in another organism).
internal causes	abnormal metabolism	internal metabolic disorders (which are sometimes related to genetical abnormalities)
	genetical causes	genetic abnormalities of chromosomes or particular gene combinations
		stresses, e.g. fear when chased

Unknown causes exist for some diseases e.g. multiple sclerosis.

The relative impact of types of disease

Until the growth of science in the nineteenth and twentieth centuries the causes of many devastating diseases were unknown and control or cure was largely by trial and error. Once causes were understood more rational procedures were possible, and of course the discovery of causes alone would not have been very useful if there had not also been parallel scientific development of treatments. The effects of different types of disease varies as discoveries are made and at any one moment the total impact is related to the state of knowledge and its application.

Bad environment can cause diseases of plants, for example deficiency of magnesium in sandy soils, otherwise suited to the growth of tobacco crops, can be remedied by supplying the metal in a suitable solution of its salts, so averting the deficiency of chlorophyll resulting from the lack of the magnesium. Deficiency diseases from lack of vitamins in the diet of humans and animals can be avoided and in most areas of the world the correct application of existing knowledge could prevent large scale famine of the kind common in a pre-scientific age.

The genetics of crops is now better understood than it was formerly and their resistance to disease can be improved by cross breeding with wild strains. In general diseases of genetic origin in animals and humans have become more prominent subjects of research in the last thirty years. West African shorthorn cattle, for instance, tolerate attack by the protozoan trypanosomes better than varieties from elsewhere, by reason of their genetic constitution.

Examples of human diseases of genetic origin are certain opacities of the lenses of the eyes, haemophilia (imperfect clotting of the blood after injuries) and some mental disorders. Sometimes the causes are the result of particular combinations of genes and sometimes there are extra chromosomes or they are absent or abnormal. Some of these disorders can be treated medically and others avoided by tracing family histories and advising parents who are likely to have affected children. Some account of these processes is given in *Heredity, development and evolution*.

Some of the greatest ravages of history have been caused by external living agents in the bodies of plants, animals and people. The agents are either pests in the form of animals belonging to a few phyla, or micro-organisms like bacteria or some fungi, or viruses. Most infections of plants are caused by fungi whereas bacteria and viruses are the principal causes of infection in animals and humans. Pests however, are chiefly different forms of worms or insects, and examples, descriptions and life-cycles are given in *The diversity of life*. Here we may briefly note a few important pests and discuss micro-organisms in detail later.

Some Nematodes (round worms) like species of *Heterodera* destroy crops by eating their roots. Other worm pests affect domesticated animals and still others infest hundreds of millions of people throughout the world, often with lasting effects on health. The control of these pests is difficult both medically and from the point of view of public health. *Schistosomiasis* occurs in many sub-tropical and tropical countries when the platyhelminth trematode causing this disease infests the veins, notably in the abdomen. *Taenia solium* is a tapeworm (cestode) infesting the intestines, sometimes attaining a length of several metres. Its eggs are shed with the faeces and if they reach pigs, pass another stage of the life cycle in them so that the pest can reach other people who eat undercooked, infested pork. *Ascaris lumbricoides* is a nematode living in the intestines, but its larva reaches the lungs. It can be picked up from raw vegetables so the risk is reduced by thorough washing and cooking. *Elephantiasis* is a disease accompanied by great swelling of the limbs in tropical countries. The cause is a nematode which blocks the lymph vessels and dams up the circulation.

Insects may damage crops by eating parts or all of them, locusts being a historic and outstanding example, still important in Africa. Some insects suck blood, like lice on the human scalp or torso. Others are of great importance as transmitters of microbial pathogens like the protozoa which cause malaria. Bacteria may also be dispersed by insects, a notable example being the bacillus of plague which is carried from black rats to humans by a flea. A recent case of a change in disease patterns is the spread of a tick, *Ixodes ricinus*, westwards from eastern European countries. The tick carries a micro-organism causing fatal inflammation of the brain.

Our control of physiological disorders has been much improved in the present century, especially of diseases resulting from defects of the endocrine organs. In 1922 Banting and Macleod discovered that insulin secreted by certain cells in the pancreas was deficient in patients suffering from *diabetes mellitus*, so-called because their urine contained sugar. The disease often proved fatal but since the preparation of insulin in a form which can be injected or taken by mouth many people can lead normal lives or have their condition relieved.

In contrast to the relief of famine and control of many devastating epidemics of crops and people, since the mid-nineteenth century, so-called 'diseases of civilisation' have mostly affected industrial nations and increased in them very much. Apart from hazards associated with some industrial practices, like the inhaling of asbestos dust, two important problems stand out: a great increase in cardio-vascular diseases and cancers. Clots of blood in the heart or brain may follow rupture of blood vessels and may cause instant death or leave much impaired health. These disabilities are precipitated by anxiety, excessive use of alcohol and tobacco and by obesity.

In proportion to other diseases cancers cause more deaths than hitherto. There are many forms of cancer and we know that some are caused by *carcinogens*, cancer inducing substances which may be absorbed in various ways. Some, like tar products, have caused cancers in people in certain industries, and it is certain that the risk of acquiring lung cancer is substantially increased by smoking tobacco, especially cigarettes. The causes of other forms of cancer as yet are imperfectly understood. Early treatment is most important; half of the cases receiving surgery soon enough are cured. Clearly there is intense scientific and medical interest in the reasons why the *tumours* (swellings) typical of the disease form and grow, and some factors in the process are now better understood.

Mental illnesses are also very prominent today and affect to different degrees one in every five patients seeking medical aid, at least in Western countries.

The micro-organisms causing infectious diseases are members of larger groups of which by no means all the species are harmful, in fact, many are essential in the decay of bodies after death and in the upkeep of soil fertility. A micro-organism comprises one or a few cells and is not often more than a few micrometres in size. Those which are infectious *pathogens* cause diseases in other, usually higher, plants, animals and humans which are then called *hosts*. Figures 109, 110, and 111, show representative micro-organisms of each main type, separately or inside hosts. Their significance will now be considered in some detail.

VIRUSES

Towards the end of the nineteenth century, after Pasteur and Koch had established that pathogenic bacteria caused a number of diseases, it was clear that many similar complaints had no comparable cause. In 1892 Iwanowsky filtered ground-up leaves of tobacco plants with mosaic disease (mottled leaves). The filter was known to hold back bacteria but the filtrate was infectious and reproduced the disease when rubbed on to healthy leaves of tobacco plants. The exact nature of the infectious filtrate was uncertain. Later, infectious filtrates were obtained from diseased tissue in many other diseases and hundreds are now known, examples being:

Organism	Average dimensions micro-metres:	Typical shape	disease caused or other notes
Staphylococcus pyogenes	1.0 diam.	in clusters	pus and boils
Neisseria gonorrhoeae	0.5 to 0.7 diameter	2 joined bean-shaped cells	gonorrhoea
Streptococcus spp.	0.5 to 0.75 diameter	Cells in chains. Some have capsules.	Many species. Infect wounds, present in milk (sour), used in making cheese.
Diplococcus pneumoniae (also called *Streptococcus*)	0.5 to 1.0	cells in pairs	one form of pneumonia (lobar)
Pseudomonas spp.	3.0 long	round ended, 1 polar flagellum	many species cause rots and wilts of plants
Salmonella typhi	3.0 x 0.5	round ended, 6 to 8 flagella	many species; intestinal diseases
Clostridium tetani	2.5 long	spore swells out end of cell	tetanus
Bacillus anthracis	5 to 6 x 1	cells in chains spore central	anthrax; large cell, contents seen relatively easily
Vibrio cholerae	2 x 0.3	1 Polar flagellum	cholera
Treponema pallidum	10 x 0.25	coil, ends taper	syphilis

Note: Bacteria are of few shapes but species and strains are numerous and differ in chemical behaviour and disease relationships. Cells of similar shapes may belong to different families, or chemical differences between identical strains may be small.

Scales for comparison: Red blood cell 8 μm (human)
Limit optical microscope 0.25
Average bacterium 3.0

Figure 109 Examples of bacteria involved in disease

IN HUMANS	IN ANIMALS	IN PLANTS
smallpox	dog distemper	tobacco mosaic
measles	foot and mouth disease	potato leaf roll
poliomyelitis	in cattle	sugar beet yellows
influenzas	myxomatosis in rabbits	
common colds		

In plants virus diseases often have visible signs in leaves as well as generally poor growth, fall of leaves or reduced amount and sizes of fruits (see Figure 112). In mammals and man the infection may be confined to given tissues. In mumps for instance, the parotid salivary glands swell. Sometimes there are typical skin rashes, as in measles. There may be general effects in man as well as local ones, e.g. fever may occur.

Often infected cells have *inclusion bodies* which may be collections of the virus as crystals or a reaction by the cell. Plant viruses travel in the phloem and although viruses do not make harmful exo-toxins, as do some bacteria, the products of infected host cells move in certain tissues like the lymph and blood in animals. Viruses thus appear as seemingly dead outside of cells yet possessing one typical property of life, namely the capacity to reproduce, but only within cells they have parasitised.

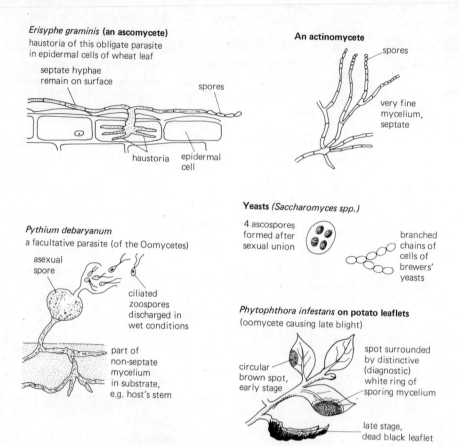

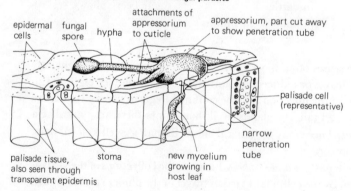

Figure 110 Some fungi and plant diseases (diagrams not to scale)

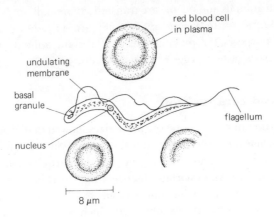

Figure 111 *Trypanosoma*; a protozoan blood parasite

Figure 112 Healthy tomato plant compared with a tomato plant infected with curly top virus

Transmission of viruses

Many plant viruses pass from diseased to healthy hosts by contact. Hairs on leaves may be broken and the virus escapes and enters broken hairs on other healthy leaves. Viruses can be passed to new crops of bulb-bearing plants from the bulbs used to start the crop, but seeds are not usually transmitters of viruses. Insects may be carriers or vectors of some viruses. In a vector, but not in a carrier, a period of incubation must pass before the insect's bite is infective. Potato leaf roll is an example of a plant virus disease transmitted by insects (aphids). (See Figure 115, aphid.)

Viruses from animals and people are transmitted in small drops of liquid from sneezes or coughs, or in faeces or dust. Figure 115 shows a sneeze. For experimental purposes, or making vaccines, certain animal viruses can be multiplied in parts of hen's eggs or in tissue culture.

Structure and composition

Experiments with filters with pores of known sizes showed that viruses comprised some sort of particles and were not chemical substances in solution. The arrival of the electron microscope made measurement of the particles and study of their structure much easier. An important discovery by Twort in 1915 and d'Herelle in 1918 threw light on virus behaviour. In some cultures of bacteria, clear areas appeared from which a filtrate was obtained which would cause similar areas to develop in new cultures and the bacterial cells there were split open, or *lysed*. From this it was concluded that the cause was a virus (*bacteriophage, or phage*) in the filtrate.

Viruses are now known to vary in dimensions from 10 to 500 nanometres, as compared to the average dimensions of bacteria of 500 to 2000 nanometres. The three chief shapes are shown in Figure 113.

(i) Cubical symmetry, many-sided and roughly spherical outer shapes, averaging 50 nanometres in diameter.

(ii) Helical symmetry, tubes 300 or more nanometres long, circular in cross-section.

(iii) Phages, in two main parts, a head and a tail.

All viruses comprise an outer protein coat containing an inner spiral or helix of nucleic acid. In all plant viruses and some animal viruses there is RNA (ribonucleic acid), and there is DNA (deoxyribonucleic acid) in the other animal viruses and in the phages. The proportion of protein to nucleic acid varies from virus to virus. The molecules of protein are packed in typical arrangements and the nucleic acid spiral can be single or double. Figure 113 shows one possible classification of viruses based on their structure and nucleic acid content. Further separations rest on serological (blood or other protein) tests, the symptoms in hosts and the modes of transmission.

Bacteriophages are valuable in genetical studies because they regenerate themselves prolifically in a few minutes and because they have only one nucleic acid strand or chromosome. Phages can also be recombined experimentally in various ways after separation of the protein from the nucleic acid. Their genetical importance is developed in *Heredity, development and evolution*.

How viruses act

From studies of viral nucleic acids separated from their coats it is clear that the type of infectivity depends upon the nucleic acids. We know much about the action of phages from one called T2 since it acts on the cells of the bacterium *Escherichia coli*, as set out in Figure 114.

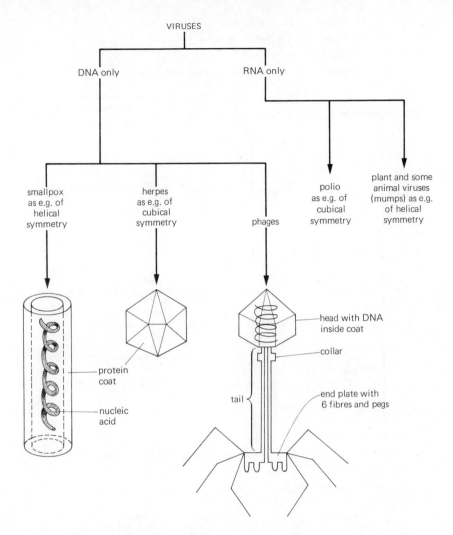

Figure 113   Types and structure of viruses

The life cycles of other viruses are similar to that of phages but may take longer and the extent of breakdown of the host cell varies. Some phages are said to be *temperate* because they do not replace the action of the host cell's nucleus totally but become associated with it. Both types of nucleic acid divide with the cell, and there is no destruction of the cell. After a number of generations however, the virus may become destructive or apparently be absorbed by the cell.

Viruses and cancer

About twelve *oncogenic* viruses cause cancers in animals but none is known to do so for certain in humans. It is thought that a few may do in humans however, including one possibly concerned with leukaemia. The oncogenic viruses may, like some phages, associate with the host's chromosomes, altering the genetic

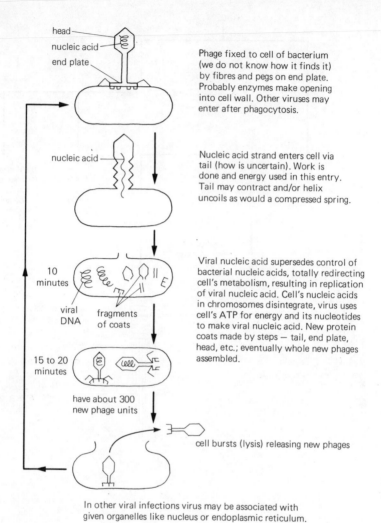

head

nucleic acid

end plate

Phage fixed to cell of bacterium
(we do not know how it finds it)
by fibres and pegs on end plate.
Probably enzymes make opening
into cell wall. Other viruses may
enter after phagocytosis.

nucleic acid

Nucleic acid strand enters cell via
tail (how is uncertain). Work is
done and energy used in this entry.
Tail may contract and/or helix
uncoils as would a compressed spring.

10
minutes

viral
DNA

fragments
of coats

Viral nucleic acid supersedes control of
bacterial nucleic acids, totally redirecting
cell's metabolism, resulting in replication
of viral nucleic acid. Cell's nucleic acids
in chromosomes disintegrate, virus uses
cell's ATP for energy and its nucleotides
to make viral nucleic acid. New protein
coats made by steps — tail, end plate,
head, etc.; eventually whole new phages
assembled.

15 to 20
minutes

have about 300
new phage units

cell bursts (lysis) releasing new phages

In other viral infections virus may be associated with
given organelles like nucleus or endoplasmic reticulum.

Figure 114   Action of bacteriophage

constitution and the activities of the genes. These effects are produced in cells in
tissue culture where viral nucleic acids are introduced into the cells and persist
there and destroy them, but, if the same virus is introduced into an animal,
cancer results. Polyoma virus of mice is an example, and has only from four to
eight viral genes concerned in the change to malignancy. There is scientific
interest in this because the RNA of the oncogenic virus initiates reproduction of
the viral RNA in the cell's DNA, which is the reverse of the usual roles of RNA
and DNA, and this property may of course be most significant in the study of the
origin of some cancers.

PARASITIC MICROBIAL PLANT DISEASES

Bacteria

Some of the fifty or so bacterial plant diseases are soft rots, reducing fruits or tubers to a mush. Others block the conducting tissues with a slime and an interesting group forms tumours like the galls on olive trees. *Pseudomonas malvacearum* damages the commercially important fruits of cotton bushes. *Erwinia amylovora* produces fire blight in pear trees and sometimes obliterates orchards. On the other hand *Streptomyces scabies* is an example of an actinomycete causing common scab in potatoes.

Fungi

Probably thousands of species parasitise plants. Facultative fungal plant parasites often kill their host, the hyphae having penetrated into the cells, using the contents as food and living on in the dead plant's remains, as a saprophyte. The hyphae of obligate parasites only penetrate the host's cells by *haustoria* (see Figure 110), finger-like projections which absorb foods and the host is not often killed. Black stem rust of wheat (caused by species of *Puccinia*) is characteristic of those fungi which have two *alternate hosts*, spending part of the life cycle in the wheat (asexual phase) and the rest in barberry plants (sexual phase).

Stages in fungal diseases

An attack takes place in three stages:

(i) prepenetration, or the spread of the parasite to the hosts,
(ii) penetration, or entry into the host,
(iii) postpenetration, or growth in the host.

Spores are spread in the air and they vary in size from single cells a few micrometres in diameter up to those with several cells and over thirty micrometres long. (See Figure 115.) Spore dispersal is medically important as well, for some fungi cause respiratory diseases. The distribution of pollen is significant to sufferers from asthma and can be followed by the same device as is used to study spores. By the Hirst spore trap and by culturing samples of air collected by aircraft it is clear that the atmosphere carries a huge population of bacteria and fungal spores as well as pollen grains. Different spores travel in different layers of the atmosphere and the movements enable the spread of plant diseases to be forecast, but recently photographs taken from satellites, orbiting the earth, provide even earlier indication of diseases by changes of the shades or colours of crops.

The distribution and movements are governed by changes in wind speed, thermal currents, humidity, the sizes and densities of the spores, drops of water, dust and gravity. In the soil, some fungi in the rhizosphere are influenced by amino acids and sugars exuded by the roots. If conditions are suitable, a spore alighting on a plant will germinate and usually contains enough nutrient to provide for a germination tube. Further supplies however, often come from juices in wounds.

Spores may enter wounds made by insects but a common mode is by formation of a swelling or *appressorium* (see Figure 110) at the tip of a hypha, which sticks to the plant surface by hairs and then pushes a narrow penetration tube into the

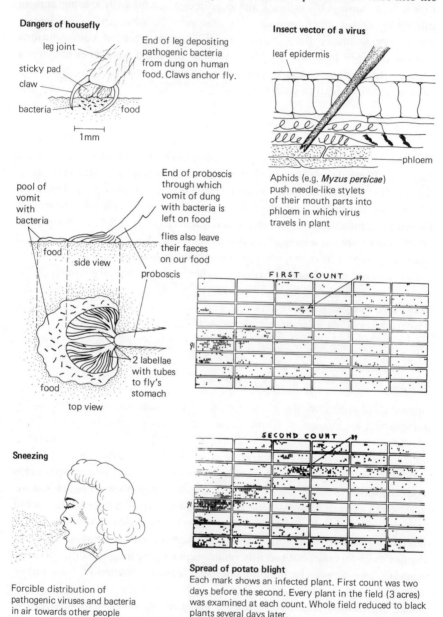

Dangers of housefly

leg joint
sticky pad
claw
bacteria
food

End of leg depositing pathogenic bacteria from dung on human food. Claws anchor fly.

1mm

pool of vomit with bacteria

food
side view

End of proboscis through which vomit of dung with bacteria is left on food

flies also leave their faeces on our food

proboscis

food
top view

2 labellae with tubes to fly's stomach

Sneezing

Forcible distribution of pathogenic viruses and bacteria in air towards other people

Insect vector of a virus

leaf epidermis

phloem

Aphids (e.g. *Myzus persicae*) push needle-like stylets of their mouth parts into phloem in which virus travels in plant

FIRST COUNT

SECOND COUNT

Spread of potato blight
Each mark shows an infected plant. First count was two days before the second. Every plant in the field (3 acres) was examined at each count. Whole field reduced to black plants several days later.

Figure 115 Dispersal of pathogens. Potato blight; Dr L. Fowden, Director, Rothamstead Experimental Station. Dr L. M. J. Kramer originator and source.

host. Once inside the tube swells and grows into hyphae. It is uncertain how appressoria operate, some penetrate the pores of stomata but others pierce the epidermis. The fixed appressorium may resist the back pressure of the penetration tube but enzymes may come from the fungus and soften the epidermis.

The extent of the internal growth varies from a limited region near the point of infection, producing externally visible spots, to total reduction of the host to a dead, evil-smelling mass. Eventually the fungus reproduces in the host and sporing structures appear from which spores are blown away by air currents. Sometimes *sclerotia*, resting bodies, are formed from tightly-woven hyphae and later new mycelium from them colonises another host. Some fungi pass the winter in the soil and infect fresh crops next season.

Resistance

At present there is no knowledge of a general mode of resistance of host plants to fungal invasion. Plant breeders have combined in single varieties resistance to given fungi with other desirable qualities like ease of cooking or flavour. For instance, some varieties of potatoes resist late blight, caused by *Phytophthora infestans*. There is evidence that thick cuticles of some plum fruits prevent fungal penetration, and spores lie on the fruits until the skins soften with ripening. It has been shown that penetration tubes from appressoria grown on metal or wax films of different thicknesses enter thin films best. Plants are protected after injury by barriers of cork or gum. One example of a substance which is able to counter infection is a phenol from the outer scales of onion bulbs: it inhibits germination of spores of the fungus *Colletotrichum circinans*. Inoculation of potato tubers with a non-parasitic strain of the late blight fungus, followed later by inoculation with a parasitic strain does result in only a little infection. Here, the potato seems to show protective mechanisms similar to those mammals possess against bacterial attack.

Control of plant diseases

Except for occasional cases, like helping a tree to survive a disease, it is not usual to try to 'cure' diseased plants. The practice is to 'control' by preventing or reducing damage to whole crops. Rational control rests on knowledge of the conditions which favour parasites and of their life cycles. It may be possible to attack the parasite more easily at one stage in the life cycle than in another.

Diseases can be partly avoided by laws which prohibit import of diseased plants or seeds, or forbidding the planting of crop varieties known to be susceptible to attack. Wise methods of cultivation are important such as correct spacing and feeding of the plants. Some plant parasites are transmitted by insects which may be controlled in various ways.

Chemicals can be used before a disease has developed or is in an early stage. Sprays can inhibit spores on the parts of plants above the ground or on seeds. Ideally, the chemicals used should damage the parasite as much as possible and the host minimally. The older inorganic substances are still valuable, like compounds of mercury, but the modern ones are organic compounds like pentachlor-phenols. Internal treatment is possible using substances which are absorbed into the tissues after external application and which reach parts not yet grown out from the buds. How internal systemic treatments act on fungi is not clear but they are very effective against some insect pests and insects which transmit viruses. Generally much knowledge and skill are needed to choose suitable combinations of methods to combat plant diseases.

PARASITIC MICROBIAL DISEASES OF ANIMALS AND MAN

Protozoa

Protozoa cause relatively few, but often dangerous, diseases of animals and man. Species of *Eimeria* cause diseases in the gut of birds and farm animals. In man, species of *Plasmodium* cause malaria, often a cause of death or chronic ill-health. *Plasmodium* is a blood parasite transmitted by insects, species of *Anopheles* mosquitoes, which pick up the protozoan when they suck blood of an infected person and later pass it on by biting a healthy person. The female mosquitoes need the blood to ripen their eggs, but the males usually live only on plant juices. Tsetse flies are vectors of *Trypanosoma* spp. which lives in the blood of man and cattle.

Fungi

Mycoses are diseases, mostly of the skin, of animals and are passed to man by contact. The fungi causing the diseases live on cats and farm animals and one, the ringworm fungus, lives on the human scalp. Athlete's foot is caused by the spores of a fungus picked up in wet places like swimming baths and itching and redness develop between the toes. Spores of the mould *Aspergillus fumigatus*, which grows on vegetable matter, cause a serious disease of the repiratory system and have been troublesome in western England.

The dispersal of pathogens

Microbial parasites of mammals and man bring about similar symptoms and signs to those in virus diseases including fever, often combined with other specific effects such as rashes. Pathogenic bacteria can be cultured for medical purposes, but, as we have seen viruses must be grown in some living tissue, like eggs for example. Bacteria and viruses pass from host to host in saliva, in drops of liquid sneezed out, in faeces and by contact. See Figure (house fly) 115. They may be dispersed in water or foods. Only two genera of bacteria, *Bacillus* and *Clostridium*, form spores which are hard to kill. An example is *Clostridium tetani* which spores in soil and can be dangerous if it enters wounds and paralyses muscles.

Bacteria lodge on skin or enter body openings like the mouth. The gut and upper respiratory passage house large populations of them. They may enter tissues through wounds. Sometimes normal bacterial populations are not pathogenic but important, like those in the guts of cattle which decompose cellulose and set free sugars or synthesise necessary vitamins of the B group. Examples of human diseases of bacterial origin are a number of the pneumonias, streptococcal throat infections and leprosy. (See Figure 109.)

Virulence

The virulence of bacteria varies from the formation of local lesions to general illness after the organisms have travelled in the lymph or blood. Even if cells do not travel from a point of infection they may still be dangerous because they make poisons (*toxins*) which circulate. The bacillus of diphtheria infects the throat but its toxins pass into the blood. Exotoxins come from undamaged bacteria but endotoxins remain in the bacterial cells and usually cause trouble only by escaping from broken cells.

In recent years clues to the nature of virulence have emerged. A form of pneumonia is caused by *Diplococcus pneumoniae* (see Figure 109) which has a capsule of carbohydrates and looks smooth (S form) in culture, and also has an R form with no capsule which looks rough. S capsules cause pneumonia but R cells do not. If live R cells and heat-killed S capsules without cells are injected into mice they succumb to pneumonia so that somehow the virulence of the dead S capsules has been transferred to the once harmless R cells. Another case is the serious result of the transference of resistance to the hitherto valuable *antibiotic* (anti-bacterial) drug penicillin possessed by some strains of bacteria to ones formerly penicillin-sensitive. The acquisition of resistance has been traced to particles of DNA (*plasmids*) transferred when the different strains of bacteria unite sexually. The resistance results from formation of the enzyme penicillinase and since DNA controls enzyme production this genetic transfer could have serious consequences in other diseases. The degree of virulence of bacteria can be reduced by culturing the pathogen above its optimum temperature or by partly poisoning it with formaldehyde (methanal).

Responses by hosts

Immune hosts never succumb to certain microbial invasions, resistant hosts may succumb but do not do so very often or only suffer mildly, whereas susceptible hosts succumb readily or suffer severely. Immunity is specific to some hosts, thus humans do not suffer from dog distemper (a virus disease) and some breeds of sheep are immune to the bacterial disease anthrax. Immunity may also be related to sex, for instance puerperal fever after childbirth is confined to women.

Otherwise immunity is produced by a range of protective devices. Some are anatomical like a thick or unbroken outer skin which keeps out microbes, or cilia in the upper respiratory tract which move bacteria away from the lungs. Others are chemicals like the acid gastric juice which inhibits the growth of bacteria swallowed with the food. The state of health is also important. It is known that breathing very cold air after spending some time in a hot room promotes respiratory infection. Poor diet can lower resistance, e.g. lack of vitamin C which if severe may lead to scurvy, common in the past among ships' crews on long voyages. Exposure to X-rays and nuclear radiations damages the lymph nodes grouped in the armpits and groins and which are important in defence against pathogenic bacteria.

The outstanding and specific internal defences are *cellular* and *humoral*. The protective cells are *phagocytes*, either neutrophil cells from the bone marrow or monocytes or macrophage cells in the liver and spleen. These cells engulf and digest pathogenic bacteria and after heavy infection they may die and become yellow pus cells (see Figure 116) as in a pimple or boil. Phagocytosis may be a small local event which prevents further invasions or more extensive in severe cases. Humoral or chemical defences comprise the formation of *antibodies* in

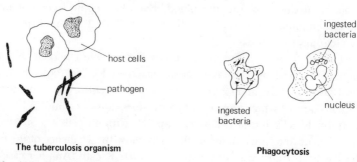

The tuberculosis organism

Mycobacterium tuberculosis
(an actinomycete) seen in sputum.
Slender rods, often with bead-like bulges.
Average dimensions 2 x 0.5 μm.

Phagocytosis

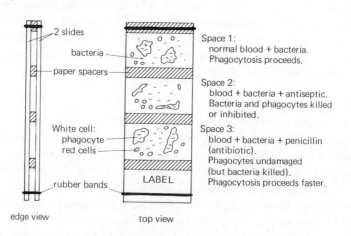

Space 1:
  normal blood + bacteria.
  Phagocytosis proceeds.

Space 2:
  blood + bacteria + antiseptic.
  Bacteria and phagocytes killed
  or inhibited.

Space 3:
  blood + bacteria + penicillin
  (antibiotic).
  Phagocytes undamaged
  (but bacteria killed).
  Phagocytosis proceeds faster.

edge view   top view

Fleming's experiment

showing penicillin harms bacteria
but not the phagocytes

Figure 116   Pathogens in tissues

response to the introduction of *antigens* which are macromolecules of proteins or carbohydrates foreign to the host's body. Antibodies accumulate as the infection proceeds and more are made than are needed for recovery. An excess therefore remains in the blood and since antibodies counteract given antigens, immunity lasts, so we are protected if that antigen is introduced to our body later. Reaction by antibody production is *active immunity*. *Passive immunity* occurs if antibodies are received from outside like those in the colostrum, the first milk an infant sucks from its mother.

Because phagocytes and antibodies are carried in the blood that fluid becomes very important medically in combating illness. Either effects can be seen in the blood, or by separating *serum*, a yellow fluid left over after a sample of blood has clotted, it can be tested for different antibodies as an aid in diagnosis. Some antibodies are *precipitins*, acting by agglutinating or clumping the bacteria together. Others are *lysins* which dissolve the contents of bacteria leaving empty cell walls, while *opsonins* stimulate the phagocytes to act quickly. Soluble antibodies are called anti-toxins. *Lysozyme* lyses bacteria below the eyelids and comes from the tears.

Medically and in veterinary practice antigen/antibody reactions are adapted for protection against microbial parasites. Active immunity can be induced to give protection against future infection. A suitably prepared antigen is injected such as a *vaccine* formed of actual bacteria weakened or killed by heat. Weakened toxins are also used and are known as toxoids. Passive immunity employs ready-made antibodies prepared from animal blood, as is done in immunising against tetanus, but this type of protection does not last for very long and is most useful for people already exposed to infection or already suffering from the disease. A booster is an injection given to increase the amount of antibodies a person has made earlier by active immunity. Thus, doctors have available many sorts of antigens or antibodies and can choose those specific to a particular disease.

Protection against viruses can be on the same lines as for bacteria in so far as the protein coat of the virus is concerned, but to inactivate the damaging nucleic acids a different form of substance appears to be required. Most host cells make *interferon* which is in fact a protein active against most viruses but because cells make it in very small amounts it is not yet available for medical use.

Chemotherapy

Broadly speaking chemotherapy means using chemicals to treat disease. As far as micro-organisms are concerned it involves choosing substances which ideally damage pathogens but not the host. Last century, Lord Lister used dilute phenol (carbolic acid) solution to inhibit those micro-organisms which cause sepsis. A *disinfectant* resembles Lister's *antiseptic* phenol because both are used to kill cells either on patients or bandages and dressings or on instruments. Since Lister's time many other substances have been used and applied externally or injected. In the late 1930s sulfa drugs were found to be effective in ailments like pneumonias. In 1929 Sir Alexander Fleming discovered the first antibiotic, an anti-bacterial substance made by another organism, usually a fungus or an actinomycete. Fleming called the substance he discovered *penicillin* after the green mould *Penicillium notatum*. An example of his elegant experiments is shown in Figure 116, by which he established the harmlessness of penicillin to phagocytes but its inhibition of certain bacteria. Since 1945 many new antibiotics have been found, some from soil organisms and active against a wider range of bacteria than pencillin alone. Many bacterial diseases have been greatly reduced or their effects minimised, including syphilis, gonorrhoea (until recent resistance by some strains of the gonococcus) and trachoma, a once incurable eye infection leading to blindness.

Blood transfusion

The ancient realisation that blood is essential to life prompted attempts to replace losses with blood from animals or healthy people. Occasionally this succeeded but after it was clear that bloods of different species of animals were incompatible transfusion into patients was confined to the use of human blood. Although methods were improved, clotting of the donor's blood was a difficulty until it was prevented by adding a little sodium citrate. Fatalities still occurred because the donor's red blood cells could be damaged within the patient.

Early this century Landsteiner discovered what must surely be some of the strangest facts in all biological science. Destruction of the donor's red cells resembles the reaction of tissues to foreign proteins in general. While it seems natural that antibodies should be produced to counteract antigenic proteins of harmful bacteria, it is very difficult to realise why human blood should be in definite groups and contain antibodies corresponding to antigens in another person's blood, for transfusion is a human invention and unlikely to have come about in nature or been practised by animals. Yet, Landsteiner indeed found that all humans belonged to one of four groups differing by the presence of antigens in their red blood cells and specific antibodies for them in their plasma. These constitute the *ABO system* and the antigens A and B which can be precipitated (O being excluded) are combined in four ways in corpuscles. The capital letters denote the antigens and the small letters the antibodies in the plasma.

Ab	41.8	per cent of the human population
Ba	8.6	
ABo	3.0	
Oab	46.6	

(4 groups)

If antigen A is passed into a recipient with antibody a in his plasma the donor's red cells are agglutinated, but if a is absent the two bloods are compatible. By arranging these combinations in a table we find which groups are compatible (shown by a minus sign) or otherwise (shown by a plus sign). Recipients belonging to group ABo have blood compatible with that from any donor and are *universal recipients*, while *universal donors* are Oab and are compatible with any other group.

	ABo	Oab	Ba	Ab
Ab	−	+	+	−
Ba	−	+	−	+
ABo	−	+	+	+
Oab	−	−	−	−

donor { Ab, Ba, ABo, Oab

There are other systems besides the ABO system, such as MNS and P, but one very interesting one comprises an antigen, the *Rhesus factor (Rh)*, called after rhesus monkeys in which it was discovered in 1940. It can cause fatal blood disease in unborn infants in late pregnancy or just after birth. People with Rh in their red cells are Rh positive and the others, who are less numerous, are Rh negative, but the rhesus antibody is not necessarily present in the plasma of Rh negative people. The Rh positive antigen can pass from a foetus into the mother's circulation and if she is Rh negative she makes antibodies which reach the foetal circulation. The maternal and foetal bloods do not mix but can exchange substances across the placenta where capillaries of the two circulations are close to each other. Such an exchange allows the antigen and antibody to meet in the foetus and its red cells are destroyed, if not at the first pregnancy possibly in a later one. The trouble is avoided by giving the mother an anti-rhesus protein. The genetics of blood groups is considered in *Heredity, development and evolution*. Obviously the value of transfusion is in saving lives after severe bleeding or shock, or to treat certain diseases. The theories of how antibodies are produced and act are rather confused although definite ones have been proposed, some based on more evidence than others.

The management of infectious diseases

Apart from medical uses of immunology hygiene has proved a primary means of controlling widespread pestilences of microbial origin, often devastating in their effects. In 1664 in London, for example, 120 000 of the population of 460 000 perished from plague. Conditions frequently favoured infection in overcrowded places with bad ventilation. Open street sewers were likely to contaminate drinking water and piles of rat-ridden stinking refuse were common. One writer remarked that people were crammed together where they exchanged caresses and parasites.

The purpose of hygiene is to reduce the numbers or breeding places or dispersal of the pathogens, and over many decades control developed on the following lines:

(i) provision of drinking water free from pathogens like the bacteria of cholera;

(ii) adequate disposal of refuse and sewage kept clear of sources of drinking water;

(iii) inspection of meat at slaughterers and of places handling and selling food;

(iv) control of insect carriers and vectors;

(v) segregation of infected persons from those still healthy;

(vi) improved personal hygiene by washing, cleaning the teeth and covering the mouth and nose when sneezing and coughing.

All methods combined reduced infectious diseases in some cases to negligible proportions. Thus cases of smallpox in the 1920s were only a ninth of those in the 1870s and typhoid fever cases were an eighth of those in the 1870s.

ZOONOSES

A number of pests, viruses and bacteria which attack animals and are transmissible to man are known as *zoonoses*. Wild and domestic animals frequently carry some diseases and the risks of transfer to us vary. Examples of viruses involved are notably those of rabies from dog bites, psittacosis from some birds and the dangerous B virus from monkeys. Among bacteria are the *Leptospira* from rats and the tuberculosis organism from badgers. The common roundworm of dogs can damage the eyes and we can get tapeworms from dogs and pigs.

One need not be put off keeping pets because wise precautions can always be observed. The sources of pets should be known and expert advice sought on how to care for and feed them. Immediate veterinary advice is essential for any illness in a pet. Wild animals, particularly if they are ill, should never be brought into the home by untrained people. The hands must always be well washed each time a pet has been handled and any wound an animal has caused must be cleaned and expertly treated at once.

SURGERY

Aseptic surgery has been one of the greatest successes in fighting bacteria. By it organisms are kept away from the sites of operations so that the suppuration of wounds common in earlier days is prevented and the precautions include the use of sterile (bacteria-free) dressings. None of the boons of modern surgery however, including the recent transplantation of organs, would have been feasible without appropriate *anaesthesia*, which chiefly uses inhaled gases. An interesting anaesthetic system long used in the east is called acupuncture and employs needles inserted into the skin at suitable points.

MICROBIOLOGY AND PUBLIC HEALTH

The scientific management of micro-organisms

The importance of micro-organisms extends beyond the treatment of disease,

Table 10 Summary of microbiological events.

A *Micro-organisms in balance of nature*	B *Micro-organisms harmful to man or to produce he wants*	C *Human actions to counteract A_3 and B*	D *Microbial activity harnessed by man*
1 Autotrophs: green plankton.			
2 Heterotrophs: as saprophytes in circulating substances.	Bacterial food poisoning, poisonous fungi, spoilage of foods from plants or animals, or of textiles or timber.	Actions against poisoning and to preserve foods by refrigeration, canning, drying, irradiation or use of preservatives.	Processed foods: bread, silage. Agricultural management of soil to promote circulation of nutrients.
3 Parasites on or in plants, animals and humans.	Parasitic diseases caused by protozoa, bacteria and fungi to plants, domesticated animals and people.	Medical, veterinary and plant disease controls. Control of vectors, crop parasites, surgery. Services: meteorological forecasts, protective legislation, breeding of stock and crops, veterinary and plant disease advice. Satellite crop forecasts. Preparations: insecticides, fungicides, antiseptics, disinfectants, toilet needs, sanitary facilities, vaccines, sera, drugs. Related activities: refuse disposal, sewage disposal, control of water supply, air conditioning.	Microbial technology for production of crops of single cells (bakers' yeasts, proteins), foods (cheeses) also organic food substances or nonfoods for industry (alcoholic beverages, industrial alcohols).

into a wide range of industries and public services without which the maintenance of health would be impossible in the modern world. In column A of Table 10 the significance of micro-organisms in nature is shown opposite to the range of human responses outlined in columns B, C and D.

The biological principles on which the control of micro-organisms rests are as follows:

(i) identification of organisms concerned and knowledge of their habitats, roles and life cycles;
(ii) their tolerance of various temperatures;
(iii) whether they are aerobic or anaerobic;
(iv) whether they need darkness or light;
(v) the need for water, general and specific foods like vitamins;
(vi) the absence or application of harmful radiations;
(vii) the absence or application of harmful substances;
(viii) if organisms grow in succession on a substrate it is necessary to know how to favour or reduce the growth of one or all of them

Control is based on depriving the cells of one or more essential needs, or by creating an unfavourable environment, or, if the organism is to be harnessed, on creating optimum conditions for it by considering each of these factors.

Micro-organisms and produce

The organic compounds in animal produce like meat change quickly after death and are good food for micro-organisms which hasten decay. Produce is affected by the way it is handled and stored. Meat is usually inspected in slaughter houses. Eggs should be kept dry and cool. Cleanliness is always important, e.g. in dairies.

Unlike meat, fruit and vegetable produce is living after harvesting so that the anti-microbial defences still operate. However, the skin of fruits should be undamaged and storage in cool and well-aired places is important.

For completeness it is desirable to mention non-food produce like timber which should be in well-ventilated conditions, both in store and when part of a building. Treatment with fungicides and insecticides by forcing them into the wood under pressure is a common practice.

Preserving produce

The chief methods are as follows.

(i) Control of temperature: this is to create conditions unfavourable to micro-organisms. The temperatures in domestic refrigerators retard microbial growth (between 0°C and 7°C) and in deep freezers the effects last much longer at about −20°C to −26°C. For long storage produce should be undamaged and quite fresh when frozen. *Pasteurisation* of milk at 71.6°C for fifteen seconds kills pathogens, except bacterial spores, without affecting other qualities and bottling excludes other live organisms. The temperatures used in canning and bottling kill both micro-organisms and bacterial spores and the sealed can excludes other live organisms (see Figure 117). Other conditions like the pH of the contents and absence of air assist preservation. Exceptionally, hazards arise, for instance spores of *Clostridium botulinum* may escape death and then germinate into live cells which form a very dangerous poison which is often fatal if swallowed.

(ii) Dehydration: this aims to deprive micro-organisms of the water essential to their life and is attained by spreading produce out in the sun or drying it in factories. Sugar is a preservative because when highly concentrated it extracts water from the cells of the tissues and they become unsuitable for microbial life.

(iii) Freeze-drying: this is a combination of removal of water and use of low temperature. Preparations of bacteria for example can be kept by it unchanged genetically for years, which is valuable when the culture is allowed to grow again.

(iv) Irradiation: sterilisation of produce, in already sealed containers, by gamma radiation, is often more practical than sterilisation by heat.

Figure 117 (opposite)   Micro-organisms and industry

One of London's gin distilleries. There are seven stills in all; the three in the background and right are flavouring stills, the remaining ones are rectifying and do not take ingredients. To the right are the condensers and spirit safes, with instruments in front for directing newly-distilled gin into receiving vessels.

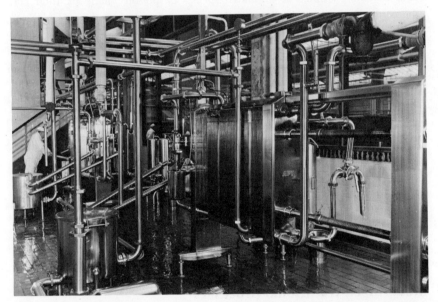

A milk pasteurisation unit

A commercial bakery. Yeast ferments sugar which makes the dough rise and form the small holes in bread. Dough is toughened and yeast killed by baking.

(v) Use of chemicals: there is control by law of what may be used safely. Smoking of fish or meats is effected by the cresols present in wood smoke which kills bacteria and gives a desirable flavour. Sulphur dioxide is used in bottled fruit juices.

Food poisoning

The effects of some organisms or their products on food may cause us slight discomfort or more serious illness or even be fatal. Some fruit bodies of basidiomycete fungi are eaten regularly like the common mushroom (*Psalliota campestris*) used in Britain. However some wild species are toxic, and one, the death cap (*Amanita phalloides*), is usually fatal even if only a little of it is eaten. Unfortunately symptoms develop when it is too late for effective treatment. The only safeguard against fungal poisoning is to know for certain what one should pick and eat by being able to identify the fungus from its botanical characters.

Other forms of food poisoning are caused by either species of the bacterium *Salmonella*, or by different unrelated species or poisons made by their cells (see botulism above). The Salmonella group set up an intestinal disease with fever and endotoxins may be eaten with a variety of foods, but the bacterial cells are destroyed by cooking. Not all the toxins are destroyed by cooking. Species of *Staphylococcus* grow in cream or on cooked meats and may also be transferred on hands. There is no fever in these cases and recovery is usually rapid.

Some serious intestinal diseases, not necessarily carried on food, have to be notified to the government in Britain; typhoid fever is an example.

HARNESSING MICROBIAL PROCESSES

In general there are historic microbial processes, like baking, once carried on by rule of thumb but now managed scientifically, and newer ones introduced as science has developed. All are called *bio-technology* or *microbial technology*, and produce useful micro-organisms in bulk or organic substances.

Modernised traditional processes

Milk is soured by bacteria for which it is a good food. To make cheese souring is arrested by pasteurisation followed by one of two main processes. Soft cheeses are produced by adding a culture of a suitable bacterium, but hard cheeses are 'started' by cultures, e.g. of *Streptococcus lactis*, and by adding rennin. A semi-solid *curd* of protein forms and is separated from a liquid *whey*. The curd is pressed and ripens slowly into cheese by the growth of a series of micro-organisms which determine the flavour. Yoghourt is milk fermented by *Lactobacillus bulgaricus* and *Streptococcus thermophilus* in 8000 litre tanks and fruit flavours may then be added. All milk processes are kept at optimum temperatures for the bacteria used.

Wines are made by letting naturally occurring or added yeasts ferment sugars from pressed grapes to ethanol. Many other changes combine with the type of grape, the soil's characteristics, and the conditions of storage to give the large range of the world's wines. Brewing requires malt sugar, obtained from starch by enzyme action in germinating barley grains. The malt is ground to *grist* and heated in water with hops which kill unwanted micro-organisms, give the correct pH and a bitter flavour. The cooled product is *wort* which is then brewed into beer in million litre vats by adding strains of the yeast *Saccharomyces cerevisiae*. (See Figure 110) This brew has about thirty per cent of solids and is stirred. For ales, yeasts are used which cling to the bubbles of carbon dioxide which form at the same time as the ethanol. These floating yeasts are saved and used again. Lager beer requires 'bottom yeast' which is also saved. After dilution to the desired concentration the beer may be aerated with carbon dioxide and bottled or put into casks. The flavours depend on the strains of yeasts and the proportions of fatty acids, esters and sterols. Whisky and gin come from distilled cereal brews and brandy from distilled wine (see Figure 117). Gin requires the addition of plant products, 'botanicals' which always include juniper berries. Distillation results in about thirty-five per cent of alcohol (ethanol) in the spirits, while in wines it is from eight to twenty per cent and in beers three to six per cent.

Bakers' yeast is a compressed mass of cells of *Saccharomyces cerevisiae* obtained by rapid growth in molasses in vats. The process is first aerobic and then anaerobic and takes place at about pH 4 and 27°C, so suppressing contaminating organisms. The yeast crop is separated by filtration. Dough rises because the yeasts release carbon dioxide gas from sugar. Baking kills the yeasts but the gas bubbles stay in the loaf and are seen as holes (see Figure 117).

Examples of newer processes

In agriculture management of the root nodule organism, *Rhizobium leguminosarum* enriches soils and the roots of leguminous crops (e.g. clover) with protein, made by fixation of free nitrogen in the soil. Correct strains of the bacterium must be matched with suitable varieties of the crops. Good effects have followed addition of the bacterium to the soil in developing countries.

Hay has to be made in suitable weather, but *silage*, to be used as cattle feed, can be made in any weather from plant residues like the tops of root crops, in a tower (the silo). Micro-organisms on the material create in a few weeks a succulent stable mass attractive to cattle. The microbes also make substances which preserve the silage, acetic (ethanoic) acid in a sweet silage and butyric (butanoic) acid in a more nutritious sour one. After consumption of the oxygen, anaerobic organisms grow at a low pH and prevent total decay.

In the food industries citric acid is obtained from microbial growth instead of by extraction from citrus fruits. Where maize is available another useful product can be made by micro-organisms in the form of fruit sugar (fructose) syrups for use in confectionery. The syrup costs about half as much as sucrose from sugar canes and is sweeter. The micro-organisms hydrolyse the starch in the maize to monosaccharides.

In the medical field production of antibiotics from moulds, such as *Penicillium notatum*, or from actinomycetes like *Streptomyces* sp., is carried on in large vats and the drugs are gathered from the liquid after the mycelium has been removed. Animal hormones, e.g. cortisone, and also sterols for oral contraceptives are made by micro-organisms. In some cases plant and animal tissues can be cultured as sources of drugs instead of using micro-organisms.

For industrial purposes alcohols (methanol and ethanol) are made by micro-organisms and have wide uses, one of which is to blend them with petrols to eke out the supply of fossil fuels.

Factors affecting bio-technology

Obviously all bio-technical processes have a scientific basis as outlined on p. 267, and today many sciences are involved including microbiology, genetics, chemistry, chemical engineering, electronics and computer control of the complex machinery. One constant problem is to avoid swamping the wanted organisms by contaminants and although it is costly to sterilise tanks, and the liquids on which the organisms live (the *substrate*), by heat it is essential to do so. Conditions may be adjusted to favour the wanted organism, as occurs when sweet wort is boiled with hops in breweries to give a pH value favouring the yeasts. Brewing is an example of a bulk process in which the vats are filled, used, and emptied again and reused, and good control is thus possible. For other types of process new types of fermenters have made continuous production possible.

Economic factors are very important. The use of fructose syrups has affected the sugar cane industry which is seeking new ways of using its products. Carbohydrate substrates are expensive so industries search for others, preferably wastes from industrial plants. The time taken to recover the cost of setting up a plant, taxation or the possession of patents may be decisive.

Industries have also to consider political aspects such as the siting and safety of a plant, employment of labour, and the effects of products on health.

Protein from single cell organisms

An outstanding example of the effects of recent technical advances is the effort to supplement or replace agriculturally produced protein which has become very expensive. A pioneer experiment was the use of a fermenter in spacecraft which was supplied with hydrogen as an energy source and carbon dioxide from the crew's breath and their urine as substrates. The bacteria grown in this were found to be toxic and unusable as food. One of the newest plants is in England and uses methane which is turned first to methanol. The bacteria used grow at $42°C$ and resemble those occurring in the hot water of the Roman baths at Bath in south-west England, where methane occurs. The process is continuous and needs much oxygen and cooling water. (See Figure 118.) The crop of non-toxic cells contains a full enough range of amino-acids for normal animal growth and it is intended to use them first for animal feed and later human use. In future hydrogen may be a better source of energy and would be released from water by electrolysis or lasers. The value of the process is indicated by the fact that the bacteria double their weight in three hours, compared to pigs, which do so in four

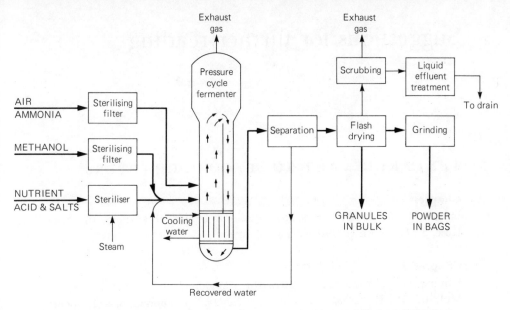

Figure 118   The ICI protein process. From ICI Agricultural Division, Billingham, Cleveland.

weeks. Moreover, the area of the plant is small and to get the same amount of protein from wheat would require 3250 hectares (8000 acres) of land.

The new biotechnology might eventually enable us to make all our needs for organic substances by microbial activity.

QUESTIONS

1   Explain the roles of homeostasis, the balance of nature and death in the biological significance of disease.
2   Give an account of the balance between the effects of the chief forms of diseases in modern times.
3   Outline the distinguishing features of virus diseases with reference to one named example. How important are viruses and how may they be controlled?
4   Choose one or two named fungal diseases of crops to illustrate their spread and effects.
5   Discuss the parasitic diseases of either plants or animals and indicate their economic importance.
6   Write notes on insect vectors, virulence, phagocytosis, zoonoses.
7   Distinguish between antigens, antibodies, immunity, lysis, agglutination.
8   By what medical and hygienic methods can infectious diseases be controlled?
9   Why is blood transfusion possible?
10   What advice would you give to firms specialising in the handling or preservation of foods, stating the scientific reasons for your proposals?
11   Describe at least three economically important processes involving micro-organisms.

Suggestions for further reading

TEXTS RELEVANT TO SPECIFIC CHAPTERS

Chapter 2
Bryant, C., *The biology of respiration*, Studies in biology 28 (Arnold, 1971).
Rose, S. *The chemistry of life* (Penguin, 1970).

Chapter 4
Jennings, T. J., *Background to biochemistry*, (Pergamon).
McElroy, W. D., *Cellular physiology and biochemistry*, Foundations of modern biology, (Prentice-Hall).
White, E. H., *Chemical background for the biological sciences*, Foundations of modern biology, (Prentice-Hall).

Chapter 5
Hall, D. O. and Rao, K. K., *Photosynthesis*, Studies in biology 37, (Arnold, 1972).
Tribe, M. A. and Whittaker, P. A., *Chloroplasts and mitochondria*, Studies in biology 31, (Arnold, 1972).
Whittingham, C. P., *Photosynthesis* (Oxford University).

Chapter 6
Morton, J., *Guts*, Studies in biology 7, (Arnold).
Wynn, C. H., *The structure and function of enzymes*, Studies in biology 42, (Arnold).

Chapter 7
Chapman, G., *The body fluids and their functions*, Studies in biology 8, (Arnold).

Chapter 8
Richardson, M., *Translocation in plants*, Studies in biology 10, (Arnold).
Rutter, A. J., *Transpiration*, Oxford biology reader, (Arnold).
Sutcliffe, J. F., *Plants and water*, Studies in biology 14, (Arnold).
Sutcliffe, J. F. and Baker, D. A., *Plants and mineral salts*, Studies in biology 48, (Arnold).
Wooding, F. B. P., *Phloem*, Oxford biology reader, (Oxford University Press).

Chapter 9
Chalmers, Crawley and Rose (editors), *The biological bases of behaviour*, (Harper and Row).
Hardy, R. N., *Homeostasis*, Studies in biology 63, (Arnold).

Hardy, R. N., *Temperature and animal life*, Studies in biology 35, (Arnold).

Langley, *Homeostasis* (Chapman-Hall).

Lewin, R., *Hormones: chemical coordinators* (G. Chapman).

Usherwood, P. R. N., *Nervous systems*, Studies in biology 36, (Arnold).

Chapter 13

Audus, L. J., *Plant growth substances* (Leonard Hill).

Hill, T. A., *Endogenous plant growth substances*, Studies in biology 40, (Arnold).

Kendrick, R. E. and Frankland, B., *Phytochrome and plant growth*, Studies in biology, (Arnold).

Torrey, J. G., *Development in flowering plants* (1967).

Villiers, T. A., *Dormancy and the survival of plants*, Studies in biology 57, (Arnold).

Chapter 14

Currey, J. D., *Animal skeletons*, Studies in biology 22, (Arnold).

Gray, J., *How animals move*, (Pelican, 1959).

Gray, J., *Animal locomotion*, (Weidenfeld and Nicolson, 1968).

Huxley, H. E., The mechanism of muscular contraction, *Scientific American* (Dec 1965).

Pennycuick, C. J., *Animal flight*, Studies in biology 33, (Arnold).

Wilkie, D. R., *Muscle*, Studies in biology 11, (Arnold).

Chapter 15

Burton, M. and Burton, R., *Inside the animal world*, (Macmillan, 1977).

Carthy, J. D., *The study of behaviour*, Studies in biology 3, (Arnold).

Lorenz, K., *King Solomon's ring* (Methuen).

Tinbergen, N., *Social behaviour in animals*, (Chapman-Hall).

Chapter 16

Barnett, H. R., *The food industry*, (Arnold).

Boycott, J. A., *The natural history of infectious disease*, (Arnold).

Clegg, A. G. and Clegg, P. C., *Man against disease*, (Heinemann, 1973).

Cowan, K., *Implant and transplant surgery*, (Murray).

Deverell, B. J., *Fungal parasitism*, Studies in biology 17, (Arnold, 1969).

Hawker, L. *et al.*, *An introduction to the biology of micro-organisms*, (Arnold).

Hunter, D., *Health in industry*, (Pelican).

Lawler, S. D. and Lawler, L. J., *Human blood groups and inheritance*, (Heinemann).

Ramsbottom, J., *Edible fungi*, (King Penguin).

Ramsbottom, J., *Poisonous fungi*, (King Penguin).

Singer, C. and Underwood, E. A., *A short history of medicine*, (Oxford University Press).

Smith, G., *An introduction to industrial mycology*, (Arnold).

Stevenson, G. B., *Biology of fungi, bacteria and viruses*, (Arnold).

Usher, G., *Introduction to viruses*, (Arnold).

van Emden, H. F., *Pest control and its ecology*, (Arnold).

Wilson, A., *Introduction to parasitology*, (Arnold).

GENERAL TEXTS

Coult, D. A., *The working plant* Principles of modern biology, (Longman).

Devlin, R. M., *Plant physiology*, (Van Nostrand Reinhold).

Hoare, *Comparative animal physiology*, (Prentice Hall).

James, W. O., *An introduction to plant physiology*, (Oxford).

Roberts, M. B. V., *Biology: a functional approach*, (Nelson, 1976).

Schmidt-Nielsen, K., *Animal physiology*, (Cambridge University Press).

Street, H. E. and Opik, H., *The physiology of flowering plants*, Contemporary biology, (Arnold).

Vines, A. E. and Rees, N., *Plant and animal biology* vol 2, (Pitman).

Wood, D. W., *Principles of animal physiology*, Contemporary biology, (Arnold).

Vertebrate structure and function, Readings from Scientific American, (Freeman).

Index